PRACTICAL BIOLOGY
FOR ADVANCED LEVEL

DR MICHAEL ROBERTS
Formerly Head of Biology at Marlborough
College and Cheltenham College

DR TIM KING
Director of Curriculum Studies,
Abingdon School

REVD DR MICHAEL REISS
Senior Lecturer in Biology, Homerton
College, Cambridge

Nelson

Thomas Nelson and Sons Ltd
Nelson House Mayfield Road
Walton-on-Thames Surrey
KT12 5PL   UK

Nelson Blackie
Wester Cleddens Road
Bishopbriggs
Glasgow
G64 2NZ   UK

Thomas Nelson (Australia)
102 Dodds Street
South Melbourne
Victoria 3205   Australia

Nelson Canada
1120 Birchmount Road
Scarborough Ontario
M1K 5G4   Canada

First published by Thomas Nelson and Sons Ltd 1994.
I(T)P Thomas Nelson is an International Thomson Publishing
Company.
I(T)P is used under licence

ISBN 0-17-448225-6
NPN 9 8 7 6 5 4 3 2 1

Printed in China

Acknowledgements

The authors and publishers would like to thank the following for all
their help and assistance in the preparation of this book:

Alison Bilsborough
Phil Bunyan
Brian Bush
J. L. Chapman
Jennifer Gregory
Stephen Johnson
Mary Jones
Tracey Monks
Elizabeth Quelch
G. Stone
Alastair Swift
Bruce Tullok
Ken Turner
Barbara Walker
P. J. Wilmore
Vanessa Woodhead

Photographs

2.6 Natural History Photographic Agency (p.31)
2.7 Institute of Biology, London, from *The Journal of Biological Education*
(p.31)
2.8 Nature Photographers Ltd (p.32)
3.1–3.6 Natural History Photographic Agency (pp.40–41)
6.9 Elizabeth Tudor, Monash University, Melbourne (p.94)
9.17 Professor John Marshall/Ophthalmology Department,
St Thomas' Hospital (p.166)
10.10 Rex Features (p.183)
11.19B Science and Plants for Schools (SAPS), Homerton College,
Cambridge (p.201)
12.18, 12.19, Gene Cox (p.227)
13.2 Heather Angel (p.238)
14.2 Natural History Photographic Agency (p.242)

Every effort has been made to trace all copyright holders,
but the publishers will be pleased to make the necessary
arrangements at the earliest opportunity if there have been
any omissions.

Contents

Preface for teachers and technicians

Preface for teachers and technicians

The purpose of this book is to provide a comprehensive coverage of the practical element in all current A/AS biology syllabuses. It should also prove suitable for students pursuing introductory biology courses in universities and colleges of further education. The book is independent of any particular theory textbook and, with the exception of this preface, is written for students. It is particularly important that students read Chapter 1 *Introducing Practical Biology* before undertaking any of the practical work. This chapter explains the rationale of the book and introduces the student to safety and other issues.

Each subsequent chapter covers a particular area of biology and contains three different kinds of practical activity as follows.

- *Practical Exercises* are structured activities in which the student is led carefully through the activity, step by step. Their aim is to enable students to carry out important biology experiments and to gain expertise in particular techniques. The great majority of these practical exercises can be carried out in 90 minutes or less in the laboratory. However, some take longer and we have indicated how much time is required in a marginal note at the start of such practical exercises.
- *Investigations* are more open-ended than practical exercises and give students more opportunity to plan their work. Students are not told exactly what to do but are given only general guidance. Some of these investigations can be carried out in 90 minutes or less in the laboratory, but many take longer than this and some are not laboratory-based but require field work.
- *Projects* are even more open-ended and require students to evaluate their findings, refine their ideas and design further investigations. Little or no guidance is given. In all, some 200 possible projects are outlined. Some of these would take, from start to finish, about 10 hours over a period of a few weeks. Others might take a total of 80 hours spread over twelve months. Some of the projects are laboratory based, others involve field work and a few can be carried out at home.

The Appendix contains a guide on how to carry out statistical analysis and presentation of biological data.

The practical exercises, investigations and projects are of different lengths and difficulty, so as to enable teachers and students to select the most appropriate ones for their specific needs. Some of the activities in this book have not appeared in print before, but on the whole we have preferred to sacrifice too much originality for reliability. All the practical exercises and investigations have been used in schools with students.

We have tried to minimise the number of activities that could cause stress to animals or harm to the environment. On the whole we have not found this too much of a constraint – indeed, it has presented us with a challenge and we have endeavoured to develop viable alternatives.

Some of the 'drawings' of dissections and microscope preparations are semi-diagrammatic. They are not intended to be photographic representations of the real thing, but to serve as a guide enabling the student to locate and identify the various structures.

In some of the cell and histology practical exercises and investigations, it is suggested that students examine electron micrographs. These are not usually included in our book. Electron micrographs are available as commercial sets or found in specialised books. Often, a polite request to a local university pays dividends.

A list of requirements is given alongside each practical exercise and investigation: apparatus first, then chemicals and finally biological material. The following abbreviations are used with respect to microscope slides: **WM** whole mount; **LS** longitudinal section; **VS** vertical section; **TS** transverse section; **HS** horizontal section; **VLS** vertical longitudinal section.

The following icons are used throughout the book to draw students' attention to specific issues of safety.

 Corrosive   Highly flammable   Risk of electric shock   Biohazard   Danger

 Oxidising   Harmful or irritant   Toxic   Eye protection must be worn   Gloves should be worn

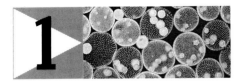

Introducing practical biology

The purpose of this book is to help you, the reader, carry out practical work for advanced level biology. The aim of practical work in biology is to explore and investigate the world of living things. Biology is a large subject and we have chosen to divide the book into 14 chapters. This chapter, Chapter 1, provides an introduction to the book as a whole. It is meant to help you to find your way around the book and get the most from the other chapters. Chapters 2–14 each cover a subject area within biology – Chapter 2 covers Ecology, Chapter 3 Classification and Identification, and so on.

Different types of practical activity

Within each chapter we have divided the material into three sections. Each section relates to a different kind of practical activity. First, there are what we call **practical exercises**. These are structured activities in which you are led carefully through the activity, step by step. The aim is to enable you to carry out an important biology experiment, e.g. studying the effect of light intensity on photosynthesis, or to help you get to grips with a particular technique, such as analysing amino acids by paper chromatography. The great majority of these practical exercises can be carried out in 90 minutes or less in the laboratory.

Secondly, there are **investigations**. These are more open-ended than practical exercises and give you more opportunity to plan your work. You are not told exactly what to do, but are given only general guidance. For example, you might investigate the distribution of woodland herbs in relation to light intensity, or you might design and use a questionnaire to determine the incidence of cigarette smoking among people of different age and gender. Some of these investigations can be carried out in 90 minutes or less in the laboratory, but many take longer than this and are not laboratory-based.

Thirdly, there are **projects**. These are even more open-ended than investigations and require you to evaluate your findings, refine your ideas and design further investigations as you carry out the project. Little or no guidance is given. In all, some 200 possible projects are outlined. Some of these would take, from start to finish, round about 10 hours over a period of a few weeks.

Others might take a total of 80 hours spread over twelve months. Some are laboratory based, others involve field work or can be carried out at home. Examples include investigating the reaction times of humans, examining the behaviour of web-building spiders, dissecting conifer cones, and relating the patterns of mosses on walls to measured environmental variables.

Having given a brief introduction to these three different kinds of practical activity, we shall now examine each in more detail. We shall show how they complement each other, and can help you build up the skills and experiences needed by a scientifically rigorous biologist. But first we need to explain how, between them, these three kinds of practical activity illustrate the **scientific method**.

The scientific method

It is notoriously difficult to provide a definition of the scientific method that holds for every aspect of science. Nevertheless, most scientists agree that progress in science involves the following:

- Making observations
- Generating hypotheses
- Making predictions
- Designing and carrying out experiments
- Constructing scientific models

In general the scientific method starts with an **observation**. The next step is to suggest an **hypothesis** to explain the observation. From the hypothesis, various **predictions**

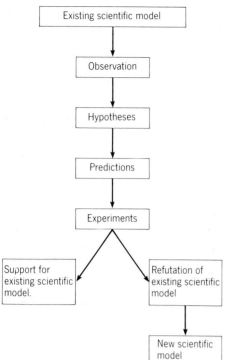

Figure 1.1 The scientific method showing the sequence of events in the emergence of scientific models.

Table 1.1 Table for recording observations and their investigation using the scientific method. Two examples are given to illustrate how to fill in the table.

Observation	Hypothesis	Prediction	Experimental test
1. An apple is shiny	The shiny layer is the waxy cuticle	If you remove the wax the shininess will disappear	Apply a wax solvent (e.g. xylene) to the surface of the apple and observe the result
2. A plant has yellow patches on its leaves	The yellowing is caused by lack of nitrogen	If you deprive a plant of nitrogen it will develop yellow leaves	Grow two groups of plants, one (the control group) in a solution containing all necessary nutrients, the other in a solution containing all nutrients except nitrogen

can be made, and these may then be tested by carrying out appropriate **experiments**. Two examples are given in Table 1.1.

The results of the experiments either lend support to the hypothesis or refute it, causing the hypothesis to be modified or even abandoned. This understanding of the scientific method is summed up in Figure 1.1.

It is important to realise that observations are *theory-laden*. This means that observations arise in the context of an existing scientific model. Consider the development of flies such as blowflies. Nowadays it is accepted that flies develop from maggots, which in turn develop from eggs. However, until the seventeenth century it was almost universally believed that some organisms were generated spontaneously from non-living matter. For example, flies were assumed to arise spontaneously within decaying meat. In 1668 an Italian physician called Francesco Redo showed that this was not the case by covering meat with a very fine gauze, which prevented female flies from laying their eggs on the meat. So biologists before the time of Redi 'observed' that maggots arose spontaneously within decaying meat.

With the benefit of hindsight, we can see how this 'observation' resulted from the assumption that some organisms could arise spontaneously from non-living matter. In other words, the existing scientific model at that time was that certain organisms (e.g. cows and humans) only arose from parents of the same species, while others (e.g. blowflies and moulds) arose from inanimate matter. It is all too easy in science for apparently accurate observations to be the result of unrealistic, hidden assumptions.

Of the three types of practical activity we have included in this book, it is the projects that illustrate most fully the full scope of the scientific method. The practical exercises and investigations emphasise particular parts of the scientific method, as we shall now show.

Practical exercises

To get the most out of the practical exercises, you need to follow carefully the instructions given. These instructions have been designed to provide you with experience in the following skills:

- Following instructions
- Handling apparatus
- Having due regard for safety
- Making accurate observations
- Recording results in an appropriate form
- Presenting quantitative results
- Drawing conclusions

We shall now look at each of these skills in more detail.

Following instructions

Instructions are provided in the order in which you need to carry them out. We would advise that before carrying out the instructions, you read through the entire exercise. This will help you to understand what you are doing and why you are doing it. In turn this will help you to remember what you have learned.

Each practical exercise in the book begins with a few lines describing its purpose. In most cases the following headings are also used:

- **Procedure** – numbered steps that need to be carried out
- **For consideration** – some questions to help you think carefully about the results you have obtained
- **Requirements** – a list of the apparatus, chemicals and biological materials you need.

Handling apparatus

Biologists need to be able to use many different types of apparatus, for example, potometers (to measure water uptake by plants), respirometers (to measure oxygen uptake or carbon dioxide production), Petri dishes (for plating out bacteria and other micro-organisms) and the light microscope (to magnify specimens). Many of the practical exercises are designed to help you derive the maximum benefit from a piece of apparatus. In some cases a particular piece of apparatus (e.g. the light microscope) or technique (e.g. handling and breeding fruit flies) is so important that we have introduced it by means of a **Box**.

Having due regard for safety

Surveys have shown that science laboratories are among the safest places to be. Nevertheless, this is no cause for complacency. On the occasions when something goes wrong and a person is injured, it is usually because one of the following common-sense rules has been broken:

- Always move slowly and carefully in a laboratory.
- Never put your fingers in your mouth or eyes after using chemicals or touching biological specimens until you have washed your hands thoroughly with soap and warm water, and dried them.
- Make sure glass objects (e.g. thermometers, beakers) cannot roll off tables or be knocked onto the floor.
- Wear safety goggles whenever there is a risk of damage to the eyes.

Situations of risk include:
- Heating anything with a Bunsen burner (even heating water has its dangers)
- Handling many liquids, particularly those identified as corrosive, irritant, toxic or harmful
- Handling corrosive or irritant solids
- Some dissection work

Throughout this book risks to eyes have been identified as far as possible, but in your own investigations and project work you will have to take advice from your teacher.
- Allow Bunsen burners, tripods, gauzes and beakers to cool down before handling them.
- Never allow your own body fluids (especially blood and saliva) to come into contact with someone else, or theirs into contact with you
- Keep long hair tied back and don't wear dangly earrings
- Don't allow electrical equipment to come into contact with water
- If you are unsure how to carry out a scientific procedure, ask your teacher first
- Make sure you understand why you are going to do something before you do it
- Wear a lab. coat when using chemicals or handling any biological specimens except prepared slides
- Follow exactly agreed procedures with regard to cuts, burns, electric shocks and other accidents (e.g. with chemicals)
- Follow exactly all specific safety instructions given in this book or provided by your teacher for particular practical exercises (e.g. use of gloves, disinfectant)

With practice, these procedures should become second nature to you. They will enable you to carry out practical work in safety.

The following icons are used throughout the book to draw your attention to specific issues of safety:

Corrosive

Highly flammable

Risk of electric shock

Biohazard

Danger

Oxidising

Harmful or irritant

Toxic

Eye protection must be worn

Gloves should be worn

Making accurate observations

In most cases the practical exercise will make it clear what you need to observe, e.g. the time taken for a certain volume of gas to be evolved or the width of a sample of cells. Ensure that you know how to use any necessary equipment before starting the practical. Think carefully about the **precision** with which you will make your observations. Common sense is needed here. If you are measuring the length and width of tree leaves so as to produce a key, there's no need to use fractions of a millimetre.

Recording results in an appropriate form

Results can be recorded in various ways. Often it is helpful to record raw data in a **table**. Most data will be in the form of numbers, i.e. they will be **quantitative** data (also known as **numerical** data). However, some data, e.g. flower colour, will be **qualitative**.

One form in which some biological findings can be recorded is a drawing. You don't need to be a professional artist to make worthwhile biological drawings. If you follow the following guidelines, a drawing can be of considerable biological value:

- Ensure that your completed drawing will cover at least a third of an A4 page.
- Plan your drawing so that the various parts are in proportion and will not be drawn too small. Small marks to indicate the length and breadth of the drawing are a great help in planning, and a faint outline can be rapidly drawn to show the relative positions of the parts.
- The final drawing should be made with clean, firm lines using a sharp HB pencil and, if needed, a good quality eraser (not a white-out fluid). If important details are too small to be shown in proportion, they can be put in an enlarged drawing at the side of the main drawing.
- Avoid shading and the use of colour *unless* you are an excellent artist *and* they really help, for example when drawing soil profiles.
- When drawing structures seen with the naked eye or hand lens, use two lines to delineate such things as blood vessels and petioles. This will help you to indicate the relative widths of such structures (see, for example, Figure 7.4).
- When drawing low power **plan drawings** under the light microscope, don't attempt to draw individual cells – just different tissues (see, for example, Figure 7.12).
- When drawing plant cells at high power under the light microscope, use two lines to indicate the width of cell walls, but a single line to indicate a membrane (see, for example, Figure 5.1).
- Always put a scale on each drawing.

Presenting quantitative results

Presentation of data is all about using graphs or other visual means to make it easier to see what your results tell you. The following four ways of presenting data are the most frequently used in biology: line graphs, bar charts, histograms and scatter graphs.

Line graphs

Figure 1.2 shows an example of a **line graph**, often simply called a **graph**. Points should be clearly marked. Encircled dots, ⊙, or crosses, ×, are appropriate. Whether the points should be joined by straight lines, as in Figure 1.2, or by a smooth curve depends on how certain you are that a smooth curve would indicate the likely position of intermediate points better than a series of straight lines. In the case of the data plotted in Figure 1.2 either would be acceptable. Whenever you are unsure of the likely position of intermediate points, it is best to use straight lines. Notice also how the axes in Figure 1.2 are labelled, and the symbol on the vertical axis to indicate that the graph jumps from 0 to 50 mg blood glucose per 100 cm^3 of blood.

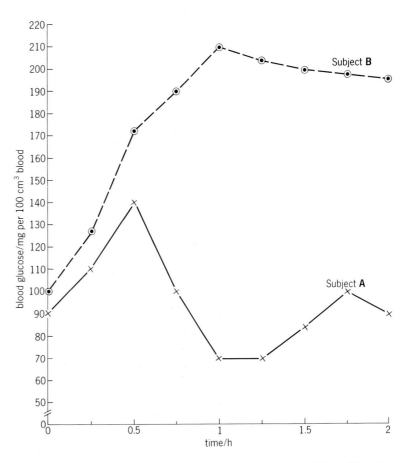

Figure 1.2 An example of a graph showing blood glucose levels in mg per 100 cm^3 blood for two human subjects, A and B.

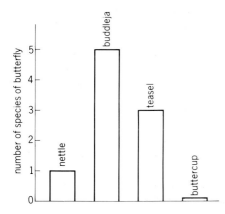

Figure 1.3 An example of a bar chart showing the number of species of butterfly that visited each of four plants during an hour's observation period. Note that the blocks are separated, as is conventional with discrete categories.

Bar charts

Figure 1.3 shows an example of a **bar chart**. In a bar chart the horizontal axis shows **discrete categories**. In the example shown here these discrete categories are four different species of plants. The vertical axis gives a numerical measure such as **abundance** or **frequency**. In the example shown here the vertical axis shows the number of species of butterfly that visited each plant during an hour's observation period. Conventionally, the blocks are of equal width and do not touch.

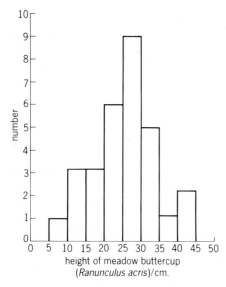

Figure 1.4 An example of a histogram showing the heights of a collection of meadow buttercups. Note that the blocks touch each other, as is conventional with continuous categories.

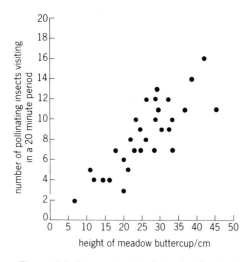

Figure 1.5 An example of a scatter graph showing the relationship between the heights of different meadow buttercup plants and the numbers of pollinating insects which visited them over a period of 20 minutes.

REQUIREMENTS

A range of biological objects, e.g. beaker of *Daphnia*, broad bean (*Vicia faba*) seeds, artery TS, vein TS, plant gall, plant with chlorotic leaves, snail, fern with spores.

Histograms

Figure 1.4 shows an example of a **histogram**. In a histogram the horizontal axis shows **continuous categories**, represented by numbers. In the example shown here the horizontal axis shows the height of meadow buttercups. The vertical axis of a histogram, like a bar chart, gives a numerical measure such as abundance or frequency. Such histograms are sometimes referred to as **frequency distribution histograms**. Conventionally, the blocks touch.

Scatter graphs

Figure 1.5 shows an example of a **scatter graph.** A scatter graph is a useful way to show the relationship between two variables. The example given here shows the relationship between the height of different meadow buttercup plants and the number of pollinating insects they attract. If one of the variables is determined by the other, it is best to put the **independent variable** on the horizontal axis and the **dependent variable** on the vertical axis. In this example, the number of pollinating insects attracted is the dependent variable because it *depends* on the other (independent) variable, namely the height of the plant. When plotting the results of an experiment, what you *control* (e.g. light intensity, enzyme concentration) goes on the horizontal axis, and what you *measure* (e.g. rate of photosynthesis, rate at which substrate is used up) goes on the vertical axis.

Drawing conclusions

Finally, you will need to draw conclusions. If your practical exercise has involved the testing of an hypothesis, for example that the enzyme pepsin works better at low pHs than in neutral or alkaline conditions, your conclusion should indicate whether the hypothesis has been **refuted** (i.e. shown not to be the case) or **supported**. Of course, even if your hypothesis has been supported, it doesn't mean that it has been confirmed with 100% certainty – in other words it isn't *proved*. Science proceeds more by showing that certain ideas are wrong than by showing that others are right (think about that!). Your conclusion might therefore include further ways of testing the original hypothesis, or might raise new possibilities to be investigated.

Often you will only be able to arrive at your conclusions after statistically analysing your data. **Statistics** are so important in biology that we have given them a section to themselves (see pages 247–258).

Sample practical exercise: Hypothesis-making and the scientific method

Here is an example of a practical exercise chosen to illustrate the scientific method. You will be presented with a number of biological objects on which you can make your own observations and suggest testable hypotheses.

Procedure

1 Draw up a table with the same headings as in Table 1.1. Make the columns as wide as possible.
2 Examine a selection of biological objects presented to you by your teacher. In each case observe *one* interesting biological phenomenon, formulate an hypothesis to explain it, make a prediction from your hypothesis and suggest an experiment to test the prediction. Fill in the table as you go along.
3 Go out of doors and find four interesting biological phenomena which you feel are worthy of investigation. Add them to your table.
4 Add suggestions from other members of your class to your table.

For consideration

1 Which of the hypotheses in your table would be particularly difficult to test experimentally and why?
2 Which experimental tests would need a **control** and what should the control be in each case?
3 Select one of the experimental tests which require a control. Identify the dependent and independent variables in the experiment. Consider how you would keep the independent variables constant and how you would measure the dependent variable.

4   Give two examples of biological investigations, not necessarily connected with the observations you have made in this practical, in which the scientific method, as outlined here, would be inappropriate.

5   Some scientists feel that there is no such thing as the 'scientific method'. What do you think?

Investigations

Each investigation in the book begins with a few lines describing its purpose. In most cases the following headings are used:

*   **Guidance** – some suggestions about issues you might consider, with ideas about how you might proceed
*   **For consideration** – some questions to help you think carefully about the results you have obtained
*   **Requirements** – a list of the apparatus, chemicals and biological materials which you may need.

By doing the investigations, you will gain experience at much the same skills attained through doing practical exercises *and* at the following skill that is more specific to investigations:

*   Planning investigations.

Planning investigations

You may already have had considerable experience at planning and carrying out scientific investigations. The importance of careful planning cannot be overstated. Your results will be of value *whatever* they are – provided you have given careful thought to the design of your investigation. Here are the sorts of things that need to be thought about when planning an investigation:

*   What hypotheses can you make?
*   How can you ensure that any experimental tests you carry out are fair?
*   What predictions can you make before obtaining any results?
*   Are your hypotheses based on scientific knowledge rather than mere hunches?
*   Can you make any mathematical (quantitative) predictions?
*   How many variables are you investigating?
*   Are your variables discrete or continuous?
*   How can you manipulate the independent variables?
*   What controls do you need?
*   How many **replicates** (i.e. repeat observations) will you require?
*   How will you collect your results?
*   What measurements are needed?
*   What techniques will you use to obtain relevant information?
*   Will you need to analyse your results statistically (see pages 247–258)? If so, does this affect the numbers of observations you need to make?
*   Is your intended procedure safe and does it show due regard for living organisms and the environment?

Your investigation may require the use of a **questionnaire**. The design, testing and implementation of questionnaires is dealt with in the Box 10.1 on page 180.

Sample investigation: Reproduction of bacteria in milk

Here is an example of an investigation: Investigate the extent to which stale milk contains more bacteria than fresh milk. Suppose you are provided with the following guidance.

Guidance

In favourable conditions bacteria on the surface of nutrient agar divide repeatedly by binary fission to form a **colony**. By the time a colony becomes visible to the naked eye it contains hundreds of thousands of individual bacteria. Milk may contain so many bacteria that if a sample was spread over an agar plate the bacterial colonies would form a continuous sheet. As a result, it would be impossible to count individual colonies.

This problem can be overcome by **serial dilution**. In serial dilution, milk can be diluted 100 times by placing 0.1 cm³ of milk in 9.9 cm³ of distilled water. Placing 0.1 cm³ of this mixture into a further 9.9 cm³ of distilled water causes the original milk to be diluted 100 × 100 = 10 000 times. Repeating this procedure a further time causes the original milk to be diluted one million times. Chances are that at *one* of these dilutions the colonies which form will be sufficiently separate to be counted individually *and* sufficiently numerous to see whether more of them are present in the stale milk than in the fresh milk.

Possible procedure

Here is a *possible* procedure you might adopt. Note that in the investigations in the rest of this book we do *not* provide detailed procedures such as this one. That's the whole point of the investigations: *you* devise and carry out *your* investigation.

Procedure

1 You are provided with six sterilised test-tubes plugged with cotton wool. Label them F1, F2, F3, S1, S2 and S3. F stands for fresh and S for stale.
2 You are provided with six sterile Petri dishes, each containing nutrient agar suitable for bacterial growth. Write on the base of each plate your initials, and one of the codes F1, F2, F3, S1, S2 or S3. Do not open any of the dishes.
3 Transfer 9.9 cm³ of sterile distilled water from the flask provided to each of the six test-tubes, using the following technique if you are right handed:
    (a) with your left hand, raise the cotton wool plug from the flask containing sterile distilled water;
    (b) holding the sterile 10 cm³ graduated pipette in your right hand, suck up 9.9 cm³ of sterile distilled water;
    (c) replace the plug on the flask and remove the cotton wool plug from a test-tube;
    (d) transfer the 9.9 cm³ of water to the test-tube;
    (e) replace the plug.
4 Using a sterile pipette, transfer 0.1 cm³ of fresh milk to tube F1. Replace the plug. Swirl the tube. Tube F1 now contains a ×100 dilution.
5 Using a different sterile pipette, transfer 0.1 cm³ from tube F1 to tube F2. Tube F2 now contains a ×10 000 dilution.
6 Using a different sterile pipette, transfer 0.1 cm³ from tube F2 to tube F3. Tube F3 now contains a × 1 000 000 dilution.
7 Using a sterile pipette or the same pipette as in Step 5, transfer 0.1 cm³ of ×100 diluted milk from tube F1 to the centre of the agar in the sterile Petri dish labelled F1. When you do this, open the lid of the Petri dish as little as possible and replace it rapidly.
8 Dip a nichrome wire or a glass spreader in 70% ethanol and pass it through a Bunsen burner flame. Keep the container of ethanol well away from the naked flame. Allow it to cool. Open the Petri dish and rapidly spread the milk as evenly as possible over the surface of the plate.
9 Using a sterile pipette or the same pipette as in Step 6, transfer 0.1 cm³ of × 10 000 diluted milk from F2 to the agar in Petri dish F3 and spread it as in Step 8.
10 Using a newly sterilised pipette, transfer 0.1 cm³ of ×1 000 000 diluted milk from F3 to the agar in Petri dish F3 and spread it as in Step 8.
11 Repeat the whole procedure, using the *stale* milk, tubes S1 to S3 and sterile Petri dishes S1 to S3.
12 Sellotape the lids to the dishes and incubate them upside down at 30 °C for 28–48 hours. Distinct colonies should then be visible.
13 *Without removing the lids*, examine the bacterial growth on the agar. Count and record the numbers of bacterial colonies, where possible. Multiply the number of colonies by the dilution to obtain an estimate of the total bacterial population in the milk.

For consideration

1 Have you obtained enough evidence to *prove* that bacteria reproduce rapidly in milk?
2 What are the main sources of error in this suggested procedure? What could you do to improve it?

REQUIREMENTS

Bunsen burner
Cotton wool
Incubator
Marker for writing on glass
Disinfectant for cleaning bench
Matches
Petri dishes (sterilised, containing nutrient agar) ×6
Pipettes (sterilised, 1 cm³ graduated) ×8
Spreader (glass or nichrome)
Test-tubes (sterilised) ×6
Test-tube rack

Distilled water, 100 cm³
Ethanol (70%)

Fresh milk
Stale milk of same type allowed to stand for 24 hours at room temperature

Highly flammable
ethanol

Biohazard
Bacteria

3   Why were the Petri dishes incubated, and why did they have to be incubated upside down?

4   What was the control in this experiment?

5   What were the dependent and independent variables in the experiment. Which independent variable was altered and which ones were kept constant?

6   How could you modify the experiment so as to estimate the *rate* at which the bacteria reproduce?

Projects

A project differs from an investigation in the following ways:
*   You have more choice in deciding what to study
*   Projects usually take longer and often involve a *series* of investigations
*   You will need to evaluate your findings as you proceed, and modify your project accordingly

Projects give you the opportunity to be creative. A successful project can give you a flavour of what it is like to be a professional research scientist. It involves working in detail on one problem, adapting your approach as you go along.

Choosing a project

Some people find it very easy to think of projects to do; others, however good they are at biology, find it very difficult. At the end of each chapter in this book some possible projects are suggested, often with some ideas to get you going. In many ways, though, it doesn't really matter *what* project you undertake, so long as it interests you. What is more important is *how* you undertake it. Having said that, several factors may help you to choose the subject of your project:
*   You may have a special interest in some part of biology
*   You may possess a particular skill (e.g. electronics, bird identification or photography)
*   An unusual opportunity may present itself (e.g. you live near a farm or get a holiday job working in a firm that makes biochemicals)
*   You may by chance come across an interesting biological phenomenon (e.g. large chunks may be missing from the leaves of a certain plant)

Here are three case studies showing how students chose their advanced level biology projects.

Case Study 1

Vanessa Woodhead was hoping to become a vet. At one point during her biology course she worked alongside a vet, gaining work experience. This brought her into contact with large numbers of dogs. These dogs routinely had their pulse rates taken in the vet's surgery. Vanessa noticed that the dogs had very different pulse rates. Some had resting pulse rates as low as 55 beats per minute, others as high as 155 per minute. Vanessa decided to investigate the factors that affect resting pulse rates in domestic dogs.

Case Study 2

Tracey Monks was unsure what to do for her biology project. Then a great gale struck. Near her home was a wood with trees belonging to a number of different species. Further from her home, but about 3 km from her Sixth Form College, was a beechwood. Here the wood consisted almost entirely of beech, believed to have been planted about 180 years earlier. Tracey decided to investigate the effects of the gale on these two very different woods.

Case Study 3

Alastair Swift hadn't the faintest idea what to do for his biology project. He had, though, found parts of ecology quite interesting and he thought it would be nice to have some guinea pigs at home. He hoped that perhaps he could do something by looking at the energetics of their growth – studying what each ate and weighing them.

Helping you to choose a possible project

- Make a list of those parts of biology that interest you
- Make a list of any experience you have that other biology students may not, e.g. ability to identify some group of organisms (e.g. cacti); relevant hobby or activity (such as keeping fish or regular childminding); distinctive habitat near where you live or which you have access to
- Make a list of some things you would really like to do for a project if only they were feasible
- Now draw together the results of the above three exercises to identify an area of biology in which you might realistically be able to do an original project. Don't worry about the precise title or detailed aims, just the area in which you might work

Identifying the aims of your project

Having identified a possible project, the next thing to do is to identify your aims. Broadly speaking, this means getting an idea of what you are trying to find out, and identifying the key questions you hope to answer. You may, tentatively, be able to suggest hypotheses and make some predictions to be tested.

Case Study 1

Vanessa had decided that she wanted to investigate the factors that affect resting pulse rates in dogs. She made a list of possible factors and came up with the following: Size of dog; Whether the dog was healthy or not; How fit the dog was; Breed of dog.

Case Study 2

Tracey knew that she wanted to compare the effects of the gale on two different woods. She decided that her project would have two main aims:
To see how the two woods differed before the gale.
To find out exactly what effect the gales had had on each wood.

Case Study 3

Alastair had decided that he wanted to look at the energetics of his two young pet guinea pigs. He therefore had two aims:
To determine exactly how much food they were eating.
To see how much of this food went into new guinea pigs (i.e. growth and reproduction).

Helping you to identify aims

- Suppose your project involved studying the succession of insects, fungi and other organisms on rotting fruits. Make a list of four questions your study might attempt to answer.
- Suppose your project involved investigating the reaction times of adults. Suggest four factors that might affect reaction times.
- Suppose your project involved identifying the invertebrates in a small river from near its source to the point where it enters the sea some 20 km away. Propose four hypotheses which you could test by collecting suitable data.
- For the area of biology which you are interested in, suggest either four key questions that could be asked or four hypotheses that could be tested.

Designing projects

Once you have identified a possible project and begun to establish its aims, you may want to get going straight away. First, though, you must have some sort of **experimental design**. This will allow you to collect the data you need in an appropriate way.

Case Study 1

Having decided to investigate the factors that affect resting pulse rate in dogs, Vanessa had identified four such possible factors: size of dog; whether the dog was healthy or not; how fit the dog was; breed of dog. She decided that all she needed to do, therefore, was to record these four bits of information and the resting pulse rate for each dog brought to the surgery where she was helping.

Case Study 2

Tracey had chosen to investigate the effects of a severe gale on two woods. She decided to study the following:
How the two woods differed in terms of the plant species they contained and the structure of their vegetation.
Whether the two woods differed in their soils and, if so, whether this was important
The strength of the wind in each wood
The effect the wind had had in each wood in bringing down trees
Whether some species of tree were more susceptible to wind damage than others
Whether the size of a tree affected its chance of being blown down

Case Study 3

Alastair was interested in studying the energetics of guinea pigs as they grew. He had decided to determine exactly how much food they ate and to see how much of this food was going into growth and reproduction. He therefore worked out the energy budgets of the guinea pigs over a period of several months, measuring the weight of food taken in, the weight of the droppings they produced and their change in body mass.

Alastair reasoned, with the help of his teacher, that these data would allow him to calculate how much energy the guinea pigs used in respiration as they grew, since, from the first law of thermodynamics, we have:

energy consumed = energy that goes into growth + energy that goes into reproduction + energy excreted and egested + energy respired.

Helping you to design projects

* Suppose your project involves studying the succession of organisms on rotting fruits. Describe a possible experimental design.
* Suppose your project involves investigating the reaction times of adults. Outline the procedure you might adopt.
* Suppose your project involves identifying the invertebrates of a small river from near its source to the point where it enters the sea. Describe a possible design for the project.
* For the area of biology which you are interested in suggest a possible experimental design, ensuring that it allows appropriate data to be collected to test a hypothesis.

Comments on the three case studies

Each of these three students completed successful projects. However, the three case studies illustrate some potential problems. In Vanessa's case (Case study 1), it was important that she had a valid way of obtaining her data. She worked alongside an experienced vet who helped her obtain a reliable measure of how fit each dog was. Because she was interested in looking at the relationship between resting pulse rate and such factors as fitness, mass and breed, she needed to obtain plenty of data in a form that could be analysed statistically. It is important before beginning a project to make sure that your experimental design will yield the right sort of data, and sufficient of it, for statistical analysis if this is appropriate to the project. Statistical analysis is dealt with on pages 247–258.

Tracey's project illustrates the difficulty of investigating a one-off phenomenon, in this case the effects of a particularly severe gale. By its very nature it is difficult to design a suitable experiment for this type of project, to test a hypothesis. There are usually problems in carrying out ecology projects that involve comparing the animals or plants of two very different areas. It is usually very difficult to determine precisely *why* the areas differ. This isn't to say that such projects should never be undertaken. However, they often work best when only one or two possible environmental variables are studied. Ecology experiments where the variable(s) can be manipulated in a controlled laboratory situation often give the best results.

Alastair's project illustrates the problem of small sample size, viz. two guinea pigs, though in his case it turned out that one of the guinea pigs was pregnant. This also complicated his original aims though it certainly ended up increasing the sample size. Alastair's experience shows the importance of being prepared, if need be, to modify your project in some way.

Modifying your project

As you proceed with your project, you should monitor your progress. Don't leave the analysis of your results to the very end. Instead, carry out preliminary analyses. These will enable you to modify your experimental design as you go along. There are several reasons why your experimental design may need modifying:

- You find you have bitten off more than you can chew and need to simplify your project. It is easy to underestimate the time required for project work.
- Unforeseen difficulties crop up, necessitating alterations.
- You find out something really interesting but unexpected, and decide to follow that up instead of your original aim.

All these are valid reasons for modifying your project. When it comes to sticking to your original experimental design, there's a fine line between showing perseverance and inflexibility. As a scientist you need constantly to evaluate your progress and think about whether to continue as you intended, or change tack.

Ethical considerations

Always consult your teacher about what you intend to do before carrying out a project. In particular:

- Don't cause any distress or suffering to animals (including invertebrates), for example by subjecting them to extremes of temperature or depriving them of food.
- Don't cause damage to the environment, for example by uprooting plants (illegal in the UK unless you have the landowner's permission) or lichens or by failing to return animals (e.g. woodlice) to the wild.
- Don't ask unduly personal questions of humans when using questionnaires.

Safety considerations

Always consult your teacher about what you intend to do before carrying out a project. Re-read the earlier section on safety (page 3).

When carrying out any field work:

- Preferably work in pairs. That way, if something goes wrong for one of you, the other can help or obtain assistance.
- Ensure you let your teacher and parent(s)/guardians know where you are.

2 Ecology

BOX 2.1 **Sampling techniques in ecology**

When you wish to investigate a population of organisms, or to test an hypothesis in ecology, it is usually impractical and too time-consuming to find and measure every individual. You need to obtain **samples**, in which the organisms or their features (length, mass, colour and so on) are in the same proportions as in the whole population.

Samples must be **representative**, and this is usually achieved by **randomising** them, using random numbers generated on a calculator or computer, or obtained from random number tables. The sampling procedure should be **repeated** enough times to allow statistical analysis of the results (see Appendix 247–258). In planning a sampling technique, the subsequent analysis of the results must always be borne in mind. Several sampling techniques, appropriate for different situations, are described below.

Quadrat sampling. A quadrat is an area in which plants or sedentary animals can be sampled. Quadrats are usually square, but can also be circular or rectangular.

The positions to be sampled can be determined by pacing out two axes at right angles and selecting random co-ordinates, using dice, random number tables or a random number generator on a computer. Alternatively, a rope can be stretched across a habitat and quadrats sampled in a straight line at regular intervals (**transect sampling**).

Assessing the occurrence of a species within a quadrat can be done in several ways. One possibility is simply to count the individuals of the species within the quadrat. After repeating this in different positions the results can then be expressed as the average number of individuals per unit area (the **density**). Alternatively, the **percentage cover** may be estimated by eye; this is the proportion of the ground area, viewed from directly above, covered by the above-ground parts of the species, such as stems and leaves. Another possibility is to calculate **percentage frequency**, which is the percentage of the quadrats in which a species occurs.

The size of the quadrat should be chosen carefully**.** The optimum size is one which includes about eighty per cent of the species in the habitat. A larger size than this wastes time and effort; a smaller size is unrepresentative and more quadrats have to be placed and sampled to compensate. The optimum size is about $0.25\,m^2$ for short grassland; $1\,m^2$ for tall grassland, rocky shore, heather moor, investigating the zonation of plants at the margin of a lake from the lake to dry land, and earthworm sampling; and $100\,m^2$ for woodlands.

Line transects. These are used for describing how species vary in a straight line across a habitat. They are particularly useful for studying different zones, for example, down a rocky shore, across a salt marsh or a sand dune system, or towards a lake or pond margin. Select a starting point at random. Stretch a rope across the habitat. Arrange quadrats at equal intervals along it. Estimate by eye the percentage cover of all the species in each quadrat. An alternative is to measure the length covered by each species which the line crosses, and then to express the data in histograms. Replication can be achieved by sampling three or more parallel transects.

Point quadrats. These are used for plant sampling in short grassland. Pointed needles, usually pushed through a horizontal wooden or metal frame in groups of ten, are lowered one by one through the vegetation. Each plant touched by the point of the needle is recorded. The results are converted to **percentage cover** (the proportion of points at which a species occurs) or **cover**

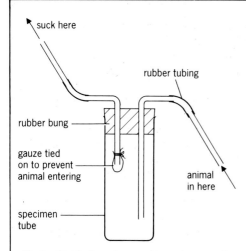

Illustration 1 A pooter, used to suck up small arthropods. There they can be anaesthetised if necessary, identified and counted.

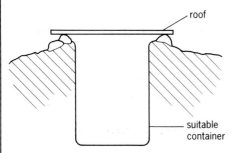

Illustration 2 A cross-section through a pitfall trap, used to sample arthropods moving over the soil surface. A wooden or glass roof can be supported above the jam jar on stones to prevent rainfall from flooding the pitfall trap.

repetition (the total number of touches on a species expressed as a percentage of the number of points sampled). Useful for annual recording in long-term experiments.

Sweep netting. This is used for sampling invertebrates from tall grassland. Take a standard number of sweeps with the open face of a net. Trap the organisms in a pooter (Illustration 1) and anaesthetise them. Identify and count the animals in the sample.

Beating. Used for sampling invertebrates from shrubs and the lower branches of trees. Lay a sheet or beating tray beneath the branches. Give the branches a standard number of thumps of the same intensity. Quickly capture the relevant organisms, for example with a pooter, and identify and count them.

Light sampling. A light trap, containing a tungsten or ultraviolet lamp, is used to attract and catch flying insects at night. The insects fly against a vertical metal plate and fall into a collection jar.

Pitfall trapping. This is used to capture arthropods walking over the soil surface. A empty jam jar, yoghurt carton or similar receptacle is inserted in the soil so that its rim is flush with the surface, and camouflaged (Illustration 2). Place several jars in each habitat. Passing arthropods fall into the containers and cannot escape. Examine each jar at frequent intervals, to reduce the likelihood that carnivores eat other arthropods, and remove the live organisms for counting and identification.

Tullgren and Baermann funnels. These devices (Illustration 3) are used to sample the organisms which inhabit the air spaces (Tullgren) and water-filled spaces (Baermann) in soil and leaf litter.

Kick sampling. This method is used to sample invertebrates from streams. Hold a fine net downstream from the place in which you intend to sample. Use a standard sideways motion of your Wellington boots to disturb the creatures on the bottom so that they swim or drift into the net. Count the

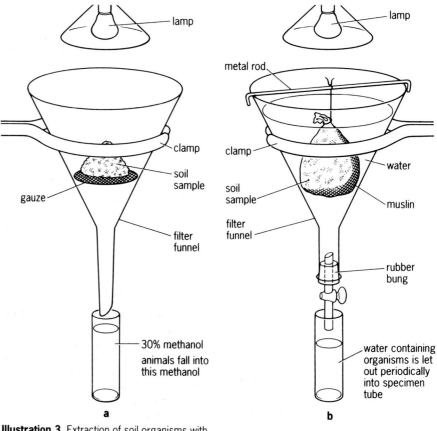

Illustration 3 Extraction of soil organisms with (**a**) a Tullgren funnel and (**b**) a Baermann funnel.

individuals of each species obtained from a certain number of kicks. For comparison, repeat the procedure exactly in different habitats.

Drift netting. Long vertical poles at each end of a net are pushed into the stream bed. After a standard length of time the organisms caught in the net are identified and counted. This is valuable in comparing different parts of a stream, assessing seasonal changes or comparing animal movements throughout day and night.

Pond sampling. In your mind's eye, divide the pond into a series of microhabitats – the sides, beneath plant leaves, open water, muddy bottom and so on. Use a simple net to remove a certain number of samples from each microhabitat. Turn each set of samples into a separate white bowl and identify and count the individuals.

Earthworm sampling. Arrange quadrats at random, or at various distances from the centre of a tree. A dilute solution of mustard (1 g mustard per litre of water) is the cheapest, most effective way to bring worms to the surface (see Projects, pages 37–39).

Sampling of individuals. If you wish to collect a sample of, say, plants, or the flowers of a species, the most unbiased procedure is to number all the plants, and to randomly select numbers and then sample the plants with these numbers.

Note: Further details of these and other sampling techniques can be found in Dowdeswell, W.H. *Ecology, Principles and Practice*, Heinemann, 1984, Slingsby, D. & Cook, C. *Practical Ecology*, Macmillan, 1986, and Williams, G. *Techniques and Fieldwork in Ecology*, Bell & Hyman, 1987.

2.1 INVESTIGATION

Investigating the microhabitats in a pond or aquarium

A pond or aquarium is a self-supporting ecosystem, but even within its limited volume, the species are not distributed at random. This investigation allows you to work out the **microhabitats** occupied by each species (it also links with Investigations 2.5, 2.10, 2.13 and 2.17). A microhabitat is a small patch of habitat which provides a distinctive micro-environment and contains a particular range of species, for example, the underside of water lily leaves, or the mud at the base of the pond.

Guidance

List as many microhabitats within the pond as possible.

Sample each microhabitat with a small net, identifying and counting the organisms (see Box 2.1, above).

If you are studying an aquarium, watch some individuals (e.g. fish, snails, water shrimps, water lice) through the glass walls and quantify the proportion of the time which they spend in different places.

Use the relevant probes, and data-logging equipment, to measure the physical variables in each microhabitat.

Devise your own experiments in which representatives of a species are provided with the choice of two distinct environments. Where do they spend their time?

For consideration

1   Summarise the ways in which particular environmental factors change in the water; in particular, light intensity, oxygen concentration, pH and the availability of living and dead plant food.
2   Does a pond provide more microhabitats than an aquarium? If so, why? How could you alter an aquarium so that it provides more microhabitats?
3   You have worked out the places in the pond, or aquarium, in which each species is most often found. For each species in turn, suggest why it 'prefers' this particular microhabitat. As well as abiotic factors, such as oxygen availability, you must consider other aspects of its **niche**, its role in the community. What does it eat, where can its food be found, and what eats it? Do these factors influence its distribution pattern?

REQUIREMENTS

Small nets or colanders for pond sampling
Data-logging equipment
Aquarium with organisms, well-established

4   Some species are restricted to one microhabitat, but others are jacks of all trades, flitting from one microhabitat to another. What are the advantages and disadvantages of each lifestyle?

The zonation of organisms on a rocky shore or a salt marsh

Between the low and high tide marks on a salt marsh or rocky shore live species which are subjected regularly, twice a day, to rapid changes in sunlight, salinity, oxygen supply, food supply and predation. Whilst some species are motile and move up and down with the tides, others are sedentary. This investigation allows you to compare the distribution patterns of these sedentary species and to speculate on reasons for the differences (see also 2.4 Investigation, page 17).

Guidance

At low tide, run a transect line up the shore (see Box 2.1, page 13, for sampling techniques). Starting at the seaward end, sample 1 m² quadrats at appropriate intervals. In each quadrat record the percentage cover of each seaweed species (see Box 2.1) and count the numbers of each recognisable animal species (barnacles, topshells, whelks and so on). Express your data in the form of histograms.

For consideration

1   The main factors that vary from the top to the bottom of a rocky shore or salt marsh, and which might affect the distribution patterns of the species growing there, are listed in the introduction. How and why does each change from low tide mark to high tide mark?
2   Can you generalise about the distribution patterns of red, green and brown seaweeds?
3   Use reference books, or use direct observation, to find out what each species of animal eats. How does their food supply vary up and down the shore, and how much do food supply and predation affect the distribution pattern of each animal species?

The distribution patterns of woodland herbs in relation to light intensity

The intensity of shade cast by the canopy of trees in a wood may influence the distribution pattern of herbs growing beneath. Obtaining evidence to test this hypothesis is an interesting sampling problem! In this investigation you will sample woodland herbs and measure the incident light energy which impinges upon them.

This investigation should be performed in summer, when deciduous trees are leafy. Even within the same quadrat, the light intensity may vary from minute to minute, let alone hour to hour. Sampling the plant species is relatively easy. To sample light intensity it is best to mark the sampled sites and return to them one after the other, taking light intensity readings from all the plots within as short a time as possible, at regular intervals throughout the day.

Guidance

Select an area of woodland with a range of tree species and a range of herb species on the woodland floor, say an area 100 m × 100 m. Sample with randomly arranged 1 m² quadrats, recording the percentage cover of up to five selected species of herb and the tree species above them. Mark each plot for a light reading later. A large sample size is necessary to provide reliable results.

After the plant sampling, wait for the light intensity to be fairly constant, and then rapidly tour the plots, recording light intensity with a light meter at each plot as many times as possible through the day. Convert these to relative light intensities and average the results for each site.

In the absence of a light meter, you could use a semi-automatic camera which has a display in the viewfinder of speed and aperture. Set the shutter to a fixed speed. Then each stop in the direction f-11, f-8, f-5.6, f-4 doubles the light intensity.

Rank the light intensities from the lowest to the highest. Divide the light intensities into five equal groups. Work out the average percentage cover of each species in each of the five groups and exhibit the results in histogram form.

For consideration

1 How could you alter your sampling technique so as to allow areas with a wide variety of light intensities to be adequately (equally?) represented in the sample?
2 Review your data. Suggest why some species are more shade-tolerant than others. What factors other than light intensity appear to influence the distribution patterns of your woodland herbs?
3 Some woodland herbs, e.g. bluebell *Hyacinthoides non-scriptus*, grow and flower before the trees come into leaf. What effect might this have on your conclusions?

2.4 INVESTIGATION

Distribution patterns of mosses or seaweeds in relation to the evaporating power of the environment

The distribution patterns of seaweeds, mosses and liverworts can often be related to evaporative stress more easily than the patterns of flowering plants.

Seaweeds, and the gametophytes of many mosses and liverworts, usually lack the waxy cuticle which prevents water loss in many other plants. Different species differ in their resistance to desiccation, and this may affect their distribution patterns. For example, on a salt marsh or rocky shore, the further away from the sea a species occurs, the shorter is the time during which it is submerged and the longer the time during which it is exposed to the air. Similarly, a moss on one side of a wall may receive more direct sunlight and be exposed to far higher temperatures, than one on the other side. The rate at which a seaweed or bryophyte loses mass in the laboratory provides a rough guide to its **desiccation resistance.**

In this investigation you are invited to investigate the distribution patterns of two or three species in their natural habitats, and to relate the patterns to their desiccation resistance in the laboratory.

Guidance

Your teacher will help you to choose a suitable habitat which contains two or three species which you intend to investigate.

Quantify the distribution patterns of the species using one or more appropriate techniques from Box 2.1, page 13.

If the species are abundant (care, conservation!) take small samples from the habitat into the laboratory; hang them on a 'washing line' to dry in similar conditions, and weigh them at intervals.

Draw graphs of their mass against time, and relate their distribution patterns to desiccation resistance.

In a parallel investigation, determine the time of death of individuals of each species as they dry. A moss cell in a leaf is regarded as dead when it remains irreversibly shrunken after being immersed in water for half an hour.

For consideration

1 How might water on the surface of the organisms at the start of the experiment affect the results?
2 How might the state of dehydration of each species when you removed it from the habitat affect the results? What precautions could be taken to ensure that each species starts at a comparable starting point?
3 What precautions did you take to ensure that your estimates of water loss in the different species were comparable and accurate?
4 What other factors apart from resistance to desiccation might affect the distribution patterns of the species you have investigated?
5 Define the cycles of wetting and drying to which each of your species is exposed. In general, photosynthesis stops when a plant is slightly dehydrated and resumes only slowly on rewetting. Bearing in mind that the species continue to respire when slightly dehydrated, what effect might the wetting-drying cycle have on the species you have investigated?

6   Many mosses and liverworts have leaves only one cell thick, in which every cell is photosynthetic. What are the advantages and disadvantages of this arrangement, compared with the leaves of flowering plants?

Analysis of the food web in a pond

Introduction

Many textbooks contain diagrams of **food webs**, showing what organism eats what in a community. How is a food web diagram arrived at? This investigation introduces the difficulties of constructing food webs, using a pond or aquarium.

Guidance

Sample the organisms in the pond or aquarium and identify them.

Find out as much as you can about the feeding habits of each species. You can (a) look up their likely foods in reference books, (b) observe each organism feeding, (c) examine the feeding apparatus of each species and draw conclusions about the nature of its food, and (d) look at the gut contents under a microscope.

Place together, in pairs, in Petri dishes, beakers, or small aquaria, a predator and a likely prey species (e.g. fish and water fleas). Observe their behaviour and note whether or not predation takes place. You can also set up beakers containing an intact plant and a possible herbivore, and find out if the plants are eaten.

Draw a food web for the pond, including the plants; some of the feeding relationships will be definite and others only tentative. Show this uncertainty in your diagram.

REQUIREMENTS

Pond or aquarium, well-established.
Pond dipping nets
Teat pipettes
Microscopes, binocular and monocular
Microscope slides and cover slips
Identification guides
Petri dishes
Beakers or small aquaria
Reference books (for feeding habits)

For consideration

1   How could you modify your techniques to estimate the dry mass of food eaten by each organism, and the proportion of its food derived from various sources?
2   What proportion of the food entering the guts of pond organisms is lost in egesta?
3   Have you included detritus, detritivores and decomposers (such as bacteria and fungi) in your web? Where would they fit in?
4   Sketch approximate pyramids of numbers and biomass for the pond or aquarium.

The energetics of a stick insect or a desert locust

The energy budget of a primary consumer can be determined in the laboratory for the Indian stick insect (*Carausius morosus*), a herbivore which can be fed on the leaves of privet (*Ligustrum* spp.) The individuals in normal laboratory populations are all females. The energy in the food they eat is egested and excreted (in faeces and uric acid), released in metabolism as heat energy, or devoted to eggs and growth in body mass.

The experiment can equally well be done with a desert locust (*Schistocerca gregaria*) provided with grass. Locusts eat more voraciously than stick insects, and need be left with food for only two days before the energy budget is determined. Locusts respire more rapidly than stick insects, and are less likely to produce eggs during the experiment, but they are more difficult to handle.

Procedure

1   Select a healthy shoot of privet with four to ten leaves. Without detaching them from the shoot, trace the outlines of all the leaves onto squared paper. Make sure that you record the position on the shoot which the leaf occupied.
2   Weigh the shoot and record its mass (P1).
3   With clingfilm, cover the top of a McCartney bottle or small beaker containing water. Push the base of the privet shoot through the clingfilm into the water. Place the bottle in the centre of half a Petri dish and stabilise it with plasticine (Figure 2.1).
4   Weigh a stick insect (to the nearest 0.01 g) and record its mass (ST1). Put it onto the privet.
5   Add to the Petri dish base a humidifier consisting of a McCartney bottle containing water with pieces of paper towelling stuck into it. Stick it to the base of the Petri dish base with plasticine.
6   Cover the privet, the stick insect and the humidifier with a bell jar or coffee jar. Leave the set-up for a week.

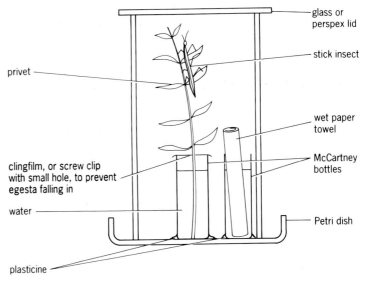

Figure 2.1 An apparatus suitable for investigating the energetics of a stick insect. If the experiment is to be performed on a locust, substitute a known fresh mass of grass for the privet. G. Monger (ed.), *Revised Nuffield A-level Biology, Practical Guide 7*, Longmans, 1986.

After a week you will need to collect the stick insect, its eggs, its egesta and the uneaten leaves. You will also have to measure the respiration rate of the insect. Proceed as follows:

7 Remove the insect and determine and record its mass (ST2).
8 Place the insect in a respirometer (2.7, Practical) and determine its metabolic rate as the volume of oxygen absorbed per unit time at room temperature. Measure its respiration rate over as many minutes as possible.
9 Weigh a cavity microscope slide (E1). Carefully collect all the egesta you can find (distinguishing them from eggs), place then in the cavity of the slide and reweigh (E2).
10 Weigh another cavity microscope slide (EGS1). Carefully collect all the eggs you can find, place them in the cavity of the slide and reweigh (EGS2).
11 Extract the remains of the privet shoot from the water. Blot it dry. Reweigh it (P2).
12 Remove each leaf from the shoot in turn. Place it on its original outline on the graph paper. Draw round the edge of the leaf.
13 The masses determined so far are all *fresh* masses. If you have time, determine the dry masses of the leaf blades (to provide a more accurate estimate of energy content per unit mass), egesta and eggs. Reweigh them after they have been heated in an oven at 105 °C for at least 48 hours.

Processing the results

The masses you have determined (in grams) can be converted into energy contents (in kJ) by applying simple conversion factors.

For the stick insect, FE = E + R + P, where FE is the energy in the food eaten, E is the energy in egesta, R is the heat lost in metabolism (crudely, respiration) and P is the energy content of the eggs and the extra mass of the insect.

14 To calculate the energy deposited in insect and eggs (P in the equation under 'Processing the results' above) add the fresh mass of eggs (EGS2 − EGS1) to the increase in fresh mass of the insect (ST2 − ST1). Calculate their energy contents by assuming that 1 g of fresh eggs or insect contains 5 kJ.
15 The fresh mass of the privet eaten is P2 − P1. Calculate its energy content, assuming that 1 g fresh privet contains 3 kJ.
16 As a check, count squares on the graph paper to estimate the area of leaf eaten by the insect. Weigh leaves of known area to calculate the mass per cm² of the leaf. Then convert the area of leaf eaten to the equivalent mass, and calculate its energy content, assuming that 1 g of fresh privet contains 3 kJ of energy.
17 The fresh mass of egesta produced is E1 − E2. Calculate its energy content, assuming that 1 g of fresh egesta contains 10 kJ.

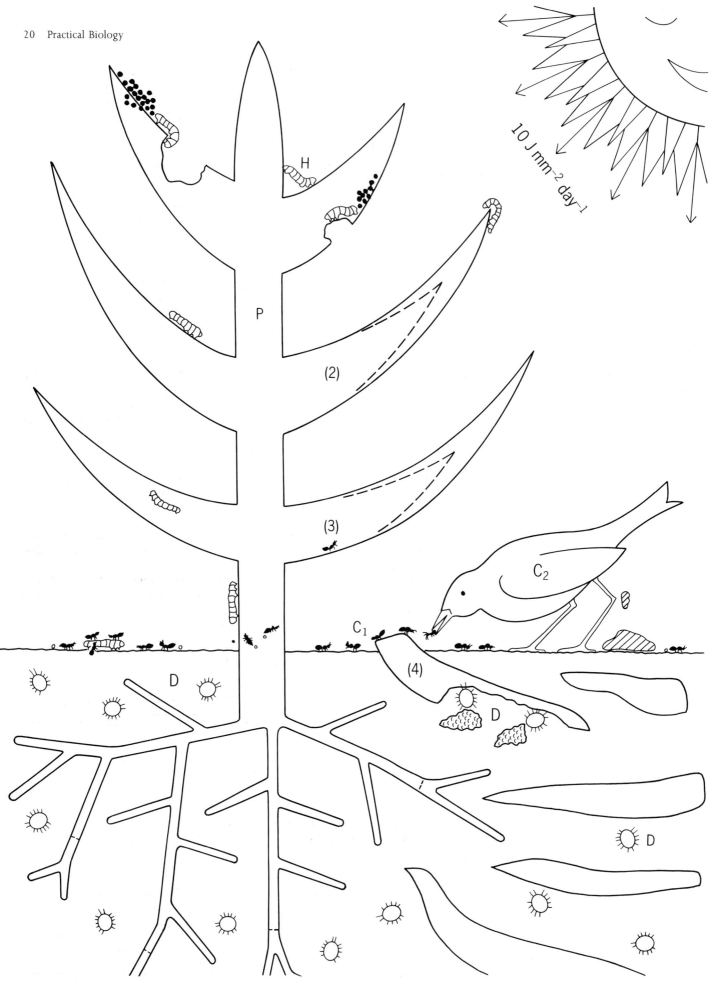

Figure 2.2 "A paper ecosystem." You will need an A3 copy of this sheet for the investigation.

18 Calculate the heat lost in metabolism *in a week*. Assume that as a consequence of the uptake of $1 \, \text{cm}^3$ of oxygen, $0.02 \, \text{kJ}$ of energy is released. Convert your respirometer measure to one hour and multiply by 168 (the number of hours in a week).

19 Put together your energy budget equation. Does it balance?

For consideration

1 List all the sources of error in the experiment.

2 Suggest three reasons why you placed clingfilm over the bottle which held the privet stem in water.

3 What effect would a change in mean temperature have had on the energy budget?

4 How might you expect the energy budget to differ in a carnivorous insect of the same size?

References

Slatter, R.J. The energy budget of the stick insect. *School Science Review*, 62 (219), 1980, and G. Monger (Ed.) *Revised Nuffield Biology, Practical Guide 7*, Investigation 29B, Longman, 1986.

2.7 PRACTICAL EXERCISE

A paper ecosystem

In this practical you are provided with a highly simplified model ecosystem as a diagram and data, and asked to work out an energy flow diagram, a pyramid of biomass and a pyramid of energy flow. The exercise is intended to provide you with a feel for the problems which an ecologist faces in investigating energy flow through a real ecosystem. A *paper* ecosystem is the next best thing.

You are asked to consider what happens to the energy entering the community shown in Figure 2.2 in one day (24 hours). You will be provided with a photocopy of Figures 2.2 and 2.3. These diagrams will help you to visualise a real ecosystem. Work in pairs. Work through the procedure, then answer the questions below.

Procedure

1 In Figure 2.2 P is a plant, H is a herbivore, C1 and C2 are carnivores and D is a detritivore. The ultimate aim of the investigation is to complete the energy flow diagram in Figure 2.3.

2 Throughout your calculations, instead of weighing organisms, assume that the area of each living and dead organism in the diagram is proportional to its mass, and its energy content, as follows:

$1 \, \text{cm}^2$ of area $(100 \, \text{mm}^2)$ is equivalent to $21 \, \text{J}$ of energy
$4 \, \text{cm}^3$ of area is equivalent to $1 \, \text{g}$ of dry mass

1 small square on the graph paper provided $(4 \, \text{mm}^2)$ is equivalent to $0.84 \, \text{J}$ of energy.

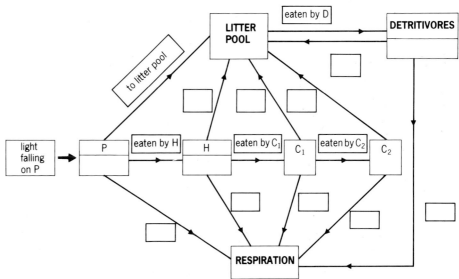

Figure 2.3 An energy flow diagram to be completed for the ecosystem. All the values will be in joules per day. The rectangles beside the arrows represent energy flows (after Aston).

3 The light energy received by the plant amounts to $10\,\mathrm{J\,mm^{-2}\,day^{-1}}$.

4 To calculate the **net primary production** (the energy contributed to dry plant mass during a day) you will need to add the energy stored in above-ground parts to the energy stored in below-ground parts.

5 To work out the energy trapped in the above-ground parts, assume that light illuminates one side of a two-dimensional plant. The dotted lines in leaves 2 and 3 of the plant show the leaf edge 24 hours ago. The solid lines show the leaf edge now. Assume that *all* the above-ground parts of the plant (the stems as well as the leaves) have grown by the same proportion as these two leaves, over the previous day.

6 To calculate the energy trapped in roots, assume that only the side roots shown beyond the dotted lines in plant P have been added in the last 24 hours.

7 Assume that of the total energy trapped in photosynthesis by the plant over one day, a quarter was lost in respiration and the remaining three-quarters was devoted to net primary production.

8 Leaf 4 was the only part of the plant to die and join the litter pool during the day. The other leaves shown underground make up, with leaf 4, the total litter pool.

9 Holes in living leaves were made by the feeding of the two herbivores H shown near them in 24 hours. Assume that all the other individuals of species H in the diagram fed at the same rate. The hole in dead leaf 4 was made in 24 hours by the two detritivore individuals D seen feeding on it. Assume that the other individuals of species D all fed at the same rate.

10 Faecal production by two individuals of species H and two of species D is shown. Assume that all the individuals of species H produce the same amount as these H individuals, and all the individuals of species D the same as these D individuals.

11 Calculate the energy devoted to body mass in a day by species H, by assuming that the individuals are now double the mass they were 24 hours ago. Calculate the energy devoted to body mass in a day by species D by subtraction: subtract from the energy in the food eaten by D in 24 hours (i) the energy lost in respiration (see below) and (ii) the energy lost in faeces.

12 The respiration rates of Species H and D were determined with a respirometer (Figure 2.4). The net meniscus movements for species H and D are shown in Table 2.1 in $\mathrm{mm\,min^{-1}}$. From these data, calculate the average net oxygen consumption over 24 hours for each species. Convert the figures to moles per day by remembering that at room temperature, one mole of a gas occupies about 24 litres.

Table 2.1 Movements of menisci in respirometers (Figure 2.4) for animals H and D, ten at a time. Units are $\mathrm{mm\,min^{-1}}$. Inward movements of the manometer fluid (positive oxygen consumption) are positive; outward movements are indicated by –.

	Reading	Experiment movement	Control movement
H	1	17.0	–2.0
	2	22.0	0.0
	3	23.5	3.5
	4	19.0	0.0
	5	21.0	–4.0
D	1	23.0	–0.5
	2	19.0	1.5
	3	20.0	2.0
	4	17.5	0.0
	5	20.0	–5.0

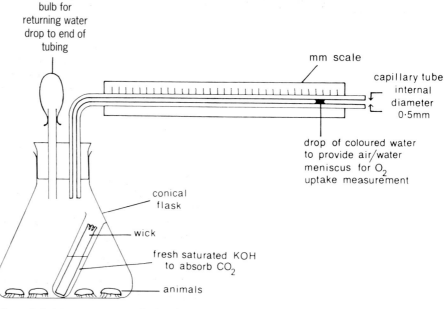

Figure 2.4 A respirometer, used to measure the rates of oxygen uptake by species H and D. The results are in Table 2.1. Notice that the rates measured are the oxygen uptakes of *ten* individuals of each species. The volumes of gas absorbed must be calculated from the meniscus movement on the basis of the internal diameter of the capillary tube.

According to the standard equation for aerobic respiration,

$$C_6H_{12}O_6 + 6O_2 \longrightarrow 6CO_2 + 6H_2O + 2880 \text{ kJ mol}^{-1}$$

six moles of oxygen release 2880 kJ of energy from one mole of glucose in aerobic respiration. Knowing the number of moles of gas which species H and species D absorb in a day, estimate the energy in kilojoules which each species releases in respiration in a day.

13 Each individual C1 eats one H per day, as shown. Only five C1 individuals produced faeces in the study period (can you find them?).

14 Animal C2 spent only 0.5 per cent of its time in our ecosystem, and ate only one C1 individual as shown. The faeces production shown for the C2 individual is the total for 24 hours across all the ecosystems in which species C2 fed.

15 Calculate as many figures as possible in the energy flow diagram for the ecosystem (Figure 2.3).

16 Calculate the energy present in the dry mass of the organisms at each trophic level and plot a pyramid of biomass for the ecosystem.

17 In terms of joules per day, calculate the rate at which energy enters the plants in the system and is transferred from one trophic level to the next. Plot a pyramid of energy flow.

For consideration

1 List as many flaws as you can in the assumptions you have been told to make at each stage of the calculations.

2 Comment on the efficiency of plant P in trapping light energy. How is the energy lost?

3 Discuss the relationship between consumption, faeces production and respiration for different animals.

REQUIREMENTS

A3-sized version of Figure 2.2
Calculator
Acetate of graph paper (2 mm squares)

Reference

Aston, T.J. Energy flow through a paper ecosystem. *Journal of Biological Education*, Vol. 22 No. 4, 275–284, 1985, which provides much of the data used here.

2.8 INVESTIGATION

Comparing the value of two woodland sites for conservation

Conservationists, particularly those belonging to local naturalists' trusts, often have to make difficult decisions in selecting land to be purchased as nature reserves. They need to be as objective as possible in evaluating sites. In this investigation you can compare the **conservation value** of two wildlife sites.

Guidance

Your teacher will help you to select two sites which support the same general type of vegetation, such as two patches of woodland or two fields.

Construct a table which assigns scores to the desirable features of each habitat from the conservation point of view. An example for woodlands is given in Table 2.2. It can readily be adapted to cater for grasslands or any other type of vegetation.

Assess the scores of each site on a four-point scale. Multiply the scores for each site together to provide its **conservation value**. Which site is more worthy of conservation?

For consideration

1 If you had taken into account the *cost* of maintaining each site as a nature reserve, including the control of visitors and paying the salary of a warden, would you still have picked the same site?

2 Should you have taken into account the total number of species which each site supports? Suggest other criteria which might also have been included in the assessment.

Table 2.2 A table suitable for evaluating the conservation value of woodlands. Each woodland is scored for eight factors. Each factor is scored on a four-point scale. The scores for all the factors are multiplied together to assess the relative value of the woodland for conservation – the higher the score, the better.

Special factors include historical association, accessibility, views and the presence of rarities.

The index can be adapted for grasslands or any other habitat type.

Factor	Points			
	1	2	3	4
1 Size of woodland	small	medium	large	very large
2 Position in landscape	secluded	average	prominent	very prominent
3 Number of people viewing each year	few	average	many	very many
4 Habitat diversity	monotonous	some paths	some rides & clearings	rides, clearings, water etc.
5 Composition & structure	young plantation or derelict woodland	mixed pole-stage crops	semi-mature or unevenly aged woodland with fairly large trees	mature or unevenly aged woodland with very large trees
6 Compatibility in the landscape	just acceptable	acceptable	good	excellent
7 Rarity value	tree & herb composition common	a few unusual species	many unusual species	unique to 50 km radius
8 Special factors	none	one	two	three or more

(freely modified from C.R. Tubbs and J.W. Blackwood, Ecological evaluation of land for planning purposes. *Biological Conservation* **3**, 169–172, 1971)

2.9 INVESTIGATION

·Preparing a management plan for a habitat

Every area managed for nature, such as a nature reserve, should have a **management plan** and this investigation provides you with the opportunity to write one. The plan should explain the aims of preserving an area of suitable habitat and the ways in which it should be managed over the next few years to achieve these objectives. It may also suggest how new habitats might be created to increase the range of species which the reserve supports. An example is given in Figure 2.5.

Rarely can a wildlife reserve be managed adequately by merely leaving it alone. The vegetation may naturally undergo **succession**, a directional change in the plant and animal species present at a site. This may make conditions less and less suitable for particular species whose preservation was intended when the reserve was set up. Alien species may invade the habitat, visitors or holiday makers may destroy it and disturb the animals, and pollution may deplete the variety of species. A management plan must suggest policies to cope with all these factors.

Guidance

Select an area which might be suitable as a nature reserve. This may be part of your school grounds, a local copse or hedgerow, a pond or stream, or even an existing nature reserve. Ideally, it should be an area where you have already carried out some ecological sampling, so that you are familiar with many of the species.

First survey the whole area, and make an annotated sketch plan showing the main types of habitat into which your nature reserve might be divided. Make a note of any interesting features or unusual species.

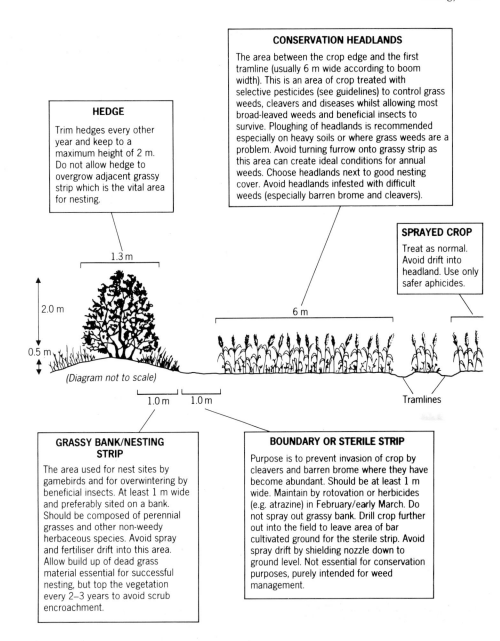

HEDGE

Trim hedges every other year and keep to a maximum height of 2 m. Do not allow hedge to overgrow adjacent grassy strip which is the vital area for nesting.

CONSERVATION HEADLANDS

The area between the crop edge and the first tramline (usually 6 m wide according to boom width). This is an area of crop treated with selective pesticides (see guidelines) to control grass weeds, cleavers and diseases whilst allowing most broad-leaved weeds and beneficial insects to survive. Ploughing of headlands is recommended especially on heavy soils or where grass weeds are a problem. Avoid turning furrow onto grassy strip as this area can create ideal conditions for annual weeds. Choose headlands next to good nesting cover. Avoid headlands infested with difficult weeds (especially barren brome and cleavers).

SPRAYED CROP

Treat as normal. Avoid drift into headland. Use only safer aphicides.

1.3 m

2.0 m

0.5 m

(Diagram not to scale)

6 m

Tramlines

1.0 m   1.0 m

GRASSY BANK/NESTING STRIP

The area used for nest sites by gamebirds and for overwintering by beneficial insects. At least 1 m wide and preferably sited on a bank. Should be composed of perennial grasses and other non-weedy herbaceous species. Avoid spray and fertiliser drift into this area. Allow build up of dead grass material essential for successful nesting, but top the vegetation every 2–3 years to avoid scrub encroachment.

BOUNDARY OR STERILE STRIP

Purpose is to prevent invasion of crop by cleavers and barren brome where they have become abundant. Should be at least 1 m wide. Maintain by rotovation or herbicides (e.g. atrazine) in February/early March. Do not spray out grassy bank. Drill crop further out into the field to leave area of bar cultivated ground for the sterile strip. Avoid spray drift by shielding nozzle down to ground level. Not essential for conservation purposes, purely intended for weed management.

MACHINERY

A specially designed sprayer is now available which can selectively spray a six-metre strip along the headland while treating the main crop with standard chemicals. Each part of the machinery is independent of the other, thus saving the need for a separate run along the Conservation Headland.

While spraying sterile strips it is vital to prevent drift into crop and hedge bottom. A very useful device, which applies the chemical safely and accurately from the tractor, has been designed for this purpose.

For further information on these two pieces of equipment contact the Conservation Headlands Field Officer.

Figure 2.5 Ways in which a field margin might be treated to make it ideally suitable for wildlife conservation. From D.J. Boatman, *Game Conservancy Review*, 1989. (N.W. Sotherton, The Game Conservancy Trust)

On this basis, think carefully about the aims of setting up the reserve, and write down your objectives. This is most important, and may require advice from your teacher.

- Which plant communities do you wish to preserve?
- Which animal species should you conserve?
- Are there any species you wish to eliminate?
- Can you create any new conditions and introduce any new species?

Then you must write your management plan. On the basis of your ecological understanding, explain how you should treat each segment of the potential reserve to conserve the communities and species you wish. Bear in mind that communities, if left alone, may change away from the species composition you wish to preserve – short grassland becomes tall grassland, and tall grassland becomes scrub, for example. You might need to mow, introduce grazing animals, cut out shrubs or even apply a herbicide to achieve the vegetation you want. The whole suite of measures should be costed.

For consideration

1 How should access to the reserve to humans be managed? Should you confine visitors to a small number of paths?
2 Examine the reserve from the point of view of 'wildlife corridors'. Can species migrate freely into and out of the reserve along ribbons of suitable habitat, such as streams or hedgerows?

2.10 INVESTIGATION

Comparing pollution levels in freshwater using a biotic index

Well-oxygenated freshwater rivers, streams, ponds and lakes support a wider range of animal species than poorly-oxygenated water bodies (Table 2.3). The addition of organic matter or fertiliser ultimately causes the water to become deoxygenated by the respiration of an expanding population of bacteria. Some water animals are more sensitive than others to depletion of oxygen, and the more sensitive ones die out when the water is polluted.

The range of animal species which occurs at a freshwater site can therefore provide a sensitive indication of the degree of pollution. In this investigation you can compare the animal species at different sites along the same river or stream, or compare different ponds or canals, and relate the differences to oxygen levels in the water and possible sources of pollution.

Guidance

Your teacher will select two ponds for comparison, one polluted and the other unpolluted. Alternatively, find or a river, stream or canal with an effluent outflow. You could sample both upstream and downstream from the outflow.

Danger

Table 2.3 Freshwater animals as indicators of pollution.

Class of waterway	Fauna	Biochemical oxygen demand (mg O_2 absorbed dm^{-3} water at 20°C in 5 days)	Waterway used for:
I	Diverse; salmon, trout, grayling, stonefly and mayfly nymphs, caddis larvae, *Gammarus*.	0–3	Domestic supply
II	Trout rarely dominant; chub, dace, caddis larvae, *Gammarus*.	3–10 (increased in summer at times of low flow)	Agriculture. Industrial processes
III	Roach, gudgeon, *Asellus*; mayfly nymphs and caddis larvae rare.	10–15	Irrigation
IV	Fish absent. Red chironomid larvae (bloodworms) and *Tubifex* worms present.	15–30 (completely deoxygenated from time to time).	Very little. Unsuitable for amenity use
V	Barren, or with fungus or small *Tubifex* worms.	> 30	None

(Adapted from D.H. Mills, *An Introduction to Freshwater Ecology*, Oliver and Boyd, 1972)

Produce a sketch map of the site, and establish as precisely as possible the volume and timing of the addition of the organic matter to the water.

Using standard sampling techniques (Box 2.1) sample the animals present at each site and identify and count them as far as possible.

If an oxygen meter is available, measure the oxygen content of the water, at a variety of depths, at each sampling point.

Alternatively, take water samples at each point and determine the 'Biological Oxygen Demand' (B.O.D.) using the Winkler method. The B.O.D. is the volume of oxygen in cm^3 absorbed by the organisms in a litre of water incubated for five days at $20\,^{\circ}C$. To determine this you will need to collect a water sample from each site with the minimum possible disturbance. Add to each sample a known volume of aerated 'dilution water'. This contains nutrient salts, so that bacterial activity will not be inhibited during the incubation by lack of nutrient ions. Pour each sample into a $250\,cm^3$ sample bottle and incubate in the dark for five days at $20\,^{\circ}C$, together with control bottles which only contain dilution water.

Determine the concentration of dissolved oxygen in each flask at the beginning and end of the five-day period by the Winkler procedure. This involves the titration of a sample of the solution against dilute sodium thiosulphate. Alternatively, use an oxygen electrode.

Relate your information about the source of the pollution to the species composition of the animal life (Table 2.3) and to your measurements of the oxygen saturation of the water.

References

For Winkler technique, see D.S. McClusky, *Ecology of estuaries*, Heinemann, 1971.
Hewitt, G. River quality investigations, Part 1: some diversity and biotic indices. *Journal of Biological Education* **25**, 44–52, 1991.

For consideration

1 Does the pollution have a significant effect on the animal life in the water and if so, what can be done to prevent the pollution in future?
2 Explain in detail why the addition of fertiliser to a stream might ultimately cause deoxygenation of the water.
3 How does the oxygen content differ with depth? How does this affect both the distribution of animal species with depth, and your sampling techniques?
4 As a conservationist, what steps might you take to increase the range of species present in the water?

REQUIREMENTS

River or stream with discharge into it of water or organic matter, e.g. from a factory, farm or sewage works.
Plankton nets
Plastic bowls
Wellington boots
Oxygen meter, or chemicals for the Winkler method of oxygen determination, involving titration of incubated samples of water against sodium thiosulphate

Identification guides, e.g. T.T. Macan, A guide to freshwater invertebrate animals, Longmans, 1959, M. Quigley, Invertebrates of streams and rivers. A key to identification, Arnold, 1977, H. Mellanby, Animal life in freshwater, 6th edn., Methuen, 1963 or J. Clegg, The Observer's Book of Pond Life, 3rd edn, Warne, 1980.

2.11 PRACTICAL EXERCISE

This exercise extends over more than one practical session.

The nitrogen cycle in an aquarium

A well-established aquarium should have in it a range of bacteria which are involved in its **nitrogen cycle**, including **decomposers** which release ammonia from the proteins, and **nitrifying bacteria** which process the ammonia to nitrite and then to nitrate.

The transfer of nitrogen in an aquarium can be followed by adding a 'pulse' of amino acids. Sensitive 'dip-sticks', such as Merkoquant reagent strips, which provide rapid colour tests for ammonia, nitrite and nitrate concentrations, allow us to trace the changes in amino acids over a week. These changes depend on bacteria.

Procedure

1 Test the water in the aquarium for ammonium, nitrite and nitrate. If the levels of any of these ions are near the maximum which the test will detect, dilute the water with deionised water, and test it again before proceeding. Record the results.
2 Add 2.5 g per litre of water of casein hydrolysate (amino acids and short-chain peptides) to the aquarium. Straight away test the water again for ammonium, nitrite and nitrate. Record the results.
3 Test the water again, at intervals of twelve hours at first, for up to a week or until the levels all return to those at the start. Record the results. At the same time, look for, and record, any changes in the plants or animals in the aquarium which might result from the addition of the nitrogen-containing pulse.
4 Plot histograms of ammonium, nitrite and nitrate concentrations against time.

For consideration

1   How do you think the relevant bacteria got into the aquarium in the first place?
2   Did the organisms in your aquarium exhibit any beneficial or harmful effects at particular phases in the experiment? If so, suggest reasons.
3   Did the nitrate return to its previous level at the end of the experiment? If so, can you suggest why?
4   Imagine that a farmer dumps some protein-rich effluent into a slow-flowing river. On the basis of your results, what might happen?

2.12 PRACTICAL EXERCISE

This exercise extends over more than one practical session.

The effect of eutrophication on the growth of duckweed and algae

Many waterways, lakes and ponds are polluted by these nutrients, a phenomenon known as **eutrophication**. The nitrates may be mainly derived from fertiliser run-off, the phosphates from sewage and detergents. What effects do these compounds have on plant growth, separately and together?

This practical exercise allows you to investigate the effect of added nitrates and phosphates on the growth of photosynthesising organisms in a controlled experiment in the laboratory or glasshouse.

Procedure

1   Place $250 \, cm^3$ of water from the same source (e.g. tap water) into each of 20 beakers. Do not use water from a source which may already have been enriched with nutrients.
2   Four control beakers (labelled C) have no nutrient additions. There are eight nutrient addition treatments, each applied to two beakers. Label each beaker with its appropriate treatment symbol: N1, N2, P1, P2, N1P1, N1P2, N2P1, N2P2. In this code N1 is a small addition of nitrate (as $1 \, g \, NaNO_3$), N2 is a large nitrate addition ($5 \, g \, NaNO_3$), P1 is a small phosphate addition ($0.1 \, g \, CaHPO_4$) and P2 is a large addition of phosphate ($0.5 \, g \, CaHPO_4$).
3   Add to each beaker the appropriate mass of salt(s) and stir thoroughly.
4   To each beaker add ten plants of a duckweed (Lemna) species, e.g. L. gibba. Count and record the total number of leaves on the plants in each treatment at the start of the experiment.
5   Arrange the beakers in a glasshouse in a 4×5 pattern. Their positions should be randomised and recorded on a plan.
6   At weekly intervals, examine the beakers. Count and record the total numbers of leaves on the plants in each beaker. Then randomise the beakers again.
7   After four weeks the growth of algae in some beakers may become obvious as a green coloration in the water or on the sides of the beakers. At each sampling date, estimate by eye the relative densities of algae in each beaker. Carefully pour some of the water from each beaker into a clean test-tube or colorimeter tube and use a colorimeter to determine how much light the chlorophyll in the sample has absorbed. Pour the sample back into the beaker once you have measured its light absorption.
8   Draw graphs of the numbers of leaves per treatment, and the chlorophyll absorption, in each treatment with time.

For consideration

1   What were the effects of nutrient addition on the duckweed and the algae?
2   Which was the more effective at promoting growth on its own, the nitrate or the phosphate?
3   Often, the addition of nitrate and phosphate together increases growth far more than might be expected from the effects of nitrates or phosphates alone. Did such an 'interaction' occur in your experiment, and can you explain it?
4   The salts were added as sodium nitrate and calcium phosphate. Design an experiment to confirm that the growth effects in this experiment are due to the nitrate and phosphate rather than to the sodium and calcium (not so easy!).
5   What was the reason for randomising the positions on the bench of the beakers from time to time?

6   How did the growth conditions in the beakers differ from those which the duck-weed might encounter in a waterway enriched with nutrients?

7   Speculate on the influence which lush plant growth in a river or stream might have on the other organisms in the community.

The effect of organic matter on oxygen depletion in fresh water

When organic matter, such as sewage or leaf litter, falls into ponds, rivers or streams, it is decomposed by bacteria and fungi, which take up oxygen from the water for their aerobic respiration. This may reduce the oxygen concentration in the water to a level at which it is impossible for some aquatic animals to survive.

In this investigation you can add leaf litter or cattle dung to fresh water in a controlled experiment, and investigate its effect on the survival and reproductive success of an aquatic animal species.

Guidance

Ideally you need sixteen tall beakers. This enables you to set up four different litter treatments, each with four beakers.

Weigh out the leaf litter or cattle dung, place it in the beakers, label them, add fresh water and then add to each beaker a fixed amount of culture of *Daphnia* or a similar aquatic arthropod. At daily intervals, measure the oxygen level at the base of each beaker with an oxygen probe, make notes on the appearance of each beaker and assess the numbers of live *Daphnia*.

For consideration

1   Under what circumstances, in real life, are waterways likely to have organic matter added to them on a scale similar to that in this experiment, and what might be the consequences?

2   What effect did the addition of nutrients (or toxins) in the organic matter have on the results of the experiment?

3   Why are ponds frequently cleaned out or dredged in autumn?

REQUIREMENTS

Tall beakers or aquaria
Tap water which has been left standing for a few days
Abundant leaf litter, grass clippings or cattle dung
Pen for marking on glass
Electronic balance
Oxygen meter, with data-logging equipment if possible
Culture of *Daphnia* or similar aquatic arthropod

Lichens as indicators of atmospheric pollution

There are over 1300 species of lichen in the British Isles and some are more sensitive than others to atmospheric pollution, particularly to sulphur dioxide. In fact the range of lichen species present at a site provides the best indication of the average level of sulphur dioxide in the air in winter. In general there are fewer lichen species in cities than in the countryside. As one moves further from a road or a polluting factory, the range of lichen species increases. In this investigation you will use a standard scale (Table 2.4) involving few easily recognisable and widespread species, to compare the pollution levels at several sites.

Whilst most of the species mentioned in Table 2.4 are lichens, *Grimmia pulvinata* is a moss and *Pleurococcus* is an alga.

Guidance

Always sample lichens in areas with broadleaved trees (conifers usually lack lichens) and old stonework (lichens take time to colonise new stonework and only grow slowly). Old churchyards are ideal. The lichens in Table 2.4 which are characteristic of the least polluted areas are found only on trees.

Only a few resistant lichens are found at the most polluted sites. These lichens may well be present at *all* the sites you sample. The 'lichen zone' of an area is determined by the lichen with the least pollution resistance. Thus a site with *Pleurococcus*, *Xanthoria* and *Caloplaca* would be in zone 3 because of the presence of *Caloplaca*.

Select a range of sites to test an hypothesis, for example, that power station X produces polluting gases. At each site, examine the lichens and record those present; record also the likely pollution sources and their distance away. Do not remove lichens or mosses; lichens only grow very slowly and must be conserved. Write a report on your findings.

Table 2.4 A biological scale, based on the occurrence of *Pleurococcus* and various lichens and mosses, which can be used to estimate the mean winter level of sulphur dioxide in the atmosphere. The scale based on that used in the ACE pollution survey. The key beneath the table provides some hints on the identification of species.

Zone	Lichens, mosses and algae	Mean winter SO$_2$ (μg per m^2)
0	*Pleurococcus* (green alga) growing on bark	over 170
1	*Lecanora conizaeoides* (lichen) on trees and acid stone	150–160
2	*Xanthoria parietina* (lichen) appears on concrete, asbestos and limestone	about 125
3	*Parmelia* (lichen) appears on acid stone and *Grimmia pulvinata* (moss) occurs on limestone or near mortar	about 100
4	Grey leafy flat lichen species (e.g. *Hypogymnia physodes*) begin to appear pressed to tree bark	about 70
5	Shrubby lichens (e.g. *Evernia prunastri*) begin to appear on trees	about 40–60
6	*Usnea* (lichen) becomes abundant	about 35

(R. Mabey, *The Pollution Handbook*. The ACE / Sunday Times Clean Air and Water Surveys, Penguin, 1974)

Pleurococcus is a bright green, unicellular alga which frequently forms a green film over the moist bark of trees.

Lecanora is a lichen which forms grey green dots, 2 mm across, closely pressed to stone or the bark of living or dead wood.

Xanthoria is a bright yellow lichen (can be orange, red) which forms distinct circular or oval patches, lobed at the edge and usually with yellow dots on the centre.

Parmelia species of lichen occur on stones and trees. They form flat grey plates. They are dark beneath and often attached to the substrate by means of root-like threads.

Grimmia pulvinata is a moss which occurs in small rounded, neat, dense cushions, 1–2 cm high, grey with the hair points of leaves, on rocks or stones.

Hypogymnia physodes is a lichen which is found on trees and fences as grey-green flat plates with the edges strongly lobed. The lobes are 2–4 mm wide and tend to stick up into the air; there are no root-like threads beneath, unlike *Parmelia*.

Shrubby lichens are erect and bush-like, or hanging and tassel-like.

Usnea lichen species are usually grey-green, intricately branched, long and trailing, hanging like long tassels from tree branches. They are known as 'beard lichens'.

For consideration

1   Suggest two ways in which lichens (and mosses) absorb nutrient ions. Suggest why these organisms are more sensitive to atmospheric pollution than flowering plants.
2   What are the advantages and disadvantages of using organisms as indicators of pollution (see also 2.10 Investigation), rather than chemical analysis?
3   Do lichens growing on walls or trees have any value? Why should they be conserved?

2.15 INVESTIGATION

Using the Lincoln Index to estimate population sizes

There are various ways of estimating population sizes depending on the species concerned. The most direct is simply to attempt to count all the individuals in the population. However, this is only feasible for populations made up of large, relatively immobile individuals.

A useful technique which can be used for mobile species is the **capture-recapture** method, also known as the **mark-release-recapture** method. The principle is straightforward. First a sample of individuals is caught, counted and marked in some way. Then these individuals are released back into their original location. After being allowed to mix with the unmarked individuals, a second sample is caught and counted and the number of marked individuals noted. An estimate of the total population size can then be made by calculating what is called the **Lincoln Index**, thus:

$$\text{Population size} = \frac{n_1 \times n_2}{n_m}$$

where:

n_1 = number of individuals marked and released;
n_2 = number of individuals caught in the second sample;
n_m = number of marked individuals caught in the second sample.

Guidance

Choose a species that is suitable for this method. You will need to catch individuals, mark them in some way and then return them unharmed. Different methods of capture and marking may be needed for different species. For instance, ground beetles can be caught in pitfall traps and marked by placing a minute drop of waterproof paint on one of their hardened front wings (elytra).

Small mammals can be trapped in Longworth traps (see Fig 2.6) and marked by clipping off a small piece of their fur. However, any Longworth, or other, traps used for catching small mammals must be adjusted so that they do not catch any shrews. It is illegal to capture shrews without a licence – the reason being that their metabolic rate is so high that they die within a few hours unless able to feed.

Other possible species for the mark-release-recapture method include, in the laboratory, flour beetles and, in the field, woodlice, pond skaters, grasshoppers and snails.

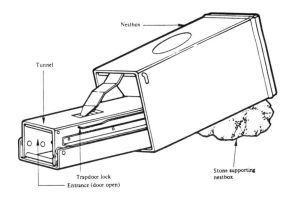

Figure 2.6 A Longworth trap, primed and baited to catch small mammals.

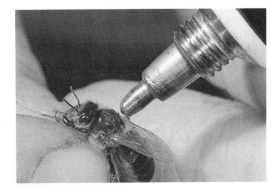

Figure 2.7 A student using a permanent marking pen to mark an individual of Honeybee queen (*Apis mellifera*).

REQUIREMENTS
Oil paint (any bright colour)
Paint brushes (size 00 for marking individuals and size 1 for moving them) or fine scissors
Longworth traps, pitfall traps or suitable nets
Other items may be required by individual students
Advice on both legal and technical aspects of mammal trapping is available from the Mammal Society, Department of Zoology, University of Bristol, Woodland Road, Bristol BS8 1UG.

Procedure

Conduct a small pilot investigation to ensure that you can catch and satisfactorily mark individuals of your chosen species (see Fig 2.7). For your main investigation you will need to mark sufficient individuals to recapture at least half a dozen marked individuals. You will also have to decide how long to wait between returning the marked individuals and obtaining your second sample. Once you have carried out your investigation, estimate the size of the population using the Lincoln Index given above.

For consideration

1 Using the Lincoln Index to estimate population sizes involves making a number of assumptions. One assumption is that marked individuals are as likely as unmarked individuals to die or to emigrate from the population before the second sample is obtained. Can you suggest at least three other assumptions made? Do you think these assumptions are realistic for your investigation?

2 Suggest ways in which your procedures could be improved.

3 In what ways might this technique be of use in ecological research?

2.16 INVESTIGATION

Niche separation in birds

The **niche** of an organism tells a biologist what the organism does in its community. For an animal, the most important aspect of its niche is usually its feeding niche. However, a full description of the niche of an animal requires much more than a description of the type of food on which it feeds. It also involves describing the physical and biological environments in which it exists and with which it interacts. The niche of an organism is sometimes said to be its *role* in the community.

An important biological principle is that no two species can be in the same habitat at the same time unless there are significant differences in their niches. If two species did have the same niche, and occurred in the same area at the same time, sooner or later one of them would exclude the other by outcompeting it. This is referred to as the **competitive exclusion principle**.

Although the competitive exclusion principle sounds reasonable enough, at first sight it may be difficult to believe that no two coexisting species share the same niche. In this investigation you can test whether different species of birds have distinct niches.

Guidance

You need to find an area where several species of birds all feed and where you can observe them without disturbing them. A garden may be a possibility or a nearby wood, provided it is safe for you to be there. If you live near the sea, you may be able to observe birds feeding on mud flats or in marshes. Clearly you need to be able to identify your birds to species level. (In some species, adult males and females can be distinguished, which enables you to investigate whether they share a niche or have distinct ones.) (see Fig 2.8).

Procedure

You need to decide on which aspects of the niche to focus. The simplest will probably be the feeding niches of the birds, though at certain times of the year you may also be able to see whether they have different nesting requirements. Decide on a method that allows you to record important characteristics of the birds' niches. For instance, in a garden you might record every minute where each species is feeding (e.g. 11.05 blue tit on artificial bird feeder, starling on lawn, blackbird at bottom of hedge; 11.06 blue tit near top of hawthorn bush; green finch on bird feeder, starling on lawn). On the seashore you might distinguish between sandy areas and rocky areas, and divide these into different zones depending on their distance from the sea.

Think about how you will analyse your data before you start collecting it.

For consideration

1 Do your data support or contradict the competitive exclusion principle? Explain your answer.
2 Can you relate any differences between the feeding niches of the birds to differences in their bill shapes and sizes?
3 How could your approach be modified to see whether the plants in a wood occupy distinct niches?

Figure 2.8 Whimbrel, Redshank, Greenshank, Terek Sandpiper, L. Sandplover on rocks.

REQUIREMENTS
Bird identification book
Binoculars
Watch or stop clock

2.17 PRACTICAL EXERCISE

The relationship between a predator and its prey

In a natural community, one animal species preys upon another. From this we can predict that the feeding relationship between these two species may influence their relative abundance.

In this investigation the predator–prey relationship between two common pond animals is analysed. The two animals are the damselfly or dragonfly nymph (predator) and the water flea, *Daphnia* (prey).

Procedure

1   Label six jars **A–F** and place an equal volume of pond water in each; they should not be more than two-thirds full.
2   Place one damselfly, or dragonfly, nymph in each jar, providing it with a short twig on which to cling.
3   After ten minutes to allow the nymph to settle down, transfer a known number of *Daphnia* specimens to each jar. To jar **A** add five *Daphnia*, to **B** add ten, to jar **C** add 15, to **D** add 20, to **E** add 30 and to **F** add 50. Leave each jar for 40 minutes.
4   After the forty minutes has elapsed, remove the predator from each jar and count the number of *Daphnia* still remaining.
5   Record your results, pool them with the class results and calculate the average number of *Daphnia* eaten (vertical axis) in each jar.
6   Plot the average number of *Daphnia* eaten (vertical axis) against the number of Daphnia in each jar before predation (horizontal axis).

For consideration

1   What can you say about the relationship between the rate of predation and prey density?
2   In the wild, could this particular predator have a significant effect in controlling the numbers of the *Daphnia* species?
3   Predict what might have happened if you had included a second prey species, at a variety of densities, in your experiment.

REQUIREMENTS

Six jars or beakers of the same size
Wide-mouthed teat pipette
Pond water

Rich culture of water fleas
Dragonfly or damselfly nymphs ×6 (starve them for 24 hours beforehand, and return them after the experiment to their natural habitat)
Short twigs ×6

2.18 PRACTICAL EXERCISE

The holly leaf miner

In Britain the leaves of holly (*Ilex aquifolium*) are very frequently parasitised by a small fly, the holly leaf miner (*Phytomyza ilicis*), whose larvae burrow through the leaves, producing yellow lines and dark blotches (mines). This practical exercise allows you to investigate the relationship between the fly, its **parasites** and **hyperparasites** (parasites which feed on parasites). It demonstrates a common situation in nature, in which animal species are parasitised by specialised solitary wasps.

The leaf miner goes through the a typical life cycle for a fly; egg, larva, pupa, adult (Figure 2.9). At least nine different species of wasp lay their eggs inside the larva or pupa. The best time to find these is early May (slightly later in the north of Britain). You can see why from Table 2.5; in May the miner should be in the late pupal stage and its major parasites either in the larval or the pupal stage. If you open up the leaves, you may find the larvae or pupae of the holly leaf miner, and you may well be able to identify the parasite from the diagrams (Figure 2.9) using the key (Table 2.6).

The three parasites which occur most frequently are described below and illustrated in Figure 2.10.

1   *Chrysocharis gemma* lays an egg into the larva of the holly leaf miner. Attacked larvae are dirty yellow, compared with the bright, shiny, pale yellow healthy larvae. The parasite then forms a shiny jet-black pupa which lies inside the mined leaf. The adult emerges by a small, round hole, leaving behind the black pupal skin.

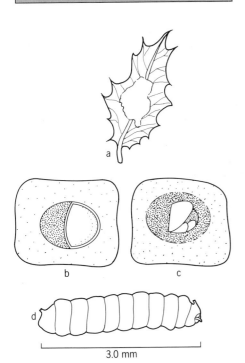

Figure 2.9 Stages in the life cycle of the holly leaf miner.
a Holly leaf mined by the holly leaf miner (*Phytomyza ilicis*).
b Pupa in a leaf before hatching.
c Pupal case in a leaf after hatching, showing emergence hole.
d Larva.

Table 2.5 The life history of the holly leaf miner and its three most frequent parasites.

	Jan	Feb	Mar	Apr	May	Jun	Jul	Aug	Sep	Oct	Nov	Dec
Holly leaf miner (*Phytomyza ilicis*)	L	L	L/P	P	P/A	A/E/L	L	L	L	L	L	L
Chrysocharis gemma	A	A	E/L	L/P	P	P/A	A	A	A	A	A	A
Chrysocharis syma	A	A	A/E/L	E/L	L/P	P/A	P/A	A	A	A	A	A
Sphegigaster flavicornis	A	A	A	A/E/L	L/P	P/A	P/A	A	A	A	A	A

Key: A = adult, E = egg, L = larva, P = pupa

Table 2.6 Identification key for the causes of death in the holly leaf miner. If the blotch has a hole (Statement 1, first alternative) the mine should be dissected to confirm that there are no larvae or pupae in the leaf.

1	Blotch with hole	go to 2
	Blotch without hole	go to 4
2	Hole a large irregular tear	bird predation
	Hole triangular, often with flap	Holly leaf miner (*Phytomyza)* emerged
	Hole circular	go to 3
3	Hole similar to feeding punctures scattered over leaf	Not holly leaf miner
	Hole neat, round, without decayed (yellow) tissue around it	*Chrysocharis gemma* emerged
	Neat round hole, surrounded by dry decayed (yellow) oval	*C. syma* or *Sphegigaster* emerged
4	Maggot large, healthy looking	*Phytomyza*
	Larval skin, flat, in brown plant tissue	Maggot killed by sucking predator
	Pupa black, hymenopterous	*C. syma* (see Fig. 2.12)
	Pupal case brown	go to 5
5	Open the puparium:	
	Adult fly (two wings) within	*Phytomyza*
	Empty	*Phytomyza* emerged
	Pupa (or cast skin)	go to 6
6	Pupa or cast skin black	*C. syma*
	Pupa blue-black with pale appendages	*Sphegigaster*

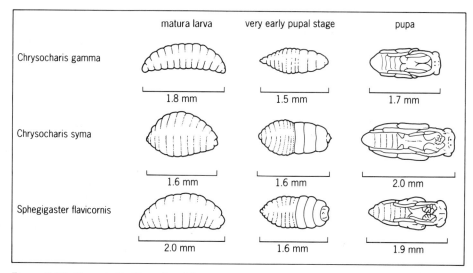

Figure 2.10 Stages in the life cycles of the commonest parasites of the holly leaf miner.

2   *Chrysocharis syma* has a similar life cycle to *Chrysocharis gemma,* except that it attacks the fly pupa, not the larva. Its pupa, once inside the pupal case of the holly leaf miner, is shiny black.

3   *Sphegigaster flavicornis* lays its egg in the pupa of the fly. The larva bores into the pupa, feeds and then pupates. The pupa is black with a bluish tinge, except for antennae, wings, and legs which are light glassy brown.

Procedure

1   Collect holly leaves from an infested tree, preferably in May, when the full range of parasites can be most easily identified. They can be kept in a refrigerator until required.

2   In the laboratory, open each mine, and use the key (Table 2.6) and the diagrams (Figures 2.9 and 2.10) to identify its contents. Record the results from each mine in the categories suggested in Table 2.7 and pool the class data.

Table 2.7 A record sheet for mines made by the holly leaf miner.

Date of collection	_____
Total leaves examined	_____
Leaves with mines	_____
Leaves without mines	_____
Empty pupal cases	_____
Dead larvae or pupae	_____
Larvae or pupae attacked by *Chrysocharis gemma*	_____
Pupae attacked by *C. syma*	_____
Pupae attacked by *Sphegigaster*	_____
Healthy unparasitised larvae	_____
Healthy unparasitised pupae	_____

REQUIREMENTS

Binocular microscope
Polythene bag for collecting leaves
Gardening gloves!
Forceps
Mounted needle
Refrigerator

Holly leaves collected from parasitised
   tree

For consideration

1   What effect does the miner have on the tree? Was there any relationship between the vigour of the trees and the intensity of infestation with the parasite?
2   What percentage of mined leaves contained the holly leaf miner? Speculate on the possible reasons why the figure is not greater – is there any evidence, for example, of predation by birds?
3   What proportion of the holly leaf miners have been parasitised? What impact do the parasites have on the population of the miner? What might happen if the parasites were eliminated?
4   Using the class data, calculate the percentage death rate from each cause and so produce a table showing the ultimate fates of a hundred holly leaf miner larvae in holly leaves.

2.19 PRACTICAL EXERCISE

This exercise extends over more than
one practical session.

Isolation of bacteria from legume root nodules

In this practical you will isolate bacteria (*Rhizobium* spp.) from legume root swellings (**nodules**), and grow them. These bacteria have a mutualistic relationship with the legume. They occupy the cytosol of enlarged root nodule cells, pick up nitrogen gas derived from the soil air and produce ammonia. The ammonia is released to the host cell, which uses it to form nitrogenous compounds such as amino acids. The **fixation** of nitrogen gas by the bacteria is an energy-demanding process, and as much as a quarter of the energy trapped by the legume in photosynthesis is used to sustain the bacteria in the nodules.

Procedure

1   Take the bottle of agar provided, remove the top and hold the neck of the bottle in the flame of a Bunsen burner for 2–3 s. Pour the contents of the bottle into a Petri dish. Replace the lid of the Petri dish as quickly as possible.
2   While the agar is setting, wash the plant roots thoroughly under the tap water to remove soil. Separate some pieces of root with nodules and place them in bleach solution for 5 minutes. Using forceps, transfer the nodules to a beaker of distilled water to rinse off the bleach.
3   With forceps, hold a microscope slide in a Bunsen flame for 2–3 s. Allow it to cool. Use a dropper to put a few separate drops of distilled water close together on the slide.
4   Flame the forceps. Then use them to place two or three nodules in separate drops of water on the slide.
5   Flame and cool a second microscope slide. Put this slide on top of the other, and press gently to crush the nodules.
6   When the agar has set, continue as follows. Remove the top slide. Dip a cotton bud into the sludge on the bottom slide. Gently wipe the cotton bud over the agar

Corrosive
Bleach
solution

in the Petri dish. Replace the lid of the Petri dish rapidly. Put your cotton bud in disinfectant. Tape the dish as shown on page 150 and label it with your name and the date.

7   Prepare a control agar plate: in a similar way, wipe a cotton bud, moistened in distilled water, over the surface of agar in another Petri dish, replace the lid, tape and label the dish.

8   Examine the agar plates after they have been incubated for at least 48 hours. Carefully record the positions and types of all the colonies. Where have most of the micro-organisms come from? Where might any other micro-organisms growing on the agar have come from?

For consideration

1   What is the source of energy for the bacteria growing on the agar plates?

2   In the intact plant the fixation of nitrogen occurs best in conditions which lack oxygen. How might the plant root nodule screen the bacteria against oxygen?

3   Explain why the association with the bacteria may be advantageous to the legume despite the sacrifice of a quarter of the legume's photosynthetic products to the bacteria.

REQUIREMENTS

Petri dishes ×2
Microscope slides ×2
Dropping pipette
Cotton buds
Forceps
Bunsen burner
Marker
Adhesive tape
Beaker
Bottles of yeast mannitol agar ×2
Distilled water
Bleach solution (10%)
Disinfectant
Plant with root nodules, e.g. pea, clover

2.20 PRACTICAL EXERCISE

Population growth of yeast

The principles involved in population dynamics can be illustrated by the reproduction of unicellular organisms such as yeast. Such organisms may have a high rate of reproduction and, therefore, lend themselves well to studies over a short period of time. Yeast cells reproduce asexually by budding.

In this practical a small number of yeast cells is allowed to multiply in a nutrient medium for about a week, and the concentration of yeast cells present is estimated at regular intervals.

Procedure

1   Using a clean graduated cylinder, measure $50 \, cm^3$ of nutrient medium (e.g. cider) and pour it into a $250 \, cm^3$ conical flask.

2   Swirl a flask containing a suspension of yeast cells and, once they are well mixed, add one drop to the flask of nutrient medium.

3   Plug the neck of the flask containing the yeast cells and nutrient medium with cotton wool and place it in a warm cupboard or incubator at 20–25 °C.

4   The yeast cells can be counted by means of a **haemocytometer**. Read Box 7.1, page 113: about how to use a haemocytometer. Then take cell counts once or twice a day for between four and seven days as follows.

   (i)   Swirl the flask before withdrawing a sample onto the haemocytometer slide – swirling helps ensure that the cells are evenly distributed before they are counted.

   (ii) There is no need to dilute the sample, but on each occasion carry out at least two independent cell counts.

   (iii) Choose an appropriately-sized square on your haemocytometer grid.

   (iv) Decide whether or not you are going to count a yeast cell in the process of budding as one cell or two, and stick to your decision.

   (v)   Count sufficient haemocytometer squares to get a reliable measure of the number of yeast cells – 100 to 200 yeast cells should be sufficient.

   (vi) Record your results systematically and use them to calculate the number of yeast cells per cubic centimetre.

5   Plot your results on linear (arithmetical) graph paper, with the number of cells per cubic centimetre on the vertical axis against time on the horizontal axis.

6   Plot a second graph of the results with, as before, time on the horizontal axis, but with the *logarithm* of the number of cells per cubic centimetre on the vertical axis. (The easiest way of doing this is to use semi-logarithmic graph paper. On this kind of graph paper the marks on the vertical axis have already been calibrated on a logarithmic scale.)

7   Compare your two graphs. Forgetting about any differences in scale, are there any differences between the two plots? If there are, suggest reasons for these differences. What is the purpose of the semi-logarithmic plot?

REQUIREMENTS

Microscope
Haemocytometer
Graduated cylinder (50 or 100 cm³)
Conical flask (250 cm³)
Cotton wool
Pipette
Linear (usual, arithmetical) graph paper
Semi-logarithmic paper
Nutrient medium for yeast (e.g. cider,
   2% sucrose solution or malt broth)
Suspension of brewer's yeast

Year	Population size
1800	8.1×10^8
1850	1.1×10^9
1900	1.7×10^9
1950	2.5×10^9
1960	3.0×10^9
1970	3.7×10^9
1980	4.5×10^9
1992	5.4×10^9

For consideration

1 Describe the shape of your plot on linear graph paper. Explain the reasons for each phase of the curve.

2 From your semi-logarithmic plot determine the length of time it takes for the population size to double (the doubling time) during the exponential phase.

3 Opposite are figures for the world human population since 1800 AD.

Plot these data on semi-logarithmic graph paper, putting population size on the vertical (semi-logarithmic) axis and the date on the horizontal (linear) axis.

How does the plot compare with the semi-logarithmic plot for yeast? What factors may affect the world human population in future?

Reference

The population growth of unicellular algae (e.g. *Chlorella*) can be assessed by colorimetric methods. See *Nuffield Advanced Science Revised Biology Practical Guide 7: Ecology* (Longman, 1986).

PROJECTS

Before starting a project, discuss your intended procedure with your teacher. Teachers should verify the safety of any site to be visited.

1 Investigate the distribution pattern of nettles (*Urtica dioica*) in relation to soil nitrate or phosphate (see G. Monger (Ed.) *Revised Nuffield Biology, Practical Guide 7*, Longmans, 1986).

2 Examine the pattern of earthworm distribution in relation to shade, soil pH and soil organic matter content. (See T.J. King *Ecology*, Nelson, 1989). Mustard in water seems a particularly efficient non-toxic worm-disturbing compound (Alan Gunn, Estimating earthworm populations, *School Science Review* 72, 86–88, 1991). For example, investigate (i) the abundance of earthworms with distance from the trunks of trees; (ii) their relative abundance in limed and unlimed soil; (iii) their relative abundance under broad-leaved and coniferous trees. The results can be followed up by choice chamber experiments in the laboratory (e.g. see Trevor Piearce, Vlare Robinson and Philip Ineson, Earthworms and soil pH, *School Science Review*, 70, 63–66, 1988).

3 Investigate factors affecting the distribution patterns of barnacles, limpets or mussels on a rocky shore, or freshwater shrimps and planarians in a freshwater stream.

4 Examine the distribution patterns of mosses on walls or gravestones in relation to aspect, or algae up a salt marsh or rocky shore, and relate the patterns of different species to their desiccation tolerances. The green protoctist *Pleurococcus*, widespread on tree trunks and fences, is also worth investigation.

5 Investigate the effects of different water table levels on plant growth in turves (see G. Monger (Ed.) *Revised Nuffield Biology. Practical Guide 7*, 1986). Turves can be cut from a lawn or a playing field (care!) and kept in large plastic bowls in which different water levels are maintained by watering, or a siphon system. The effects of these treatments on plant growth can be monitored and related to the natural microhabitats of the species.

6 Compare the distribution patterns of any two species of woodlouse, and then explain them as far as possible by laboratory experiments, with choice chambers or by providing a range of microhabitats within a glass jar, to investigate the environmental preferences of the species.

7 Investigate the effect of different salinities on the hatching success and growth of the brine shrimp, *Artemia salina*. Eggs are available from most aquarists or aquatic centres (see Kirsty Ward-Booth and Michael Reiss, *Artemia salina*: an easily cultured invertebrate ideally suited for ecological studies, *Journal of Biological Education* 22, 247–251, 1988).

8 Using a pH probe attached to a data-logging device, record the fluctuations in pH in the same place in an aquarium over a period of one day. Alter the position of the probe and read the pH in different parts of the aquarium. Interpret your observations in terms of the balance between photosynthesis and respiration, and fluctuations in temperature. Can you test your conclusions experimentally by altering the environmental conditions and predicting the effects of your changes on the diurnal pH fluctuations?

9 Use some of the sampling techniques outlined in Box 2.1 to compare the animal or plant species of two or more contrasting habitats. Possibilities include hedge and roadside verge, slow-flowing and fast-flowing parts of a stream, or shady woodland and clearings.

10 Measure the growth of duckweed (*Lemna* spp.) at different levels of added detergent to simulate pollution in an experiment designed rather like 2.12 Practical Exercise.

11 The effects of acid rain can be investigated by watering seedlings of cress (*Lepidium sativum*) or mustard (*Brassica nigra*) in a replicated experiment with simulated rainfall consisting of buffer solutions of different pH, using a range of pH 1–7. Similar investigations can be performed on seed germination and early seedling growth of a variety of species. To test the effects of acid rain on leaves, different marked leaves on large plants kept in the laboratory, a frame or a greenhouse can be exposed to artificial rainfall of different pH.

12 The predator–prey experiment (2.17 Practical Exercise) can also be carried out with small fish provided with prey at different densities, e.g. water fleas or midge larvae (bloodworms). Alternatively, investigate the effects of providing the insect predator with a choice of two different prey, at a variety of densities.

13 Competition experiments between two different plant species can be carried out by growing them at different relative numbers in pots

PROJECTS (cont.)

in a greenhouse. This is easiest to set up from the seedling stage. Mustard (*Brassica nigra*) and cress (*Lepidium sativum*) can be sown together and a range of densities achieved by removing some of the seedlings which emerge. Experiments are more convincing if the competing species normally occur together in nature, for example a crop plant and a weed which is found in it, or two species of duckweed (*Lemna* spp.) which can be competed in water-filled beakers (see G. Monger (Ed.) *Revised Nuffield Biology, Practical Guide 7*, Longmans, 1985). Alternatively, it is fascinating to sow seeds of competing species at different relative times.

If you perform such experiments it is important to reproduce each treatment three or four times. At the end of the experiment, the best measure of relative growth is usually the dry mass of the harvested plants.

14 Using the technique suggested in 2.6 Practical Exercise, compare the energy budgets of stick insects of different sizes and ages. To what extent does the pattern which occurs during the development of a stick insect resemble that in a human as (s)he grows from childhood to adulthood?

15 Determine the energy budget of a domestic mammal, such as a guinea pig. It can be fed weighed amounts of food. Note that the energy content per gram of lipids is about twice that of carbohydrate and protein, and so it is desirable to know the proportion of these various constituents in the diet.

16 Investigate the early stages of succession on bare rock by looking at the lichens and mosses on gravestones of different ages. Are some surfaces more resistant to colonisation than others by virtue of their texture and composition? Can you relate the diameters of certain lichen species to the ages of the gravestones on which they are growing? Can you work out the successional sequence by recording whenever one species is growing on top of another? Relate the speed of colonisation to aspect and slope.

17 Investigate succession on herbivore dung.

18 Determine the pyramid of biomass or energy flow on a mixed farm (with the farmer's permission!).

19 Study the population growth of a species other than yeast – for instance, a snail in an aquarium or pond, or an annual weed (e.g. annual meadow-grass, *Poa annua*) on a newly exposed area of soil or waste ground. See Box 2.1 on 'Sampling techniques in ecology' on page 13. Find situations where the species concerned looks likely to increase in numbers. How do your results compare with the idealised shape of a population growth curve shown in textbooks?

20 Obtain data from tombstones or national newspapers to see whether women and men live to different ages. Data from tombstones will also enable you to see whether life spans have increased over the last few hundred years.

21 Set up small aquaria, for example using large plastic ice cream cartons, with duckweed (*Lemna*). Investigate whether carrying capacity depends on the nutrient status of the water. See 'The effect of eutrophication on the growth of duckweed' on page 28.

22 Devise a project to study some aspect of biological control. For example, do ladybirds control the numbers of aphids?

23 Design a questionnaire to see whether people of different ages differ in the number of children they would like to have. Do women and men have the same preference?

24 Study some aspect of the population biology of an introduced species, e.g. grey squirrel (*Sciurus carolinensis*), rabbit (*Oryctolagus cuniculus*), Japanese knotweed (*Fallopia japonica*), rhododendron (*Rhododendron ponticum*), swamp stonecrop (*Crassula helmsii*). How abundant is the species in a given area? How many offspring can each individual produce? How old are individuals before they reproduce?

25 Do different species of slugs or snails occupy the same feeding niche? Collect the faecal pellets by keeping individuals in separate containers for 24 hours. Estimate the proportions of various constituents under the microscope: living (green) flowering plant tissue; dead (brown) flowering plant tissue; living moss; dead moss; fungi; pollen grains; arthropods; the rest. Do the diets of species differ? Do the species compete with one another for food?

26 Follow the development of frog or toad spawn in a pond. Can you work out what causes mortality at different stages of the life cycle?

27 Investigate the growth rates of clover (*Trifolium repens*) and grass, in turves containing both, exposed to different fertiliser treatments. Clover is a legume, and therefore likely to have an independent source of nitrogen through nitrogen fixation by bacteria in its root nodules. Carefully map the relative positions of clover and grasses on squared paper in six turves collected from a grassland. Leave two of the turves as controls, add a low dose of nitrogenous fertiliser to two more, and a high dose to the other two. Keep the turves in shallow trays in a glasshouse, and at intervals map the areas covered by grass and clover.

28 Alternatively, investigate the effects of providing the insect predator with a choice of two different prey, at a variety of densities.

29 Galls are abnormal lumps of tissue produced on plants, formed as the result of the plant's reaction to invasion by a parasite. Survey a local oak woodland for galls in winter, and try to hatch out some of the parasites of the gall-making insects. Amongst the galls present in abundance in the litter of oak shoots beneath oaks in winter are knopper galls (Figure 2.11 a, b). Marble galls (Figure 2.11 d, e, f) occur on the trees themselves.

Knopper galls are best collected in January or early February from leaf litter. Keep large numbers (about twenty in each jar) in 5–6 glass jars covered with fine muslin (some of the wasps which attack the knopper gall wasp are as small as 1 mm across). Wasps and parasites emerge, and can be identified, from late February onwards (Figure 2.11c). Intact marble galls produced by *Andricus kollari* and *A. lignicola*, without emergence holes, can be collected in winter from the current shoots of oak trees (if it has buds on, it's a shoot). Their gall-wasps and parasites can be captured and identified in the same way as those of the knopper galls. Little is known about the natural parasites of these gall-forming insects, and ecologists at the Department of Biology at Imperial College at Silwood Park, Ascot, Berkshire SL5 7PY would be pleased to help.

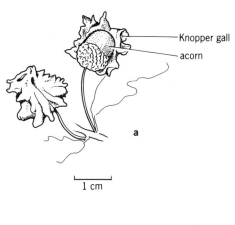

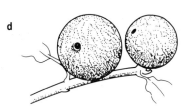

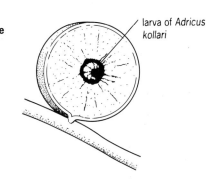

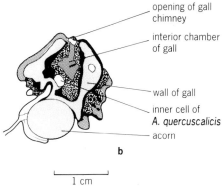

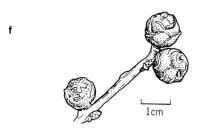

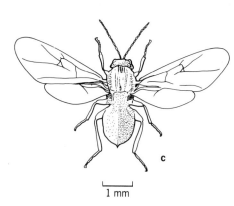

Figure 2.11

Galls on oak twigs beneath oak trees in winter (courtesy of Dr G. Stone).

a Knopper gall on an acorn.

b An opened knopper gall.

c The female of the gall-wasp *Andricus quercuscalicis*, which produces knopper galls.

d A marble gall, produced by the gall-wasp *Andricus kollari*. The surface of the gall is woody, smooth, and brown, and reaches 25 mm diameter.

e An opened marble gall.

f The gall produced by *Andricus lignocola*. This looks like a rather uneven, scruffy, marble gall. It is usually dark brown in colour and 5–10 mm across.

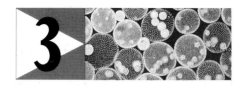

Classification and identification

Construction of an identification key

About one and a half million species alive today have been assigned scientific names in the **binomial system**. The name of the genus (e.g. *Homo*) is followed by the specific name (e.g. *sapiens*). Organisms named in this way can be identified to species level by means of **identification keys**. For example, botanists use keys for plants and entomologists keys for insects. When a geographical area contains relatively few species, an identification key may not be necessary. Ornithologists, for instance, rarely use keys to determine the scientific name of a bird. Instead, they compare the appearance of the bird with accurate paintings or with precise written descriptions. The same applies to mammals. For most groups, however, identification keys are used.

An example of a key

To illustrate how an identification key can be constructed, consider the following descriptions and photographs of the adults of the six species of reptiles native in Britain.

*   The grass snake, *Natrix natrix*, has two rows of spots down its back. There is a yellow, orange, white or pinkish collar behind its head, usually divided in the middle and surrounded posteriorly by black blotches (Figure 3.1). It is the only British snake which lays eggs. Adults are typically 60–90 cm in length. It is commonly found close to, or even in, water and occurs throughout England and Wales.
*   The adder (or viper), *Vipera berus*, has a dark zig-zag stripe down the middle of its back (Figure 3.2). Adults average 45–55 cm in length. When disturbed, the adder moves moderately quickly and often hisses. It is found throughout England, Scotland and Wales.
*   The smooth snake, *Coronella austriaca*, has a series of small ill-defined spots down its back. It lacks both a zig-zag pattern of dorsal markings and a pale collar. There is a characteristic dark streak along the side of the head, starting from the nostril, passing through the eye and continuing backwards for a few centimetres (Figure 3.3). Adults average 40–50 cm in length. It is confined to southern heathlands in England.
*   The common lizard, *Lacerta vivipara*, has a very variable coloration and patterning. There is usually a dark stripe, more or less entire, extending from the back of the head to the base of the tail (Figure 3.4). Adults average 12–18 cm in length. It is widespread throughout the British Isles.
*   The sand lizard, *Lacerta agilis*, has three longitudinal rows of irregularly shaped dark spots, each with a cental white dot or streak, down its back (Figure 3.5). Adults average 15–23 cm. It is confined to southern heaths and sand dunes in England.

Figure 3.1 The grass snake, *Natrix natrix*.

Figure 3.2 The adder (or viper), *Vipera berus*.

Figure 3.3 The smooth snake, *Coronella austriaca*.

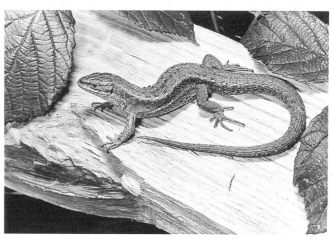

Figure 3.4 The common lizard, *Lacerta vivipara*.

Figure 3.5 The sand lizard, *Lacerta agilis*.

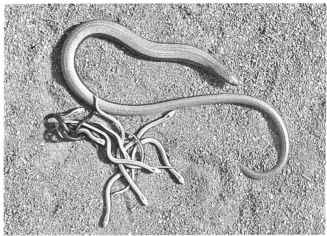

Figure 3.6 The slow-worm, *Anguis fragilis*.

The slow-worm, *Anguis fragilis*, is a legless lizard and resembles a snake. The eyes, unlike those of snakes, have moveable eyelids. The body is covered with small smooth scales which give the animal a characteristic polished appearance (Figure 3.6). Adults are typically 30–40 cm in length. It is confined to southern England.

There is no single perfect identification key to any group of organisms, but here is a possible key for these six reptiles:

1	Limbs present	go to 2
	Limbs absent	go to 3
2	Three longitudinal series of irregularly shaped dark dots along back, each with a central white dot or streak; confined to southern heaths and sand dunes in England	Sand lizard
	No such regular patterning; found throughout the British Isles	Common lizard
3	Back with rows of spots	go to 4
	Back with zig-zag stripe or no patterning	go to 5
4	Pale collar behind head; no dark streak along side of head from nostril through eye; often over 50 cm in length; found throughout England and Wales	Grass snake
	Pale collar behind head absent; dark streak along side of the head, starting from the nostril, passing through the eye and continuing backways for a few cm; confined to southern heathlands in England	Smooth snake

5 Eyelids moveable; highly polished appearance; no dark zig-zag stripe down middle of back; confined to southern England	Slow-worm
Eyelids not moveable; dark zig-zag stripe down middle of back; found throughout England, Scotland and Wales	Adder

Notice that the key is **dichotomous**, that is, at each point in the key the user is faced with just two choices. The great majority of keys are dichotomous. Notice too that certain information has not been used. For example, information about the length of an organism is of little use unless there are clear cut differences between species. Similarly, questions that require the user to know whether or not an individual lays eggs are unhelpful in the middle of winter or if the specimen is male. It is also best if information about the geographical distribution and size of specimens is only used in a supporting role alongside anatomical differences.

A good key minimises the number of questions the user has to answer before identifying a specimen. This can be done by phrasing descriptions early in the key which apply to several of the species, rather than devising a key which simply eliminates one species with each description. See, for example, questions 1 and 3 in the above key.

Guidance

1   With these principles in mind, devise a dichotomous key to distinguish between about eight to ten specimens, each belonging to a distinct species. You may be provided with specimens or you may have to collect your own. The specimens could be from entire organisms (e.g. arthropods) or from parts of organisms (e.g. leaves from trees). Assign a different letter to each specimen and ensure that your key keys out all the specimens, referring to each specimen by its letter.
2   Use characteristics which are easily observed and unambiguous – someone else may not judge various shades of green as you do unless you define your terms with precision.
3   When you have completed your key, ask someone else to check it. See whether they can give each specimen its correct letter.

For consideration

1   Did the person you asked to check your key find some questions more difficult than others? If so, why was this?
2   Variation between organisms does not take place only between different species. There is variation within a species too. Suppose you intended to publish a guide to identify the native trees of Britain by their leaves. How might you cope with the problem of variation within species?

REQUIREMENTS

Eight to ten specimens belonging to different species
Hand lens
Other items may be required by individual students (e.g. size 1 paint brush for moving specimens)

3.2 PRACTICAL EXERCISE

The taxonomic hierarchy

Organisms can be classified into species, and species can be grouped together into genera, genera into families, families into orders, orders into classes, classes into phyla and phyla into kingdoms. This is called the **taxonomic hierarchy**.

As one progresses down the hierarchy, from kingdom to phylum to genus, fewer and fewer species are found within each group. At the same time, they have more in common. For example, the phylum Mollusca (molluscs) contains some 80 000 living species which share certain fundamental features. Nevertheless, molluscs include such different organisms as slugs, clams and squids. However, within the phylum Mollusca, the genus *Patella* contains just *some* of the organisms known as limpets, and it takes an expert to distinguish certain species of *Patella* from one another.

In this investigation you will examine some of the significant features used by taxonomists to classify certain plants. We shall begin with the genus *Ranunculus*, which includes the buttercups. The way one species in this genus fits into the taxonomic hierarchy is shown in Table 3.1.

Procedure

1   Examine, either in the field or in the laboratory, at least some of the species of *Ranunculus* listed in Table 3.2 while they are in flower. Note similarities and differences between the different species.

Table 3.1 How the meadow buttercup (*Ranunculus acris*) fits into the classification of plants.

Taxonomic category	Taxon
Kingdom	Plantae
Phylum	Angiospermophyta
Class	Dicotyledoneae
Order	Ranales
Family	Ranunculaceae
Genus	*Ranunculus*
Specific name	*acris*
Species	*Ranunculus acris*

Table 3.2 Scientific names, common British names and habitats of eleven species of *Ranunculus*.

Scientific name	Common British name	Habitats
R. acris	Meadow buttercup	Grassland, especially damp and calcareous
R. aquatilis	Common water-crowfoot	Ponds, ditches, canals, slow rivers
R. arvensis	Corn buttercup	Weed of cultivated ground, especially cornfields
R. auricomus	Goldilocks	Woods, hedgebanks
R. bulbosus	Bulbous buttercup	Dry grassland, fixed dunes
R. flammula	Lesser spearwort	Wet places
R. ficaria	Lesser celandine	Damp meadows, woods, hedgebanks, beside streams
R. fluitans	River water-crowfoot	Larger rivers of moderate flow-rate
R. lingua	Greater spearwort	Marshes and pondsides
R. repens	Creeping buttercup	Wet grassland, woods, streamsides, marshes, dune-slacks, and as a weed of grassland and waste places
R. sceleratus	Celery-leaved buttercup	Marshy fields, ditches, ponds, streamsides

2 From your observations, suggest (i) which features might cause all these species to be placed in the same genus; and (ii) which features distinguish one species from another.

3 *Ranunculus* belongs to the family Ranunculaceae. This family contains many other genera besides *Ranunculus*. These genera include:

Anemone, e.g. *A. nemorosa* (wood anemone);
Caltha, e.g. *C. palustris* (marsh-marigold);
Clematis, e.g. *C. vitalba* (traveller's joy);
Aquilegia, e.g. *A. vulgaris* (columbine);
Helleborus, e.g. *H. foetidus* (stinking hellebore).

Examine flowering and/or fruiting specimens of all or some of the above genera. Suggest which features distinguish one genus from another.

4 These genera, and therefore the species they contain, are placed in the same family because of certain similarities between their flowers. What features of the flowers do they share?

5 The Ranunculaceae is a family within the phylum Angiospermophyta (flowering plants). There are over two hundred families of angiosperms. These include the following: Asteraceae (e.g. daisy, thistles, groundsel); Brassicaceae (e.g. shepherd's purse, wallflower); Convolvulaceae (e.g. bindweed); Fabaceae, also known as Leguminosae (e.g. pea, clover, gorse); Lamiaceae, also known as Labiatae (e.g. dead-nettle); Primulaceae (e.g. primrose, cowslip); Rosaceae (e.g. strawberry, roses); Scrophulariaceae (e.g. speedwells, foxglove, snapdragon); Violaceae (e.g. violets).

Examine representatives of some or all of the above families. In what respects do they differ from the Ranunculaceae and from each other? What features do they have in common which cause them to be placed in the same phylum of the plant kingdom, the Angiospermophyta?

For consideration

1 With reference to the plants you have studied, is it true that the similarities between organisms increase as you go down the taxonomic hierarchy?

2 Can you suggest why characteristics of flowers and fruits are more widely used in the classification of plants than are vegetative characteristics, such as leaves?

REQUIREMENTS

Ranunculus species (see Table 3.2) – either live in the field or herbarium specimens in the laboratory
Species belonging to some or all of the following genera: *Anemone, Caltha, Clematis, Aquilegia, Helleborus*
A few other angiosperms (see list in step 5)
Hand lens

3.3 PRACTICAL EXERCISE

Classification of organisms

At one time, the classification of organisms made up a substantial proportion of the time advanced level biology students spent on their course. Nowadays this is rarely the case unless you are studying an option concerned with the diversity of organisms. However, every student of biology, whatever their particular interests, should be able to classify organisms at least into their major groups. Accordingly, we present below a classification of living organisms down to the level of phyla, sometimes classes, and invite you to use it to identify a number of specimens provided by your teacher.

Procedure

Assign each organism to its correct kingdom, phylum and – if appropriate – class, using the classification below. If any of the terms are unfamiliar to you, you will need to consult a standard advanced level biology textbook (e.g. Roberts, M.B.V., Reiss, M.J. and Monger, G. *Biology: Principles and Processes*, Nelson, 1993), a dictionary of biology (e.g. Abercrombie, M., Hickman, M., Johnson, M.L. and Thain, M. *The New Penguin Dictionary of Biology*, Penguin, 1990) or a book on the classification and identification of living organisms (e.g. Monger, G. and Sangster, M. *Systematics and Classification*, Longman, 1988). The classification is based on that provided in the Institute of Biology's (1989) *Biological Nomenclature: Recommendations on Terms, Units and Symbols*, Institute of Biology.

Kingdom Prokaryotae

Unicellular; lack nuclei and membrane-bound organelles.

Kingdom Protoctista

Eukaryotic organisms which are not animals, plants or fungi; often unicellular.

Phylum **Rhizopoda** (rhizopods)
Pseudopodia for locomotion.

Phylum **Zoomastigina** (flagellates)
At least one flagellum for locomotion; heterotrophic.

Phylum **Apicomplexa** (sporozoans)
Multiple fission stages in the life history; mostly parasitic.

Phylum **Ciliophora** (ciliates)
Cilia for locomotion and/or feeding.

Phylum **Euglenophyta** (euglenoid flagellates)
Flagella; distinctive biochemistry (including paramylon as the cytoplasmic storage product); photosynthetic and non-photosynthetic members.

Phylum **Oomycota** (oomycetes)
Sexual reproduction by fertilisation of male and female gametangia; asexual sporangia produce biflagellate spores; hyphae non-septate (no cross walls).

Phylum **Chlorophyta** (green algae)
Photosynthetic, with green chlorophyll pigments as in plants; unicellular, colonial and filamentous.

Phylum **Rhodophyta** (red algae)
Photosynthetic, with plastids containing red pigments as well as chlorophyll.

Phylum **Phaeophyta** (brown algae)
Photosynthetic, with plastids containing brown pigments as well as chlorophyll.

Kingdom Fungi

Eukaryotic with a protective wall containing chitin; heterotrophic with absorptive methods of nutrition; usually organised into white thread-like multi-nucleate hyphae; spores without flagella.

Phylum **Zygomycota** (zygomycetes)
Sexual reproduction by gametangia producing a zygospore; hyphae non-septate.

Phylum **Ascomycota** (ascomycetes)
Sexual reproduction involving spore production inside a slender container (ascus); hyphae septate.

Phylum **Basidiomycota** (basidiomycetes)
Sexual reproduction involves spores produced externally on a basidium; hyphae septate.

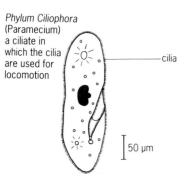

Phylum Ciliophora
(Paramecium)
a ciliate in which the cilia are used for locomotion

— cilia

50 μm

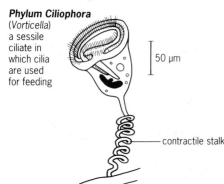

Phylum Ciliophora
(*Vorticella*)
a sessile ciliate in which cilia are used for feeding

50 μm

— contractile stalk

Phylum Euglenophyta (*Euglena*)

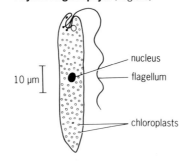

10 μm

nucleus
flagellum

chloroplasts

Phylum Rhizopoda (*Amoeba*)

200 μm

— pseudopodia

Phylum Basidiomycota mushroom

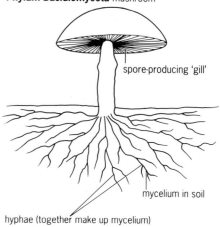

spore-producing 'gill'

mycelium in soil

hyphae (together make up mycelium)

Kingdom Plantae

Eukaryotic, multicellular and photo-synthetic; cell walls contain cellulose.

Phylum **Bryophyta** (bryophytes)
Conspicuous gametophyte generation; no true roots (body anchored by filamentous rhizoids).

Class **Hepaticae** (liverworts)
Body either a flat thallus or with leaves in three ranks; unicellular rhizoids; spore capsule opens by splitting into four valves.

Class **Musci** (mosses)
Leafy body with leaves spirally arranged; multicellular rhizoids; spore capsule with elaborate dispersal mechanism.

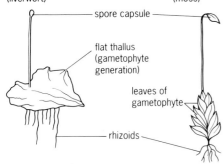

Class Hepaticae (liverwort)   **Class Musci** (moss)

- spore capsule
- flat thallus (gametophyte generation)
- leaves of gametophyte
- rhizoids

Phylum **Lycopodophyta** (club mosses)
Small spirally arranged leaves; sporangia usually in cones.

Phylum **Sphenophyta** (horsetails)
Leaves in whorls around the stem; sporangia in cones.

Phylum **Filicinophyta** (ferns)
Young leaves coiled in bud; sporangia in clusters (sori).

Phylum **Coniferophyta** (conifers)
Cone-bearing without flowers or fruits; ovules not surrounded by an ovary wall.

Phylum **Angiospermophyta** (angiosperms – also called flowering plants)
Seed-bearing plants with flowers; seeds enclosed in a fruit.

Class **Monocotyledoneae** (monocots)
Leaves usually with parallel veins; embryos with one cotyledon; flower parts usually in multiples of three; vascular bundles scattered in stem; roots without a definite xylem 'star'.

Class **Dicotyledoneae** (dicots)
Net-veined leaves; embryos with two cotyledons; roots with two, four or five points on a xylem 'star'; secondary thickening present in trees and shrubs.

Kingdom Animalia

Eukaryotic, non-photosynthetic multicellular organisms with nervous coordination.

Phylum **Cnidaria** (cnidarians)
Two cell layers separated by a mesogloea; nematoblast cells; radial symmetry with tentacles.

Phylum **Platyhelminthes** (flatworms)
Flat unsegmented animals; often with a mouth, but lacking an anus.

Class **Turbellaria** (turbellarians)
Ciliated outer surface; free-living; aquatic.

Class Turbellaria (*Planaria*)

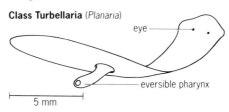

- eye
- eversible pharynx
- 5 mm

Class **Trematoda** (trematodes – also called flukes)
Non-ciliated outer surface; endo-parasites; one or more suckers.

Class Trematoda (*Fasciola*)

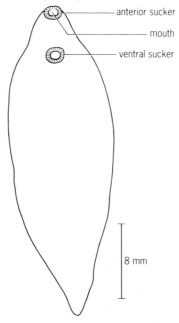

- anterior sucker
- mouth
- ventral sucker
- 8 mm

Class **Cestoda** (tapeworms – also called cestodes)
Non-ciliated outer surface; endo-parasites; scolex bearing suckers and hooks; flat, elongated body usually divided into sexually reproducing sections (proglottids).

Class Cestoda (*Taenia*)

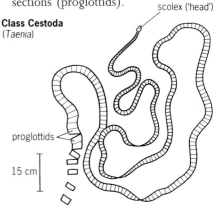

- scolex ('head')
- proglottids
- 15 cm

Phylum **Nematoda** (nematodes – also called roundworms)
Unsegmented cylindrical body; both a mouth and an anus.

Phylum Nematoda (*Ascaris*)

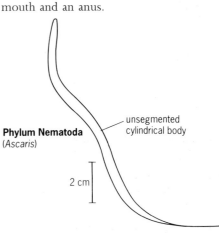

- unsegmented cylindrical body
- 2 cm

Phylum **Annelida** (annelids – also called segmented worms)
Worm-like animals with clear segmentation.

Class **Polychaeta** (polychaetes – also called marine worms)
Distinct head; numerous chaetae on projections (parapodia); marine.

Class Polychaeta (*Nereis*)

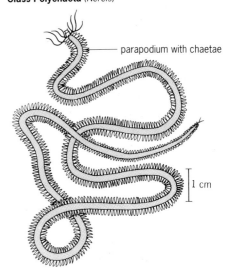

- parapodium with chaetae
- 1 cm

Class **Oligochaeta** (oligochaetes – also called earthworms)
No distinct head; few chaetae per segment and no parapodia; in fresh-water and soil.

Class Oligochaeta (*Lumbricus*)

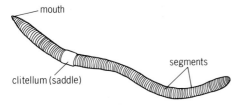

Class **Hirudinea** (leeches)
No distinct head; no chaetae or parapodia; usually ectoparasites or predators with two suckers.

Class Hirudinea (*Hirudo*)

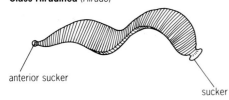

Phylum **Mollusca** (molluscs)
Unsegmented, with a head, foot and visceral hump; often with a calcareous shell.

Class **Gastropoda** (gastropods)
Head, eyes and sensory tentacles; shell – if present – single, often coiled; radula used in feeding.

Class **Pelycopoda** (bivalves)
Head reduced, no tentacles; shell of two hinged valves; filter feeding.

Class Pelycopoda (*Anodonta*)

Class **Cephalopoda** (cephalopods)
Conspicuous head and tentacles; well developed eyes; beak and radula used in feeding; no shell in living forms.

Phylum **Arthropoda** (arthropods)
Hard exoskeleton; segmented; jointed limbs; bilaterally symmetrical.

Superclass **Crustacea** (crustaceans)
Head not clearly defined; two pairs of antennae; mostly aquatic. (There is a great deal of morphological diversity

in this superclass which contains several classes.)

Superclass Crustacea

(*Astacus*)   (*Asellus*)

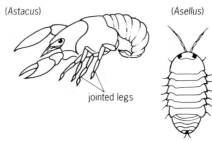

Class **Chilopoda** (centipedes)
Long flattened body with many segments; distinct head; one pair of antennae; one pair of legs per segment; terrestrial; carnivorous.

Class Chilopoda

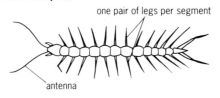

Class **Diplopoda** (millipedes)
Long cylindrical body with many segments; distinct head; one pair of antennae; two pairs of legs per segment; terrestrial; herbivorous.

Class Diplopoda

Class **Insecta** (insects)
Body divided into head, thorax and abdomen; three pairs of legs; head usually with compound eyes; frequently terrestrial; usually winged as adults.

Class Insecta (silverfish)

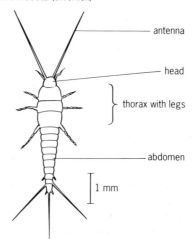

Class **Arachnida** (arachnids)
Four pairs of legs attached to what appears to be a combined head and thorax; no true jaws; no compound eyes; terrestrial.

Class Arachnida (spider)

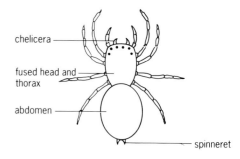

Phylum **Echinodermata** (echinoderms)
Water vascular system with tube feet; 5-way radial symmetry; marine.

Class **Stelleroidea** (starfish and brittlestars)
Flattened; five (sometimes more) arms.

Class Stelleroidea (starfish)

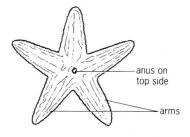

Class **Echinoidea** (sea urchins)
Globular; no arms.

Class Echinoidea (sea urchin)

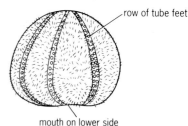

Phylum **Chordata** (chordates)
Notochord; hollow dorsal nerve cord; visceral clefts; post-anal tail.

Class **Chondrichthyes** (cartilaginous fish)
Skeleton of cartilage; mouth ventral; fleshy fins; separate gill openings.

Class **Osteichthyes** (bony fish)
Skeleton of bone; mouth terminal; fins supported by rays; gills covered by a bony flap (operculum).

Class **Amphibia** (amphibians)
Soft skin; aquatic larvae with gills;
land-living adults with lungs.

Class Amphibia (*frog*)

soft skin

Class **Reptilia** (reptiles)
Scaly skin; usually limbed; lungs; eggs
with shells.

Class Reptilia (*crocodile*)

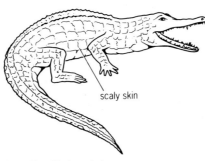

scaly skin

Class Reptilia (*tortoise*)

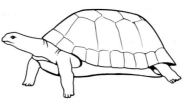

Class **Aves** (birds)
Skin with feathers; winged; lungs;
endothermic; eggs with shells.

Class Aves (*gull*)

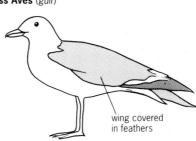

wing covered
in feathers

Class **Mammalia** (mammals)
Skin with hair in follicles; lungs;
endothermic; mostly viviparous;
young fed on milk.

Class Mammalia (*kangaroo*)

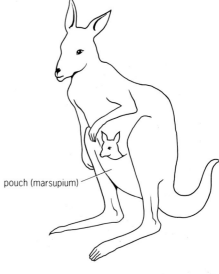

pouch (marsupium)

Class Mammalia (*duck-billed platypus*)

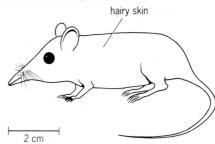

Class Mammalia (*common shrew*)

hairy skin

2 cm

REQUIREMENTS

Microscope
Blunt seeker
Live specimens of some of the
   following organisms:
   Mucor;
   Locusta or *Drosophila*;
   Helix or *Arion* or *Cepaea* or *Achatina
   fulica*;
   Daphnia or *Asellus* or *Gammarus*;
   Euglena;
   Lumbricus or *Allolobophora*;
   Paramecium;
   Poa or *Triticum* or *Lolium* or *Agrostis*;
   Chlamydomonas or *Spirogyra*;
   Amoeba.
Prepared slides of some of the
   following organisms:
   Bryum or *Funaria* or *Mnium* or
   Polytrichum;
   Plasmodium,
   Fasciola;
   Phytophthora;
   Trypanosoma.
Preserved specimens of some of the
   following organisms:
   Dryopteris or *Pteridium*;
   Scyliorhinus;
   Taenia;
   Ascaris;
   Clupea or *Salmo* or *Gadus*;
   Rattus;
   Asterias or *Ophiothrix*;
   Fucus or *Laminaria*.

For consideration

1   Explain why you found some of the organisms easier to classify than others.
2   One of the five kingdoms is generally thought to be less 'satisfactory' than the
    other four. Which do you suppose this is? In what way do you think it is less
    'satisfactory'?

References

Abercrombie, M., Hickman, M., Johnson, M.L. and Thain, M. *The New Penguin Dictionary
of Biology*, Penguin, 1990.
Institute of Biology's Biological Nomenclature: Recommendations on Terms, Units and Symbols, Insti-
tute of Biology, 1989.
Monger, G. and Sangster, M. *Systematics and Classification*, Longman, 1988.
Roberts, M.B.V., Reiss, M.J. and Monger, G. *Biology: Principles and Processes*, Nelson, 1993.

3.4 INVESTIGATION

Table 3.3 Orders of insects found in Britain.

Thysanura (silver-fish and other bristle-tails)
Diplura (tiny soil-living insects)
Protura (minute soil-living insects)
Collembola (springtails)
Ephemeroptera (mayflies)
Odonata (dragonflies)
Plecoptera (stoneflies)
Orthoptera (crickets and grasshoppers)
Dermaptera (earwigs)
Dictyoptera (cockroaches)
Psocoptera (booklice)
Mallophaga (biting lice)
Anoplura (sucking lice)
Hemiptera (true bugs)
Thysanoptera (thrips)
Neuroptera (alder flies, snake flies and lacewings)
Mecoptera (scorpion flies)
Lepidoptera (butterflies and moths)
Trichoptera (caddis flies)
Diptera (true flies)
Siphonaptera (fleas)
Hymenoptera (bees, wasps and ants)
Coleoptera (beetles)
Strepsiptera (stylopids – parasites of bees)

REQUIREMENTS

Suitable identification books, e.g. Chinery, M. (1973) *A Field Guide to the Insects of Britain and Northern Europe*, Collins; Croft, P.S. (1986) *A Key to the Major Groups of British Freshwater Invertebrates*, Field Studies Council; Gilbert, F.S. (1986) *Hoverflies*, Richmond Publishing; Prys-Jones, O.E. & Corbet, S.A. (1987) *Bumblebees*, Richmond Publishing; Tilling, S.M. (1987) *A Key to the Major Groups of British Terrestrial Invertebrates*, Field Studies Council; Majerus, M. & Kearns, P. (1989) *Ladybirds*, Richmond Publishing.
Appropriate sampling facilities (e.g. insect net, beating tray, pooter)
Binocular microscope or hand lens

Diversity of insects

The insects contain more species than any other class. Indeed, there are more species of beetles – one of the orders of insects – than are found in any other class. The biologist J. B. S. Haldane, a convinced atheist, was once asked what he could conclude about the nature of the Almighty from his knowledge of the natural world. 'An inordinate fondness for beetles', he replied.

The twenty-four orders of insects listed in Table 3.3 are found in Britain. It is both relatively easy and scientifically valuable to be able to distinguish them.

Guidance

You are most likely to carry out a meaningful investigation if you compare the insects in two different sites. For instance in short grass and neighbouring long grass; or in a lake and a stream that feeds it.

Obtain two sample of insects, one from each site. Box 2.1 'Sampling techniques in ecology' on page 13 provides details of several ways in which insect samples may be obtained. Then, using one or more of the books listed in the Requirements below, identify the insects in each sample at least to their order. A pooter is particularly useful for holding an insect in a confined space while you are identifying it. Once identification is complete, the insect can then be returned to the wild. It may be safest not to allow any of the insects to come into contact with you. Everybody knows about bees and wasps, but there are other insects which can sting or cause an allergic reaction.

For consideration

1 How confident are you about your identifications? How could you check them?
2 What did your comparisons of two different areas tell you? Did you find different insects in the two areas? If so, can you propose any hypotheses to explain these differences?
3 How might you attempt to determine the total number of individual insects in an area?
4 How might you attempt to determine the number of insect species in an area?

PROJECTS

Before starting a project, discuss your intended procedure with your teacher.

1 Investigate the extent to which variation occurs within species as well as between them.

2 Conduct a survey at a garden centre to see whether people prefer to use scientific or common names and why.

3 Carry out a project similar to the 3.2 Practical Exercise, page 42, but using a variety of annelids (e.g. earthworms, lugworms, ragworms, fanworms and leeches).

4 Find out about the principles of numerical taxonomy and attempt to use them to classify a group of organisms (e.g. different molluscs). Compare your classification with the usual one given in zoology textbooks and suggest explanations for any similarities and differences.

5 Identify the birds that come to a particular place, for instance a garden or a copse of trees. Investigate the relationship between the number of individuals you see and the number of species you identify. See how many different bird species are there in the first 8 birds you see, the first 16, the first 32, the first 64, etc. Compare your results with those obtained in the same place studying a different taxonomic group, or with those obtained in a second place when studying the same taxonomic group.

6 Obtain identification books that identify different organisms in the same geographical area to species level (e.g. flowering plants, butterflies and moths, birds, mammals, all in the UK). How many different species are there on average in a genus? Does this figure differ for different organisms (e.g. flowering plants compared with birds)? If so, can you suggest why this is?

4

The chemicals of life

Eye protection
must be worn

BOX 4.1 **Food tests – identification of the necessary components of a balanced diet and the compounds in intact tissue**

This box describes methods of identifying the main classes of chemical compounds in ground-up tissue, intact cells, foodstuffs and extracted juices. A suitable investigation involving these methods appears in 9.5 Practical Exercise. You will need to wear your safety spectacles for these tests. It is safer to use water baths for heating.

Carbohydrates

Sugars (monosaccharides and disaccharides)

All monosaccharides (e.g. glucose, galactose, fructose) and certain disaccharides (e.g. maltose) will reduce copper (II) sulphate, producing a precipitate of copper (I) oxide on heating. Such sugars are known as **reducing sugars,** and can be tested for by heating with **Benedict's reagent,** which contains copper (II) sulphate. Add an equal quantity of Benedict's reagent to the substance to be tested. Shake, and bring to the boil by heating the test tube in a water bath. A green precipitate indicates relatively little sugar, yellow somewhat more, brown even more and red the most.

The disaccharide sucrose, however, gives a negative Benedict's test. Its presence can be detected by Benedict's solution provided it is first hydrolysed into glucose and fructose, and *then* tested with Benedict's solution, which will yield a positive result.

To test for the presence of sucrose in a compound which has already tested negative with Benedict's solution, add a few drops of dilute hydrochloric acid and boil. Neutralise with sodium hydrogencarbonate (check the pH with pH paper) and test with Benedict's reagent again.

Corrosive
dilute
hydrochloric
acid

Starch

The addition of dilute iodine solution to a solution or a tissue containing starch yields a blue-black colour. If you are testing a foodstuff in water, the blue colour sometimes appears on the foodstuff itself rather than in the solution, as starch is relatively insoluble.

Cellulose

Cellulose stains purple with **Schultz' solution**.

Irritant
Iodine
solution

Corrosive
Schultz'
solution

Lipids

Shake a foodstuff in **absolute ethanol** for a minute. Then pour the ethanol (not the foodstuff) into a test tube containing water. A cloudy white emulsion indicates lipid. The whiteness of the precipitate is proportional to the concentration of lipid in the substance being tested.

Highly flammable
Ethanol

Lipids also take up the red stain **Sudan III**. Another way to detect lipid in tissue which has been ground up is to transfer the tissue to a test tube containing water and boil. If lipids are present, oil droplets will escape from the tissue and rise to the surface. Add Sudan III, shake, allow the oil to settle and the oil will now be stained red.

Corrosive
Phloroglucinol
concentrated
hydrochloric
acid

Harmful
Phloroglucinol

Corrosive
Potassium
hydroxide

Corrosive
Millon's
reagent

Toxic
Millon's
reagent

Toxic
DCPIP

Corrosive
DCPIP

REQUIREMENTS

Test-tubes
Test-tube rack
Bunsen burner
Pestle and mortar
Watch glass
Spatula
Safety goggles
Lab coat
Iodine solution
Benedict's reagent
Schultz' solution
Phloroglucinol (benzene-1,3,5-triol)
Concentrated hydrochloric acid
Dilute hydrochloric acid
DCPIP
Methylgreen pyronin
Acetic orcein
Sodium hydrogencarbonate
Sudan III
Millon's reagent
Potassium hydroxide (approx. 10–20%)
Copper (II) sulphate solution (1%)
Ethanol (absolute and 70%)
Litmus paper

BOX 4.1 Food tests (continued)

Lignin

Lignin, a hydrocarbon polymer characteristic of xylem tissue, stains red with **acidified phloroglucinol**. Add phloroglucinol first, and then a few drops of concentrated hydrochloric acid; or use a made-up solution of acidified phloroglucinol.

Proteins

The **biuret test** is suitable for soluble proteins. Add a little potassium hydroxide to the solution until it clears. Then add a drop of dilute copper (II) sulphate solution down the side of the test-tube. A blue ring at the surface of the solution indicates protein. On shaking, the blue ring disappears and the solution turns purple.

For insoluble proteins **Millon's reagent** is suitable but you may not be allowed to use it because it is both toxic and corrosive. To a small amount (3 cm^3) of the solution or a suspension of the protein, add about six drops of Millon's reagent and boil. If protein is present a brick red precipitate appears on the surface of the substance being tested.

Vitamin C

Use the decolourisation of **DCPIP** (4.3 Practical Exercise) as a quantitative test for Vitamin C.

Tests on intact tissue

The advantage of testing intact tissue is that the distribution of individual compounds within the cells can be studied in detail. Examples are as follows:

The distribution of DNA and RNA in intact broad bean cells is investigated with **methyl green pyronin** (13.8 Practical exercise).
The chromosomes of dividing cells are shown up with acetic orcein stain (11.1 Investigation).
The cellulose in plant cell walls can be detected with **Schultz' solution** (Box 4.1)
The starch grains within onion cells are stained with **dilute iodine solution** (Box 4.1)
The lignified tissue within a plant root, plant stem or macerated tissue is stained with **acidified phloroglucinol** (11.2, 11.4 Practical Exercises)
The waxy cuticle on a plant leaf, and the Casparian bands within the endodermis cell walls of a root, can be highlighted with **Sudan III**.

4.1 PRACTICAL EXERCISE

This exercise extends over more than one practical session.

Analysis of the amino acids in a protein by paper chromatography

The purpose of this practical is to find which amino acids are present in the protein albumen (egg white). The protein is first hydrolysed by treating it with the digestive enzyme trypsin. The amino acids are then separated and identified by paper chromatography.

The principle behind paper chromatography is as follows. A small amount of solvent is put at the bottom of a jar. A strip of absorptive paper, with a concentrated spot of the mixed amino acids towards the bottom, is suspended in the jar so that its end dips into the solvent. The latter moves slowly up the strip of paper, carrying the amino acids with it. As the amino acids travel at different speeds, they separate from one another. The paper is then treated with a reagent which stains the amino acids so that they can be detected and identified.

Note: Chromatography solvents are usually highly flammable. Extinguish Bunsen burners.

Procedure

This experiment takes several days and so it is advisable that you should draw up a timetable.

1 To break down the protein, half fill a test-tube with the trypsin solution provided. Then add the protein: either 2 g of egg white, or 5.0 cm³ of albumen. Finally, add a crystal of thymol to kill bacteria. Leave the mixture to incubate at 30 °C for 48–72 hours.

2 In a fume cupboard, pour the solvent into the jar to a depth of 3 cm. Put the lid on the jar so that the atmosphere inside becomes saturated with vapour.

3 Wash and dry your hands to remove amino acids. Handling the paper as little as possible, cut a strip of chromatography paper long enough for one end to dip into the solvent to a depth of about 5 mm, and the other end to stick out of the top of the jar by about 2 cm.

4 Draw a pencil line across the strip 4 cm from one end. Using a fine pipette, place a small drop of the amino acid mixture in the middle of the pencil line. Let this dry, place another drop on top of the first and dry again. Repeat this about six times, keeping the spot as small as possible.

5 Lower the strip carefully into the glass jar so that the bottom end dips about 5 mm into the solvent. Then bend the top end over and attach it to the lid (Figure 4.1). Leave the apparatus alone for 8–16 hours.

Corrosive
Butan-1-ol

Flammable
Butan-1-ol

REQUIREMENTS

Fume cupboard
Boiling tube
Glass jar (approximately 40 cm high × 7 cm diameter, gas jar recommended)
Lid for gas jar
Strip of chromatography paper (about 40 × 2 cm)
Pencil and ruler
Dropping pipette with fine point
Measuring cylinder (10 cm³)
Adhesive
Kitchen gloves
Crystallising dish (125 mm diameter)
Hair dryer or small convector heater

Trypsin solution (10 cm³)
Thymol crystals
Solvent, 200 cm³ (see below)
Distilled water
Ninhydrin solution (sufficient to fill crystallising dish to a depth of 10 mm)

Egg white (2 g) or fluid albumen (5 cm³)

Make up the solvent as follows:

4 parts of butan-1-ol, 1 part glacial ethanoic acid and 1 part distilled water
Make up ninhydrin reagent as follows:
1.0% solution of ninhydrin in butan-1-ol
Make up trypsin solution as follows:
dissolve 2.0 g trypsin in 100 cm³ of 1.0% sodium hydrogencarbonate

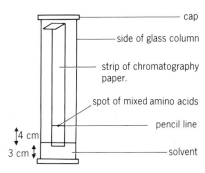

Figure 4.1 Diagram of paper chromatography apparatus for the separation of amino acids.

6 After 8–16 hours have elapsed, remove the strip from the jar; the solvent should have risen 20–25 cm from the pencil line. Draw another line across the strip at the highest point reached by the solvent. Then hang the strip in a warm place to dry.

Developing the chromatogram

7 Developing the chromatogram involves staining the amino acids. This is done by means of a dilute solution of ninhydrin in butan-1-ol. Use the fume cupboard, wear gloves and take care. Pour a small amount of the ninhydrin reagent into a glass crystallising dish and slowly draw the chromatography paper through the liquid. Ensure that the whole of the area between the two pencil lines is thoroughly soaked.

8 Dry the strip rapidly by holding it close to a source of heat, e.g. a hair dryer. Do not use a Bunsen flame; ninhydrin is inflammable. If you continue to heat it after it is dry, purple spots will appear along its length. Continue heating until the colour in the spots is as dense as possible.

Interpreting the chromatogram

9 Each purple spot corresponds to one or more amino acids. To identify them we make use of a measurement called the R_f value; R_f stands for 'relative front'. This is

Flammable
Ninhydrin

Toxic
Ninhydrin

Irritant
Ninhydrin

the ratio of the distance moved by the spot to the distance moved by the solvent:

$$R_f = \frac{\text{distance moved by spot}}{\text{distance moved by solvent}}$$

10 Draw a horizontal line through each spot and calculate its R_f value. By comparing your R_f values with those listed in Table 4.1, try to identify the amino acid responsible for each spot in your chromatogram. Write alongside each spot the name of your amino acid, together with the measured R_f value.

For consideration

1 How many different amino acids occur in albumen, according to your analysis?
2 Albumen is known to contain fifteen amino acids (see Table 4.2). List several reasons why they do not all appear on your chromatogram.
3 Some of the spots are so close together that it is impossible to distinguish between them. How could you extend the chromatographic technique in order to show if this explanation is correct?

Table 4.1 The amino acids present in the protein albumen (egg white), listed in order of R_f value (in this solvent only).

Amino acid	R_f value
Lysine	0.14
Arginine	0.20
Aspartic acid	0.24
Glycine	0.26
Serine	0.27
Glutamic acid	0.30
Threonine	0.35
Alanine	0.38
Proline	0.43 (yellow)
Tyrosine	0.45
Methionine	0.55
Valine	0.60
Phenylalanine	0.68
Isoleucine	0.72
Leucine	0.73

Table 4.2 The amino acids present in the protein albumen (egg white), listed in order of decreasing concentration.

Amino acid	Approximate % protein
Glutamic acid	16.5
Aspartic acid	9.3
Leucine	9.2
Serine	8.2
Phenylalanine	7.7
Valine	7.1
Isoleucine	7.0
Alanine	6.7
Lysine	6.3
Arginine	5.7
Methionine	5.2
Threonine	4.0
Tyrosine	3.7
Proline	3.6
Glycine	3.1

4.2 PRACTICAL EXERCISE

This exercise extends over more than one practical session.

Analysis of the amino acids in a protein by paper electrophoresis

One aim of this experiment is to determine which amino acids occur in casein, the major protein in milk. Another is to illustrate paper electrophoresis, an important technique for separating and identifying organic compounds in mixtures.

When a mixture of amino acids is placed on moist filter paper between two electrodes, and the current is switched on, the amino acids with no net charge will stay in place, the positively-charged molecules will move towards the negative electrode and the negatively-charged molecules will move towards the positive electrode. When the current is switched off, the paper is dried and treated with a reagent which stains the amino acids so that they can be located and identified. Identification is far easier if solutions of known amino acids have also been included in the experiment.

Procedure

1 Take a 30 × 10 cm sheet of filter paper. Handle it carefully on the edge; do not finger the paper. Rule a pencil line across it halfway down, 15 cm from either end. Starting 1 cm from the edge, make nine pencil dots on this line, each 1 cm apart. Number these dots 1–9.
2 Dissolve 5 g of casein hydrolysate in 10 cm³ of water in a test-tube. Stopper the test-tube and shake thoroughly. After five minutes, use a dropping pipette with a fine point to pipette drops of this solution onto dots 3 and 6. Do not let the spots become larger than 3 mm diameter.

REQUIREMENTS

Fume cupboard
Electrophoresis apparatus with power
  supply
Chromatography or filter paper
Crystallising dish (diameter 12 cm or
  more)
Hair dryer or convector heater
Dropping pipettes (with fine points) ×10
Pencil and ruler
Glass beakers (50 cm³) ×8
Amino acids
Buffer solution (pH 3.6) – see below
Ninhydrin solution (sufficient to fill
  crystallising dish to depth of 10 mm) –
  see below
Casein hydrolysate (available from
  suppliers)
Make up buffer solution as follows:
  carefully add 13.8 g glacial ethanoic
  acid and 1.5 g pyridine to 234.7 g dis-
  tilled water

Make up ninhydrin reagent as follows:
  200 mg ninhydrin in 100 cm³ propanone

3 · Dry the spots by placing the paper some distance from a blow heater. Then add another drop of casein hydrolysate to each spot. Repeat this procedure another eight times.

4 Using a separate clean pipette in each case, add solutions of pure amino acids to the remaining dots as follows:
  1-arginine, 2-lysine, 4-glycine, 5-aspartic acid, 7-glutamic acid, 8-valine, 9-trypto-phan. For each dot, about ten applications of amino acid solution are needed.

5 To moisten the filter paper, first place some buffer solution in a crystallising dish in a fume cupboard. Draw both ends of the filter paper through the buffer so that the paper is wetted at both ends up to 2 cm from the pencil line, but remains dry in the centre.

6 Set up the paper in a tank; an example is shown in Figure 4.2. Moisten the centre of the paper, but not the spots themselves, with buffer solution from a dropping pipette. Replace the top of the tank firmly.

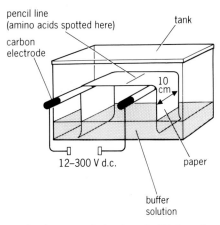

Figure 4.2 One type of apparatus for paper electrophoresis. Whatever the apparatus, the charged compounds to be separated are placed between the electrodes on a moist medium in a buffer solution which conducts electricity.

Caution
Current

Irritant   Flammable
Ninhydrin   Ninhydrin

7 Connect the electrodes to a 12–300 volt d.c. supply. Run the current for half an hour (high voltage) or several hours (low voltage).

8 Switch off the current. Remove the paper from the jar, and hang it up to dry in a warm fume cupboard.

9 When the electrophoretogram is dry, you can stain it. In a fume cupboard, pour a small amount of ninhydrin solution into a glass crystallising dish. Slowly draw the electrophoresis paper through the liquid. Ensure that the whole of the area of the paper is thoroughly soaked. Then dry the paper in the fume cupboard and observe the stained amino acids.

10 Write alongside each spot the name of the amino acid responsible.

For consideration

1 List the amino acids which occur in casein.

2 There are known to be 17 different amino acids in casein. Why do they not all appear in your electrophoretogram?

3 One possible answer to the previous question is that all the amino acids occur in your electrophoretogram, but some of the spots are so close to one another that it is impossible to distinguish between them. How could you extend the technique in order to investigate this possibility?

4 How do the charges on amino acid molecules originate?

5 If you altered the pH of the solution, would the pattern of spots obtained be the same? Explain your answer carefully.

6 Electrophoresis is frequently used to separate whole protein molecules. In protein synthesis the amino groups of one amino acid join to the carboxylic acid groups of the next. Why then are proteins charged?

Reference

Brown, G.D. and Creedy, J. *Experimental Biology Manual*, Heinemann Educational, 1970.

Vitamin C content of various fruits

In this investigation you can compare the vitamin C contents of different fruits (or any other foodstuff) by a simple colour test, the decolourisation of the blue dye **DCPIP (dichlorophenolindolephenol)**. Vitamin C is an anti-oxidant, and reduces DCPIP to a colourless solution (pink in the case of some fruits – it is the disappearance of the blue colour that you should look for). Vitamin C prevents the deficiency disease **scurvy**, and is particularly abundant in citrus fruits such as oranges, lemons and limes.

First you must estimate the volume of a known concentration of Vitamin C solution required to decolourise 2 cm^3 of a DCPIP solution. Then you must determine the volume of fruit juice which decolourises 2 cm^3 of DCPIP solution. This provides an estimate of the concentration of vitamin C in fruit juice, in units of 1 mg (see Guidance). This figure is then multiplied by the volume of the fruit to obtain its total vitamin C content.

Guidance

First try a 'test run' to establish a suitable technique which you can apply to all the fruits.

To determine the volume of your fruit, put it in a beaker and cover it with water. Mark the level of the meniscus on the outside of the beaker. Remove the fruit, make the water up to the mark with water from a measuring cylinder. The volume of water you add is equivalent to the volume of the fruit.

Add the vitamin C solution, drop by drop, with a pipette, to 2 cm^3 of the DCPIP solution in a test-tube. Shake the tube gently after the addition of each drop and continue to add drops until the DCPIP solution is decolourised. Record the exact volume of vitamin C you added. Repeat the procedure and average the results.

You can now calculate the mass of vitamin C which is required to decolourise 2 cm^3 of DCPIP solution, knowing that the vitamin C solution was made up to contain 1 mg vitamin C in 1.0 cm^3 water.

You can now repeat this procedure with the fruit juice, containing vitamin C at unknown concentration, instead of the known concentration of vitamin C. If only one or two drops of fruit juice are required to decolourise DCPIP, dilute the juice five times and try again. Using the same technique, you should be able to compare the vitamin C contents of several different fruits or vegetables.

For consideration

1   Vitamin C (ascorbic acid) is derived from a 6-carbon sugar. Suggest why it is so abundant in fruits and vegetables. What functions might it serve?
2   List all the sources of error you can think of in calculating the vitamin C content of a fruit merely from its concentration in fruit juice and the volume of the fruit.
3   A typical human needs about 10 mg of vitamin C a day to prevent scurvy and the British government recommends a daily intake of about 30 mg. To what extent can these needs be met by a single lemon or orange?

Beaker (100 cm^3)
Beaker (500 cm^3)
Container to collect a small volume of lemon juice
Measuring cylinder (250 cm^3)
Pipette or syringe to measure 2 cm^3 volume
Pipette or syringe to measure accurately volumes up to 1 cm^3
Test-tube
Spatula
Distilled water (50 cm^3)
Vitamin C (0.1%, fresh, 0.1% is 1 mg per cm^3 or lg per L)
DCPIP (dichlorophenolindolephenol) (1% aqueous solution, freshly made up)
Fruits and vegetables

Comparison of the chemical composition of various foodstuffs

The relative concentrations of starch, reducing sugars, lipids and proteins in a variety of foodstuffs can be compared by using the techniques outlined in Box 4.1 on food tests. Then you can relate the composition of the foodstuff to its value to the organism which produced it, or the way in which the food was processed.

You can include almost any foodstuff in your investigation, but following are recommended: milk, butter, cheese, apple, brown bread, white bread and meat.

Guidance

Test for starch with iodine solution, for reducing sugars with Benedict's solution, for lipids with the ethanol test and for proteins with the Biuret test. You may also have time to test for lignin with acidified phoroglucinol. The methods are described in Box 4.1.

Cut up the solids with a sharp knife. Try to make the tests as quantitative as possible. By standardising the amounts of foodstuffs to be tested, and the quantities of reagents, you will be able to make a valid comparison.

Harmful
Iodine
solution
phloroglucinol

flammable
Ethanol

Corrosive
Phoroglucinol

Apply the same test to all the foodstuffs, and compare the results, before you test for a different compound. Record the intensity of the colour produced in each test on a five-point scale.

For consideration

1 Relate the composition of milk to its function. Account for the differences in composition between milk, cheese and butter in terms of the way in which cheese and butter are produced from milk.
2 Why does meat have such a high protein content? Which named proteins might be responsible?
3 Speculate on the advantages to an apple fruit of its high content of reducing sugars.

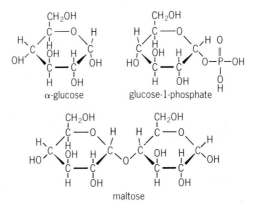

Figure 4.3 The structural formulae of the three substrates from which starch might be made; glucose, glucose-1-phosphate and maltose.

REQUIREMENTS

Test-tubes
Test-tube rack
Test-tube brushes
Sharp knife or razor blade
Ceramic tile
Spatula
Bunsen burner
Test-tube holder
Safety spectacles

Iodine solution
Benedict's reagent
Ethanol (absolute)
Millon's reagent
Potassium hydroxide (dilute)
Copper (II) sulphate (1%)
Phoroglucinol
Concentrated hydrochloric acid

Meat (white meat, e.g. chicken is best if Millon's test is used)
Milk
Cheese
Butter
Apple
White bread
Brown bread
Suspension of brewer's yeast

4.5 PRACTICAL EXERCISE

Synthesis of starch using an enzyme extracted from a potato

Potato tubers contain an enzyme which catalyses the synthesis of starch, a polymer of glucose units, from simple 'building blocks'. The aim of this investigation is to find out which compounds the enzyme can act on to produce starch. We shall investigate three possible substrates: **glucose**, **glucose-1-phosphate** (formed from a reaction between glucose and ATP) and **maltose**, a disaccharide of two glucose units (Figure 4.3).

Procedure

Extracting the enzyme from potato tissue

1 Peel a medium-sized potato and cut it into small pieces. Grind a few pieces of potato in a pestle and mortar with some sand and 20 cm^3 of water.
2 Pour the liquid part of the extract into two centrifuge tubes so that each contains an equal volume. Try not to let sand and solid matter get into the tubes – any which is added should be distributed equally between the two.
3 Spin the extracts in a centrifuge for a few minutes at 5000 rpm. The object is to deposit the starch, cell walls and other solid matter to the bottom of the centrifuge tubes. The starch-free liquid above the deposit should contain the enzyme.
4 Stop the centrifuge. Using a teat pipette, carefully withdraw from the centrifuge tube as much as possible of the clear enzyme solution, without disturbing the deposit beneath. Transfer it to a test-tube.
5 This 'enzyme' solution must be starch-free. To check, transfer a few drops into a test-tube containing 3 cm^3 of iodine solution. If a blue colour appears, the solution contains some starch and the potato extract needs to be centrifuged again.
6 Distribute the enzyme solution equally between three test-tubes.

Harmful
Iodine
solution

REQUIREMENTS

Centrifuge and centrifuge tubes
Test-tube rack
Pestle and mortar
Scalpel
Marker for writing on glass
Test-tubes ×7
Teat pipette
Syringes (5 cm³) ×3
Glass rod
White tile

Glucose solution (3 cm³, 1%)
Glucose-1-phosphate solution (3 cm³, 1%)
Maltose solution (3 cm³, 1%)
Iodine solution

Potato tuber

4.6 PRACTICAL EXERCISE

REQUIREMENTS

Test-tubes ×5
Test-tube rack
Labels or wax pencil
Stopclock
Pipettes or syringes (5 cm³) ×2
White tile
Glass rods ×6
Water baths maintained at 25 °C, 40 °C, 60 °C and 100 °C
Thermometers
Beaker

Amylase solution (allow 50 cm³), concentration up to 1% depending on age
Starch solution (1%) (allow 50 cm³)
Iodine solution
Ice

Harmful
Iodine
solution

Attempting starch synthesis

7 Label three clean test-tubes G, G-1-P, and M respectively. Using a separate syringe in each case, place 3 cm³ of glucose-1-phosphate in the G tube, 3 cm³ glucose solution in the G-1-P tube, and 3 cm³ of maltose solution in the M tube.

8 To attempt starch synthesis, pour the contents of an enzyme tube into the substrate tube, mix well, note the time, and immediately withdraw one drop of the solution with a glass rod. Touch the drop onto a drop of fresh iodine solution on a white tile and record the colour produced. Repeat at intervals of one minute for fifteen minutes, recording the colour each time. You should be able to try to synthesise starch in the three tubes simultaneously. If you make starch, the extract will eventually turn the iodine solution blue-black.

For consideration

1 The chemical structures of the three substrates are shown in Figure 4.3. What feature of the starch-synthesising substrate molecule might have been recognised by the starch-synthesising enzyme?

2 The synthesis of polymers such as starch requires metabolic energy. What was the energy source in the successful reaction?

3 The enzyme isolated from potatoes is known as **starch phosphorylase**. In the intact potato tuber it is also used to break down starch. How did conditions in the test-tube favour starch synthesis? In what circumstances does the enzyme bring about starch synthesis in a potato?

4 In plant leaves, starch accumulates in chloroplasts. The synthesis of starch requires ATP. Where do you think this ATP comes from?

Effect of exposure to different temperatures on molecular structure of an enzyme

Enzyme molecular structure is affected by temperature. To assess the effect of temperature on enzyme structure, you can expose samples of the enzyme to different temperatures for the same length of time, and then find how long each sample takes to catalyse its reaction under standard conditions.

In this experiment samples of **amylase**, a starch-digesting enzyme, are exposed to various temperatures for five minutes. The time required for each sample to digest the same quantity of starch at the same temperature is then estimated by using iodine solution (which turns blue-black in the presence of starch) as an indicator.

Procedure

1 Label five test-tubes – room temperature (measure it!), 25 °C, 40 °C, 60 °C and 100 °C. Add 5 cm³ of amylase solution to each.

2 Keep the first tube at room temperature. Place each of the other tubes in the appropriate water bath for exactly five minutes. During this time prepare a results sheet with time on the vertical axis and one column for each temperature.

3 Immediately remove the tubes from the water baths and cool them rapidly to room temperature with ice in a beaker (care!).

4 Once you are satisfied that the contents of each tube are at the same temperature, add 5cm³ of starch solution to each and mix with a clean glass rod.

5 At intervals of one minute test each tube for the presence of starch. Withdraw one drop of the starch-enzyme mixture, place it on a white tile and add one drop of iodine solution. Use a separate glass rod for each tube and a different one for the iodine solution.

6 Carefully record each result as it is obtained, in terms of a consistent colour scheme. Do not continue your observations for longer than fifteen minutes. Note how long it takes in each case before a blue-black colour *ceases* to be obtained when iodine solution is added to the mixture.

For consideration

1 The assessment of the colour of an iodine solution is subjective. Can you think of a *quantitative* way to compare reaction rates?

2   Speculate in detail on the influence of temperature on the molecular structure of the enzyme. What types of bond probably hold the molecule together and which is most likely to be broken by heat energy?

Harmful Iodine solution

Effect of temperature on the rate of reaction

Design an experiment to assess the influence of temperature on the reaction rate, using the digestion of starch by the enzyme amylase as the enzyme-substrate system. Try to make the reaction as quantitative as possible, so that you can say how much faster the reaction occurs at one temperature than another.

In this investigation the time required by amylase to digest the same quantity of starch at a series of different temperatures is estimated by using iodine solution as an indicator.

Guidance

Use a technique similar to that in 4.6 Practical Exercise. Make sure that the starch and amylase solutions reach the temperatures of the water baths *before* you mix them.

Test each tube for the presence of starch at intervals of one minute. Carefully record in a table each result as it is obtained, in terms of a consistent colour scheme. Do not continue your observations for longer than fifteen minutes.

For consideration

1   Suggest how you might relate the colour of the iodine to the proportion of the starch which has been broken down.
2   On the basis of the data you have collected, compare the rates of reaction at different temperatures.
3   Give two reasons why the rate of reaction increases with temperature, up to a point.
4   In conventional brewing, hot water is mixed with the mashed malt in order to stimulate the *rapid* breakdown of any remaining starch to maltose. What temperature of water would you advise the brewmaster to add?

Effect of enzyme and substrate concentrations on the hydrolysis of sucrose

To investigate the effect of enzyme and substrate concentrations on the rate of a reaction, a convenient system is provided by the hydrolysis of the disaccharide sucrose by the enzyme **sucrase** (**invertase**) into its constituent monosaccharides, glucose and fructose. On the basis of the information provided here, you can devise your own experiment.

The reaction is as follows:

$$C_{12}H_{22}O_{11} + H_2O \longrightarrow C_6H_{12}O_6 + C_6H_{12}O_6$$
Sucrose   Glucose   Fructose

To determine the effect of enzyme concentration, you will need to add the same volume of sucrase solution, containing different enzyme concentrations, to standard volumes of sucrose solution. To investigate the effect of substrate concentration, a standard concentration of enzyme needs to be added to different concentrations of substrate.

The progress of the reaction can be followed by testing for the substrates and products. Sucrose does not give a positive test when heated with Benedict's solution, but glucose and fructose both yield a yellow, brown or red precipitate.

Whichever experiment you attempt, it is essential to measure the *initial* rate of the reaction, that is, the reaction over a short period of time, say 30 seconds. The rate of reaction declines with time, and if you continue the experiment for longer, the effect of this decline of the reaction rate becomes confused with the effect of the enzyme or the substrate concentrations.

Eye protection
must be worn

Guidance
Summary of the technique

Using a syringe, place 1 cm^3 of Benedict's solution in a test-tube, and place it into a test-tube rack. Then place 5 cm^3 of 2% sucrose in one test-tube, and 5 cm^3 of 1% sucrase in another, and put both into a water bath at 38 °C.

Leave both test-tubes in the water bath for five minutes to allow their temperatures to reach the temperature of the water. Then, simultaneously, start the stop clock and pour the contents of the sucrase solution into the sucrose solution. Swirl the contents of the test-tube and rapidly put it back into the 38 °C water bath.

After thirty seconds, remove 1 cm^3 of the reaction mixture with a syringe and squirt it into the test tube of Benedict's solution in the test-tube rack. Now transfer the test-tube to a water bath at 50 °C for five minutes, and during this time record both the timing of the colour changes and the approximate amount of precipitate formed.

Carrying out the investigation

Now plan and carry out an investigation, using dilutions of the sucrase and sucrose solutions provided, into the effect of altering the enzyme or substrate concentration on the rate of reaction. Write down your plan before you start. Are any controls necessary? Keep detailed records of what you did and the results you obtained, and be prepared to modify your technique (e.g. by allowing the reaction to take place for a minute instead of thirty seconds) to obtain more satisfactory results.

For consideration

1   Examine your results. What relationship is there between the initial rate of reaction and either enzyme or substrate concentration?
2   Explore ways of making your results into figures which can be plotted on a graph. For example, if you calculate the rate of reaction as 1/reaction time for the first reducing sugars to be detected, you may then be able to plot it against enzyme or substrate concentration.
3   Explain your results in terms of the interactions between enzyme and substrate molecules.
4   Why do you think that sucrose yields a negative Benedict's test when the two sugars of which it is composed both give positive tests?

Reference

Green, N.P., Stout, G.W., Taylor, D.J. *Biological Science*, Cambridge University Press, 1984.

REQUIREMENTS

Water baths at 38 °C and 50 °C with metal
    test-tube racks
Test-tubes
Test-tube rack
Stopclocks
Syringes (1 cm^3, 5 cm^3)
Marking pen or chinagraph pencil
Measuring cylinders
Safety goggles

Benedict's reagent
Distilled water
Sucrase (invertase) solution, 1%
Sucrose solution, 2%

4.9 PRACTICAL EXERCISE

Influence of pH on the activity of potato catalase

The activity of most enzymes, including catalase, is influenced by changes in pH. Catalase occurs in many plant and animal tissues. It breaks down toxic hydrogen peroxide, formed as a by-product of various biochemical reactions, into water and oxygen.

In this experiment, you can test the hypothesis that the optimum pH of catalase is about the same as the pH of potato cells (7.4). One way to do this is to place potato discs in hydrogen peroxide solutions of known pH and measure the rate at which oxygen is evolved. This reflects the activity of the catalase enzyme in the potato.

Procedure

Danger
Razor blade

1   With a cork borer, cut a cylinder of potato tuber tissue about 1 cm in diameter and at least 6 cm long. Slice the cylinder into discs 1 mm thick and, as you do so, place them under water in a Petri dish. You require at least sixty discs.
2   Assemble the apparatus shown in Figure 4.4. Take particular care against breakage as you insert the manometer tube into the bung.
3   Remove the bung from the boiling tube. With a syringe, place into the boiling tube 5 cm^3 of buffer solution at pH 3. Carefully add ten potato discs. Then, with another syringe, add 5 cm^3 of hydrogen peroxide.

REQUIREMENTS

Razor blade
Cork borer
Ruler
Ceramic tile
Forceps
Boiling tube (with bored rubber bung)
Stand, bosses and clamps
Manometer tube (approx 3 mm diameter)
Beaker
Syringes (5 cm^3) ×2
Spring clip
Stop clock
Wax pencil
Potato tuber
Manometer fluid
Hydrogen peroxide ('20-volume')
Citric-acid phosphate buffers, made up as
   shown below from Na$_2$HPO$_4$ (0.2 mol
   dm^{-3}) and citric acid (0.1 mol dm^{-3}) to
   give 100 cm^3 of buffer in each case:

pH	Na$_2$HPO$_4$ (cm^3)	Citric acid (cm^3)
3.0	20.55	79.45
4.0	38.55	61.45
5.0	51.50	48.50
6.0	63.15	36.85
7.0	82.35	17.65
8.0	97.25	2.75

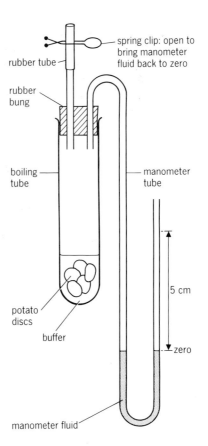

Figure 4.4 Technique for measuring the rate of evolution of oxygen from hydrogen peroxide when living tissue is present.

4 Replace the bung immediately, making sure that it provides an airtight seal, and note the time. Mark on the right hand manometer tube the position of the meniscus and draw a line 5 cm above it.

5 Gently agitate the boiling tube (why?). As the reaction begins and oxygen is produced you should see the manometer fluid being pushed down the left hand side of the manometer tube and rising on the right hand side. Time how long it takes for the fluid to rise through 5 cm on the right hand side.

6 Open the clip at the top of the boiling tube so that the manometer fluid returns to its original position. Then close the clip and time the production of a second 5 cm of oxygen. Work out the average reading.

7 Remove the bung and thoroughly wash out the boiling tube.

8 Now carry out five further tests, each with a fresh set of ten potato discs. Follow the same procedure, but with buffer solutions of pH 4, 5, 6, 7 and 8 in turn. Make sure that you use a *clean* syringe each time.

9 Take each of your average readings and express the rate of reaction, in arbitrary units, by dividing 1000 by the time taken in seconds for a 5 cm rise in the manometer fluid.

10 Plot a graph of the rate of reaction (vertical axis) against pH.

For consideration

1 What is a 'buffer' solution? Why was it valuable to use buffer solutions in this experiment?

2 What was the relationship between the activity of potato catalase and pH?

3 Is the relationship important for the potato cells?

4 At the molecular level, how might pH affect the efficiency with which an enzyme works?

5 Using the same apparatus, how would you measure the *volume* of gas given off per unit time?

Effect of bead size on the activity of immobilised yeast or catalase

The **entrapment** of enzymes or yeast and other microorganisms in beads has become a standard technique in biotechnology. The beads can be easy replaced, removed, counted or handled, they can be cleaned with distilled water and used to create columns in which compounds are modified as they trickle down. Bead diameter influences surface area, which affects the rates of diffusion of compounds into and out of the beads. In this practical exercise we shall enclose yeast in alginate beads of different sizes, and use the rate of production of carbon dioxide gas as a measure of the rate of respiration. The same technique can be used to investigate the effect of bead size on the production of oxygen by the enzyme catalase acting on hydrogen peroxide. In this case it would be necessary to trap the *enzyme* in beads.

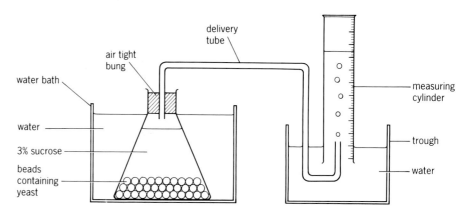

Figure 4.5 Simple apparatus for collecting CO_2 evolved from immobilised yeast, or O_2 from immoblised catalase acting on hydrogen peroxide.

Procedure

1 Add 0.8 g sodium alginate to 20 cm^3 distilled water, and stir this viscous liquid until it achieves an even consistency. Leave the solution to soak for five minutes.
2 Stir 1 g of yeast into 20 cm^3 distilled water and leave it to soak for five minutes.
3 Add the yeast suspension to the alginate solution and mix well with a glass rod.
4 Draw up 10 cm^3 of the mixture into a syringe and drop the mixture, using a constant pressure so that the beads are all the same size, from a height of about 10 cm, into a beaker containing 100 cm^3 of 1.4 % calcium chloride solution.
5 Repeat this procedure twice more with different beakers of calcium chloride solution. In each case use a different speed of flow so as to produce beads of different sizes.
6 Allow the beads to stand in the calcium chloride solution for twenty minutes. Whilst they are standing, measure the average diameter of representative beads from each solution, with a ruler, under a binocular microscope, and then replace the beads. Strain with a tea strainer to remove the beads from the calcium chloride.
7 Set up three fermentation vessels as shown in Figure 4.5 with 3% sucrose solution and the beads. Investigate and record the relative rates of reaction.

REQUIREMENTS

Beakers, 250 cm^3, ×4
Glass rod
Plastic syringe, 10 cm^3
Tea strainer
Binocular microscope
Ruler
Fermentation apparatus (×3) as in Figure 4.5 (conical flask, bung and delivery tube, trough, 100 cm^3 measuring cylinder)
Sodium alginate, 2.4 g
Distilled water
Calcium chloride solution, 1.4%, 500 cm^3
Sucrose solution, 3%, 750 cm^3
Dried yeast

For consideration

1 The volume of the beads is the same in all three solutions. Estimate the total surface areas of the beads in each solution, and the distance from the surface of a spherical bead to the centre.
2 Explain your results in terms of the ease with which sucrose enters a bead, the distance the molecules have to diffuse, and the average distance of the yeast cells from the surface of the bead.

4.11 PRACTICAL EXERCISE

Removal of urea from solutions using immobilised urease

In patients with kidney failure, urea accumulates in the blood rather than being excreted. One way to remove urea from the blood is to treat it with the enzyme **urease**, which decomposes urea into carbon dioxide and ammonia. This may be done in a reactor column containing the immobilised urease enzyme and 'activated' charcoal. **Immobilised enzymes** are enzyme molecules which have been trapped in beads of gelatine or on the surface of another compound to allow them to be handled more easily. The ammonia produced in this particular reaction is retained by the activated charcoal. The blood, free of urea, can then be returned to the patient. This practical simulates this process.

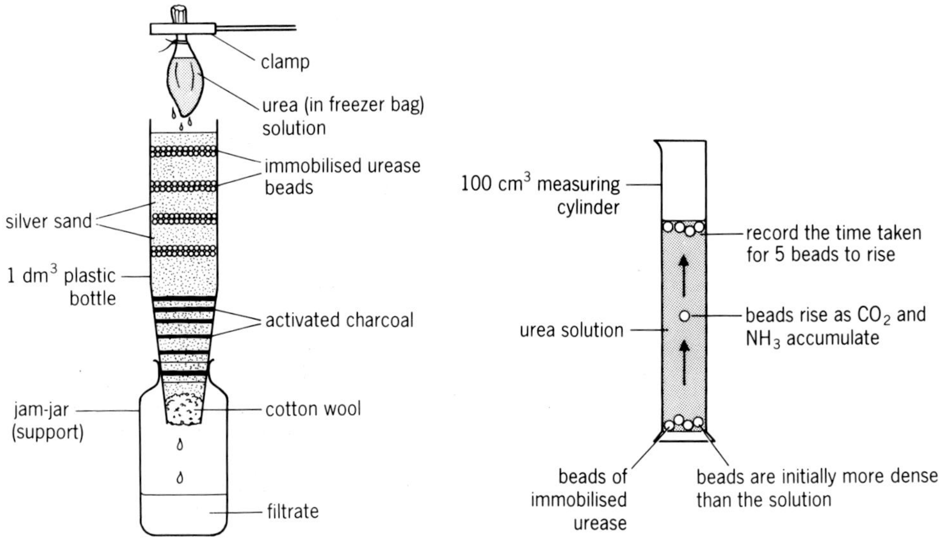

Figure 4.6 The apparatus for (a) removing, and (b) estimating urea. (*After P.W. Freeland*)

REQUIREMENTS

Jam jar
Screwtop plastic bottle (1 dm³)
Scissors
Cotton wool
pH papers (pH 1–14)
Freezer bags (2)
String
Clamp stand, boss and clamp
Pin
Beaker, 250 cm³ (two)
Plastic syringe, 10 cm³
Tea strainer
Boiling tubes
Boiling tube rack
Measuring cylinder, 100 cm³
Glass rod

Urea solution, 2%, 500 cm³
Urease solution, 60 cm³ (crush 15 urease tablets in a polythene bag, and dissolve the resulting powder in 1 dm⁻³ distilled water)
Sodium alginate, 3%, 75 cm³
Calcium chloride, 3%, 100 cm³
Distilled or deionised water
Silver sand, 500 g
Activated charcoal, 250 g

Procedure

1   Mix 50 cm³ urease solution and 50 cm³ sodium alginate solution in a beaker. Draw this mixture into a plastic syringe. Inject it, drop by drop, into calcium chloride solution, in a beaker, to form about three hundred uniformly-sized beads. Remove the beads from the solution by straining through a tea strainer. Collect about eighty beads in boiling tubes, in groups of ten, ready for the calibration and estimation.

2   Set up the apparatus shown in Figure 4.6. First, remove the bottom of the plastic bottle, then turn it upside down and plug the neck with cotton wool. Place the neck of the inverted bottle in the jam jar (Figure 4.6a). Pack alternating layers of silver sand and activated charcoal into the bottom 10 cm of the bottle at the neck end. Then add alternating layers of silver sand, and beads of immobilised urease, to within 1–2 cm of the top.

3   Test and record the pH of the 2% urea solution provided. Pour about 150 cm³ of 2% urea solution into a freezer bag. Tie the bag with string. Clamp the bag above the inverted bottle. Prick the bag to establish a *slow* drip of urea solution through the apparatus.

4   Now establish a calibration curve. Fill a measuring cylinder to the 100 cm³ mark with 2% urea solution. Drop ten beads of immobilised urease into the cylinder and note the time. The beads will sink, then slowly rise as they fill with carbon dioxide and ammonia, produced by the reaction between urease and urea. Record the time taken for five beads to rise to the surface (Figure 4.6b).

5   Repeat the procedure in step 4 using solutions containing 1.5, 1.0, 0.5 and 0.25% urea. In each case record the time taken for five beads to rise to the surface. Express the rate of reaction as 1000/time in seconds for the beads to rise. Plot a calibration curve showing the rate of reaction against the concentration of urea.

6   Now determine the concentration of the urea in the filtrate in the jam jar. Record the pH of the filtrate. Pour 100 cm³ of this filtrate into the measuring cylinder (Keep the remaining filtrates.) Use ten beads of immobilised urease, and your standard curve, to determine the concentration of urea.

7   Pass the remaining filtrate from the jam jar through the column a second time. Again, measure the pH, and find out how much urea the filtrate contains by repeating the measuring cylinder experiment and using the calibration curve.

For consideration

1   Did the passage of the urea solution through the column alter its pH, and if so, why?

2   Might this process have any commercial value besides the treatment of blood by dialysis?

Refererence

Freeland, P.W. *Focus on Biology: Micro-organisms in action. Investigations*, Hodder and Stoughton, 1990.

4.12 INVESTIGATION

The efficiency of various treatments intended to preserve milk

This experiment allows you to test the efficiency of different methods of milk preservation. Milk contains microorganisms, particularly *Lactobacillus* bacteria, which can reproduce rapidly at favourable temperatures. The lactic acid they produce in anaerobic respiration sours the milk and makes it unpalatable. The rate of microbial respiration in milk can be detected with rezazurin dye and the accumulation of lactic acid can be estimated with a pH meter.

Several types of treated milk are commercially available, such as skimmed milk, semi-skimmed milk, ultra-heat treated (UHT milk) and pasteurised milk. Unpasteurised milk might serve as a control. You can test these milks after they have been allowed to stand for various lengths of time at room temperature. In addition you can test the efficiency of your own methods of preservation, such as heat treatment, refrigeration, or the addition of sodium nitrite, vinegar, or concentrated salt. Don't forget to incorporate controls!

Guidance

A standardised test is required in order to assess the microbial activity in milk. The simplest is to mix the milk with rezazurin dye at 37 °C and to record the rate at which the colour changes.

Add 1 cm³ of rezazurin dye to each of a series of test-tubes in a rack. Add 10 cm³ milk to one of the tubes, replace the bung, and with your thumb on the bung, turn the tube upside down three times. Label the tube with the sample number and replace it in the rack. Repeat for the other tubes in turn. Record the colour of the contents of each tube, using the names blue, lilac, pink/mauve, pink and colourless. Record the colours every 5 minutes for thirty minutes. The more rapidly the colour changes, the greater the microbial activity in the milk.

The pH of milk samples can also be measured, preferably with a pH meter or probe but, failing that, with pH paper or universal indicator.

If you would like a more precise estimate of the numbers of microbes in milk, you can use a serial dilution technique (see page 8) and estimate the numbers of colonies growing on china blue lactose agar.

For consideration

1   Why is milk particularly suitable for microbial growth?

2   Where do the *Lactobacillus* bacteria in milk come from?

3   Look up the various methods of pasteurisation used by dairies. How effective are they?

4   Try to find out the time which elapses between milk production and either its delivery to the doorstep, or its sale in a shop or supermarket. How much does its microbial population increase during that time?

5   Can you find an effective preservative which does not alter the taste of milk? (Do not taste the milk)

REQUIREMENTS

Water bath at 37 °C
Test-tubes with bungs
Test-tube racks
Plastic syringes, 2 cm³, 10 cm³
Glass marker
Stopclock
pH meter with probe or pH paper or universal indicator

Various types of milk; skimmed, semi-skimmed, UHT, pasteurised and unpasteurised
Rezazurin dye solution
Sodium nitrite
Spirit vinegar
Salt
China blue lactose agar

The optimum conditions for dry matter production by a fermenter

A **bioreactor** is a chamber in which defined conditions are maintained to encourage the production of useful compounds by the organisms inside. Several types of bioreactor are commercially available. Maintaining a pure culture of an organism inside a bioreactor for several weeks, with the continuous removal of the product, provides a useful insight into commercial biotechnology.

Another valuable exercise is to develop your own bioreactor and to test and refine various versions over several weeks. Some of the factors to be considered, and the problems to be overcome, are outlined here. The object is to attain a continuous flow process, in which some compounds are continually added and products are continually removed.

Guidance

Although this investigation can be done by individual students, it is probably better to work in a group and to share responsibilities.

(a) The simplest bioreactor may be a boiling tube, with a cotton wool plug, containing an organism and its substrate, placed in a water bath.

(b) Contamination with invading microorganisms is likely to be a problem, so all the materials should be autoclaved, or sterilised with a dilute bleach solution.

(c) To prevent contamination, it will be necessary to seal the top of the tube, but then the shortage of oxygen, the accumulation of waste gases or the pressure of accumulated gases may be a problem.

(d) One solution to this would be to connect the reactor to an aquarium pump, connected to a cotton wool dust filter, and to provide an air exit, again with a filter to prevent the entry of foreign microorganisms. The entry of air must be slow to avoid cooling the culture.

(e) The addition of another glass tube to the cork at the top of the reactor would then allow sampling of the reaction mixture, and perhaps the harvesting of the products. A finger over the air exit builds up pressure sufficiently for some of the solution to pass through this sampling tube to be collected.

(f) At this stage the circulation of the liquid within the reaction vessel needs to be measured and improved. You may have to change the shape of the reaction vessel.

(g) The addition of a further tube to the cork at the top allows the addition of extra nutrients or drops of acid or alkali to maintain a certain pH. If this can be done by drip feed under gravity, it begins to convert this process into a continuous one.

(h) An additional degree of sophistication would be provided by incorporating a motorised stirrer and and internal aquarium-style heater into the reaction vessel. An infra-red detector would allow the turbidity of the solution to be monitored, and a pH probe (perhaps linked to a microcomputer with suitable datalogging software) would allow a continuous read-out of pH to be obtained.

For consideration

1   How could you alter the conditions to maximise the output of useful product from your reactor?
2   What problems might you encounter in 'scaling up' the process a hundred thousand times to an industrial scale, and how might you overcome them?

REQUIREMENTS

This is an open-ended investigation and access to general laboratory glassware, bungs and glass tubing is required. It is valuable to have an autoclave (to sterilise glassware), an aquarium air pump and a water bath or aquarium heater with thermostat.

The reactor can be tried out with a variety of organisms. Examples include: *Saccharomyces cerevisiae* or *S. elipsoideus* in a sucrose or glucose-containing medium (at 25–30 °C?) to produce ethanol and carbon dioxide; *Acetobacter aceti* which produces vinegar when cultivated on dilute ethanol (at 30 °C?); *Alcaligenes eutrophus* which produces polyhydroxy-butyrate, a polymer to make plastic, when grown on dilute nutrient broth (at 30 °C?).

Effect of temperature on the oxygen consumption of organisms

In organisms such as plants and arthropods, which cannot control their own body temperatures, the temperature inside the organism generally fluctuates with that of the environment. The respiration rate of such organisms changes accordingly. The aim of this experiment is to find out how temperature affects the rate of respiration of broad beans, mung beans, maggots, mealworms or woodlice. It also illustrates the principle of using an important piece of apparatus, the **respirometer.**

Principle

If a group of organisms is oxidising glucose by aerobic respiration, the volume of oxygen taken up equals the volume of carbon dioxide produced. In a closed vessel containing respiring organisms, the concentration of oxygen will decrease and the concentration of carbon dioxide will increase.

Suppose, however, that a compound which absorbs carbon dioxide is placed inside the closed vessel. The respiring organisms still absorb oxygen, and the rate at which the pressure falls is a measure of the rate at which the organisms take up oxygen.

Two identical closed vessels are used. One contains living organisms, and the other (the control) contains either dead organisms or an exactly equal volume of an inert material. The control is necessary because temperature changes affect the volumes of the gases. Any differences between the two vessels can then be attributed to gaseous exchange by the living organisms.

Procedure

1 Fill a beaker half full with cold water to act as a water bath. Place it on a tripod and gauze and take the temperature of the water with a thermometer. If it is below 20 °C, heat the beaker gently with a Bunsen burner until it reaches 20 °C.

2 Label two boiling tubes L and D. Place living organisms in tube L and the equivalent number of dead organisms, or volume of inert material, in tube D. If the living organisms are seeds, push a plug of cotton wool into each tube and put an equal mass (5 g) of self-indicating soda lime on top. If the organisms are animals, put the soda lime into the tubes first, then the cotton wool and then the animals on top.

3 Pour a coloured manometer fluid into the reservoir of one of the manometers. If air bubbles appear in the capillary tube of the manometer, use a pipette filler to blow air down the long arm of the manometer tube to remove them (care!).

4 Gingerly, without creating air bubbles in the fluid, fit the long arm of the manometer tube into the rubber tubing attached to one of the rubber bungs. Fit the bung securely into one of the boiling tubes (care!).

5 Repeat steps 3 and 4 with the other manometer tube and bung. Clamp the two boiling tubes vertically in the water bath, making sure that both spring clips are open. Your apparatus should now look like Figure 4.7.

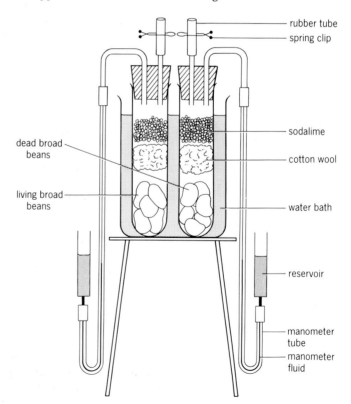

Figure 4.7 A respirometer, with control, for measuring the rate of oxygen uptake by small organisms, in this case broad beans. If animals such as blowfly larvae are used, the soda lime is better placed at the base of the tube and the animals above the cotton wool. This is to prevent the soda lime from falling onto the animals.
(*After D.G. Mackean*)

6 Make sure both spring clips are open. Check that your water bath is at 20 °C. Mark the levels of the menisci of the coloured fluid in both manometer tubes. Close both the spring clips. Note the time.

7 Record the levels of the fluid in both manometers, for example after 3, 6 and 9 minutes. If the level of the manometer fluid attached to boiling tube L does not change, check carefully for leaks and start again.

8 Open both spring clips. If a constant-temperature water bath is not being used, heat the beaker with a Bunsen burner until the water temperature reaches 33 °C. Remove the Bunsen burner. Allow at least five minutes for the beans to reach this temperature and for the volume of the air in the boiling tubes to stabilise. By this time the water should have cooled to about 30 °C. Repeat steps 6 and 7 at this temperature.

9 Open both spring clips. Pour away the water at 30 °C and replace it with cold tap water. Add a few cubes of ice until the water reaches 8 °C. Allow ten minutes for the beans to reach this temperature and for the volumes of air in the boiling tubes to stabilise. By this time the water in the beaker should have reached about 10 °C. Repeat steps 6 and 7 at this temperature.

10 Plot your data on a graph which shows the volume of oxygen evolved against time for each of the three temperatures.

For consideration

1 How much faster is the respiration rate at 20 °C than at 10 °C? How much faster is the respiration rate at 30 °C than at 20 °C? In working out these values you are calculating two estimates of the Q_{10}. The Q_{10} indicates the extent to which the rate of reaction increases with a 10 °C increase in temperature. The Q_{10} is slightly in excess of 2 for a large number of enzyme-controlled reactions. Do your results agree with this?

2 Explain in terms of the behaviour of individual molecules why the rate of an enzyme-controlled reaction doubles with a 10 °C increase in temperature (there are two main reasons).

3 Suppose that the uptake of oxygen suddenly stops but the seeds remain alive. Suggest an explanation.

4 If you have been using soaked seeds they may be respiring anaerobically as well as aerobically. How might this have affected your results, and why?

4.15 INVESTIGATION

Determination of the respiratory quotient

Using a modified respirometer (Practical Exercise 4.14), it is possible to determine the **respiratory quotient (R.Q.)** of organisms. This is the ratio of the volume of carbon dioxide produced to the volume of oxygen absorbed. This provides clues to the substrate being respired and the extent to which the tissue is respiring anaerobically.

Principle

If an organism is only respiring glucose aerobically, the volume of carbon dioxide produced equals the volume of oxygen absorbed so the R.Q. should be 1.0.

If a tissue is respiring fats aerobically, the respiratory quotient should be about 0.7. Imagine, for example, that stearic (octodecanoic) acid is being respired:

$$C_{17}H_{35} COOH + 26O_2 \longrightarrow 18CO_2 + 18H_2O$$

the respiratory quotient is $18/26 = 0.69$.

When anaerobic respiration to lactate is taking place, no carbon dioxide is produced, but organisms respiring anaerobically to ethanol, such as yeast and plant tissue, produce CO_2. Their respiratory quotient is very high.

In practice many organisms carry out aerobic and anaerobic respiration simultaneously. The relative extents of aerobic and anaerobic respiration can then be estimated from the respiratory quotient. Imagine, for example, that seeds produce twice as much carbon dioxide as the oxygen they absorb (R.Q. = 2). The aerobic respiration of a gram of glucose produces three times the volume of carbon dioxide as anaerobic respiration, so this respiratory quotient might indicate that glucose was being broken down three times faster by anaerobic than by aerobic respiration. Think about it!

Guidance

Batches of broad bean seeds which have been soaked beneath the surface of water (i) for 48 hours, (ii) for 42 hours and removed for 6 hours, (iii) for 36 hours and removed for 12 hours make ideal material.

The apparatus required is a pair of respirometer tubes in a water bath (Figure 4.7), but in this case one contains soda lime and the other does not. It is important that the volume of gas is identical in each tube so that any temperature fluctuations will be equally reflected in both. The tubes must both contain equal masses of the same species of respiring organisms, and the one without soda lime must contain an equivalent volume of an inert compound. Above all, the temperature of the water bath must not fluctuate during the experiment. You may wish to devise your own system of thermostatic control – a good opportunity to apply technology to biology.

Since soda lime absorbs carbon dioxide, the tube containing it measures oxygen uptake. The other tube measures net gas exchange. The carbon dioxide output is the difference between these two readings. A fall is negative and a rise is positive.

For consideration

1 Suppose that your germinating seeds appeared to have a net oxygen production. Suggest two possible reasons for this result.
2 Look up how fatty acids are respired in a cell. Why cannot they be respired *anaerobically*?
3 Imagine that you obtained a respiratory quotient of 0.9. Discuss possible reasons.

REQUIREMENTS

As for Practical 4.14
Thermostat (if available).
Inert compound equivalent in volume to
    soda lime
Broad bean seeds in batches which have
    been (i) soaked under water for
    48 hours, (ii) soaked for 42 hours and
    exposed to the air for 6 h and (iii)
    soaked for 36 hours and exposed for
    12 hours.

4.16 PRACTICAL EXERCISE

Effect of temperature on the rate of anaerobic respiration of yeast

Many yeasts of the genus *Saccharomyces* can grow in the absence of oxygen; some do not even have mitochondria for aerobic respiration. Under these conditions, yeast respires anaerobically; glucose is converted to carbon dioxide and ethanol in the process of **fermentation**:

$$C_6H_{12}O_6 \longrightarrow 2CO_2 + 2C_2H_5OH$$

The rate at which carbon dioxide is produced can be used to measure the rate of anaerobic respiration of yeast. In this experiment we shall determine the effect of temperature on the rate of fermentation.

Procedure

1 You are provided with a yeast culture set up an hour before. Using a pipette or syringe, transfer 10 cm^3 of the culture to each of six test-tubes.
2 Place two tubes in each of three water baths, at 20 °C, 35 °C and 50 °C. If thermostatically-controlled water baths are not available use three water-filled beakers, each containing a thermometer, supported on a tripod and gauze, over a Bunsen burner.
3 Leave the tubes in the water baths for five minutes to allow the temperatures of their contents to reach the temperature of the water bath.
4 Now fill a fermentation tube and insert it upside down into each test-tube. Carry out the following procedure for each of the six tubes:
    (i) Insert a teat pipette into the culture, suck up some of it and fill the fermentation tube to the brim.
    (ii) Hold the test-tube at an angle. Invert the fermentation tube and quickly push it down the wall of the test-tube.
    (iii) If the fermentation tube collects a bubble on the way down remove it, refill it and try once more.
5 At intervals of ten minutes, record the length of the carbon dioxide bubble within each fermentation tube. Work out the average bubble length for each temperature at each time interval.
6 Draw a graph of average bubble length (vertical axis) against time (horizontal axis). Plot three lines on it, one each for 20 °C, 35 °C and 50 °C. Estimate the rate of fermentation at each temperature by measuring the slope of each line.

For consideration

1 In what way does the rate of fermentation vary with temperature? Most enzyme-controlled processes approximately double in rate for each ten degree Celsius rise in temperature. Do your results confirm this general rule, or not?

REQUIREMENTS

Balance
Beaker (250 cm^3)
Fermentation tubes ×6
Graph paper
Dropping pipettes ×3
Pipette or syringe (3 cm^3) ×3
Ruler with mm scale
Spatula
Stopclock or stopwatch
Test-tubes ×6
Water baths (at 20 °C, 35 °C and 50 °C)
Test-tube racks in water baths
Thermometers

An hour before the practical starts set up
    a culture of yeast in a beaker containing
    glucose (3 g), dried yeast (2 g), yeast
    extract (1 g) and water (100 cm^3).
    Place it in an incubator or water bath at
    35 °C for an hour to allow fermentation
    to begin.

2   Carbon dioxide is very soluble in water. Why did it accumulate at the end of the tube, instead of dissolving in the water?

3   What lessons might brewers learn from the results of this experiment?

Reference

Revised Nuffield A level Biology, *Practical guide 2 – Chemical reactions in organisms*, Longman, 1985.

PROJECTS

Before starting a project discuss your intended procedure with your teacher.

1   Investigate the effect of preservation techniques on the vitamin C content of different foods, using the technique outlined in 4.3 Practical Exercise. For instance, you can compare the effect of leaving food to decay naturally, with heating to different temperatures for various lengths of time, chilling, deep freezing and/or pickling, or you can compare the vitamin C contents of fruit juices sold commercially with those of juice freshly extracted from fruits.
Other food sources containing high concentrations of vitamin C are spinach and peas.

2   Compare the distribution patterns of various chemical compounds within the seeds of different plant species, using the techniques outlined in Box 4.1 page 49. Include both endospermic and non-endospermic seeds, some of which store carbohydrate and some of which store lipids. Separate the parts of the seed from one another and test them separately, or stain thin sections of the seeds and examine them under the microscope. Relate the distribution of the compounds to their functions in the seeds.

3   Compare the concentrations of reducing sugars in various soft drinks with Benedict's reagent. First make the test quantitative, by heating various known concentrations of glucose with Benedict's reagent for a standard time and recording the colours you obtain.

4   Compare, by paper chromatography, the range of pigments present in the petals of several closely-related plant species, and explain why the flowers are that particular colour.

5   Use the catalase apparatus (4.9 Practical Exercise) to investigate in more detail the effect of temperature, enzyme concentration and substrate concentration on the reaction rate.

6   Investigate the distribution pattern of the enzymes nitrate reductase and nitrite reductase in leaves, stem and roots of seedlings of dwarf French bean (*Phaseolus vulgaris*). Incubate mashed up tissues in water and use reagent strips to assess the rate of appearance of nitrite and ammonia (see Freeland, P.W. *Problems in Practical Advanced Level Biology*, Hodder and Stoughton, 1985).

7   Investigate the properties of the protein-digesting enzyme 'stem bromelain'. Derived from pineapple fruit and stems, this enzyme is commercially available and can be purchased as a meat tenderiser. It can be used to break down the protein gelatin. See Dickson, S.R. and Bickerstaff, G.F., Pineapple bromelain and protein hydrolysis, *Journal of Biological Education* 25, 164–166, 1991.

8   Investigate the properties of the enzyme rennin, which is cheaply available from food stores as rennet. It acts on the soluble protein caseinogen in milk to produce insoluble casein. Since it acts in the stomach, its optimum pH might be expected to be on the acidic side.

9   Investigate the properties of the enzyme lipase, using pH sensors and datalogging equipment. The hydrolysis of lipids (triacylglycerols) produces fatty acids and glycerol. As the fatty acids are released, the pH of the solution falls. Using a calibrated pH probe connected to the analogue port of a microcomputer, the reduction in pH can be logged over a period of thirty minutes or so. The effects of different treatments (initial pH, temperature, enzyme concentration, substrate concentration) on the rate of enzyme activity can be assessed. Suitable software is available from Philip Harris Ltd.

10   Investigate the effect of various factors on the expansion of dough. Obvious factors include temperature and the composition of the mixture (yeast, sugar and flour). To measure expansion, mix 75 g of flour, 2 g of dried yeast and 50 cm^3 of water at room temperature. Place the mixture in a measuring cylinder and record the volume of the dough every minute.

11   Tears contain an enzyme known as lysozyme, which kills bacteria by breaking down the polysaccharides in their cell walls (lysis). Investigate the lytic activity of human tears. You can induce tears with a freshly cut onion. Add drops of serially diluted tears to populations of *Staphylococcus aureus* or *Escherichia coli* growing on agar plates. Be sure to employ suitable sterile techniques.

12   Compare the effects of different antibiotics on the growth of bacteria. One way of doing this is to grow colonies of bacteria (e.g. *Bacillus subtilis*, *Chromobacterium lividum*, *Staphylococcus aureus* or *Escherichia coli*) on agar plates, on whose surfaces are placed discs of filter paper impregnated with the antibiotics. In a similar way you could compare the efficiency in killing microbes of various toothpastes, antiseptics, deodorants or disinfectants.

13   Compare the abilities of different 'biological' washing powders to break down starch and proteins. A possible technique is to use a cork borer to cut wells in starch-iodine agar and milk nutrient agar. Solutions of the detergents can be placed in the wells, and their efficiency compared by measuring the area of the clear zones which appear around each well.

14   Assess the value of the enzyme pectinase for manufacturing fruit juice from certain fruits. Pectinase is released from certain fungi when they rot fruit, but is widely available for home brewing.

15   Using a respirometer, compare the respiratory quotients of germinating seeds which store fats (e.g. castor oil bean, sunflower) with those which store carbohydrates (e.g. wheat, maize) (see 4.15 Investigation).

16   Determine the respiration rates per gram of plant material (e.g. germinating broad bean seeds) and animal material (e.g. blowfly maggots) at the same temperature. List as many reasons as you can to explain the difference.

From cells to individuals

Examination of plant cells

Plants provide excellent material for the study of cells. However, the features typical of a plant cell cannot all be seen in one cell. It is necessary to look at several different types of plant cell in order to build up a complete picture. This is what we shall do in this practical exercise. Before you start, it is useful to have in mind a theoretical conception of what a generalised plant cell looks like (Figure 5.1).

Procedure

1 Strip off a piece of epidermis from the inner lining of one of the fleshy scales of an onion, mount it in dilute iodine solution and observe one cell under low and high powers. Observe the granular **cytoplasm** surrounding the clear **vacuole**. The **nucleus** is located in the cytoplasm close to the **cell wall**.

2 Repeat step 1 but this time mount the piece of epidermis in water instead of dilute iodine solution. What difference does this make to how much you can see? What does this tell you about the value of *staining* cells before you look at them under the microscope?

3 Open up one of the flowers of *Tradescantia* and remove a stamen. Mount the stamen in water and examine one of the hairs under high power. Adjust the illumination carefully or, better still, use phase contrast. The hair is a single cell. The nucleus is suspended in the centre of the cell by thin bridles of cytoplasm (Figure 5.2). Streaming of the cytoplasm, indicated by movement of granules, can sometimes be seen in these bridles and in the peripheral cytoplasm.

4 Neither of the cells examined so far contains **chloroplasts**. To see these organelles, mount a small leaf of moss in water and examine its cells under high power. The cells are so packed with chloroplasts that little else can be seen. What gives the chloroplasts their green colour?

5 Many plant cells store starch in the form of starch grains. Nowhere can these be better seen than in a potato tuber. Scrape some tissue from the cut surface of a

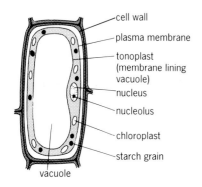

Figure 5.1 Drawing of a generalised plant cell. In reality there is no gap between the cell wall and plasma membrane; normally the plasma membrane presses against the inner side of the cell wall.

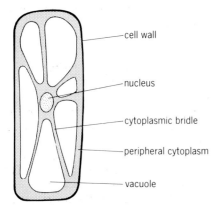

Figure 5.2 Staminal hair cell of *Tradescantia* showing how the nucleus is suspended in the centre of the cell.

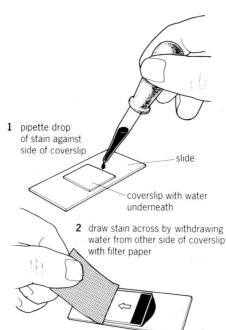

Figure 5.3 The technique of irrigation in which a stain is introduced under a coverslip.

1 pipette drop of stain against side of coverslip — slide

coverslip with water underneath

2 draw stain across by withdrawing water from other side of coverslip with filter paper

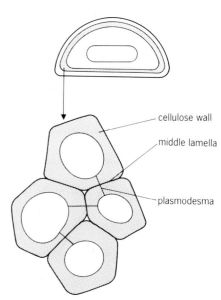

Figure 5.4 Transverse section of a pine needle showing where you can find cells with exceptionally thick walls.

cellulose wall

middle lamella

plasmodesma

potato tuber and mount it in water. Observe starch grains under low and high powers. They can be stained with dilute iodine solution by a technique called **irrigation** (Figure 5.3). Watch the starch grains turn blue as the stain moves across the slide. The starch grains are located inside tightly packed cells whose cell walls can just be seen. How would you describe the shape of these cells?

6   To see details of the **cell wall** you need to examine cells with exceptionally thick walls. Such cells can be seen in a transverse section of a pine needle (Figure 5.4). Layers of **cellulose** making up the secondary walls should be visible. The thin line between the cell walls of adjacent cells is the **middle lamella**. What does it consist of? Notice fine channels traversing the cell walls. They contain **plasmodesmata** which connect adjacent cells.

For consideration

1   If you want to see the nuclei of plant cells it is best to look at onion cells rather than potato or moss leaf cells. Why?

2   There is no such thing as a *typical* plant cell. Explain.

3   Suggest possible disadvantages of staining cells before viewing them under the microscope.

5.2 INVESTIGATION

Examination of animal cells

One of the best places from which to obtain animal cells for viewing under the microscope is the epithelium lining various organs in the body of a mammal. If the organ is a solid one, such as the kidney, the epithelium lining its outside may be used. In the case of hollow or tubular organs, such as the trachea, the epithelium lining the inside can be used.

The purpose of this investigation is to examine cells obtained from such sources in an attempt to build up a picture of a typical animal cell.

Guidance

Samples of epithelium can usually be removed by gently scraping the surface of the organ with a scalpel blade. The tissue thus obtained should be mounted in a drop of stain on a slide. A suitable stain is methylene blue.

Try taking scrapings from, for example, the inner surface of the trachea of sheep or pig. See if you can detect any cells. If you can, examine them under high power, using oil immersion if possible. Try other organs if available.

In some cases, for example the cornea of the eye, the epithelial cells come away so readily that all you need to do is touch the surface of a dry slide with the organ. Try this with a sheep's or pig's eye. Cells adhering to the slide may then be immersed in a drop of methylene blue and covered with a coverslip. (The eyes of cattle should not be used because of the slight *theoretical* risk of transmitting bovine spongiform encephalopathy (BSE).)

If you wish to examine *human* cells, the best source is the inner surface of the cheek. To avoid possible transmission of disease, cheek cell sampling should be carried out only under the close supervision of a teacher using the procedure outlined in the Box on page 70.

Another source of human cells is the base of a hair. The cells come away with the hair when it is plucked.

A typical epithelial cell from the human cheek is shown in Figure 5.5. How do the cells which you have studied in this investigation differ from this one?

Mount a sample of epithelial cells in water instead of methylene blue. What difference does this make to how much you can see? Try observing the cells with dark ground illumination and, if available, phase contrast.

For consideration

1   How were your observations of animal cells helped by (a) staining and (b) different kinds of microscopy?

2   Which structures, visible in typical plant cells, are absent from typical animal cells?

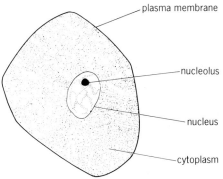

Figure 5.5 A squamous epithelial cell from the inner lining of the human cheek as seen under high power after staining with methylene blue.

References

Lewis, J.G.E. and Chester, M.F. Bullocks corneal cells: an alternative to human cheek cells, *School Science Review*, Vol. 70, No. 252, March 1989. The instructions can be applied equally to sheep or pig eyes.

Wells, J. Observing cells in plucked hair follicles, *Journal of Biological Education*, Vol. 25, No. 1, Spring 1991.

Biohazard
Cheek cells

Corrosive
Sodium
hypochlorite

BOX 5.1 | Cheek cell sampling

The following safe procedure is recommended by the Institute of Biology. It should be carried out only under the close supervision of a teacher.

1 Take a cotton bud from a newly opened pack.
2 Move the cotton bud over the inside of the cheek on one side of the mouth and along the outer lower side of the gum.
3 Smear the cotton bud over a small area of a clean microscope slide.
4 Place the used cotton bud immediately in a small volume of 1% sodium hypochlorite in a suitable container (e.g. 5 cm³ of hypochlorite solution in a 10 cm³ specimen tube).
5 Place 3 drops of 1 per cent methylene blue from a teat pipette onto the smear and cover with a coverslip.
6 Observe the smear under the low power magnification of a microscope. When the cells are in focus increase the power of the objective to achieve maximum magnification and resolution. The cytoplasm will be stained pale blue and the nucleus will be stained a darker blue.
7 After the cells have been observed, immerse the slide and coverslip in a beaker of laboratory disinfectant.
8 The teacher or laboratory technician should place the used cotton buds in a polythene bag which should be sealed and then disposed in accordance with local regulations governing the disposal of laboratory waste.
9 Slides and coverslips should be washed thoroughly, dried and reused according to normal practice.

If the above safe procedure is followed there are absolutely no reasons why any student or teacher should be exposed to the risk of infection by the transmission of pathogens.

REQUIREMENTS

Cotton bud, sealed
Slide and coverslip
Teat pipette
Sodium hypochlorite, 5 cm³ of 1% in a 10 cm³ specimen tube
Methylene blue, 1%
Disinfectant, in beaker
Polythene bag

5.3 INVESTIGATION

The fine structure of cells

The electron microscope is much more powerful than the light microscope, but exactly how much more detail of cells does it reveal? In this investigation you will have an opportunity to find out.

Guidance

You will be given a prepared slide of a transverse section of mammalian liver and an electron micrograph of part of a liver cell.

Examine the slide under the light microscope, first under low power then high power. Concentrate on one particular cell. Make a careful record of what you can, and cannot, see. If available, try using oil immersion to see if that helps. Then look at the electron micrograph. Identify as many structures and organelles as you can, using Figure 5.6 to help you. By how many times is the liver cell more magnified in the electron micrograph than under your light microscope?

Using the most effective method of presentation you can think of, compare the information about the structure of a liver cell provided by the electron microscope with that provided by the light microscope.

REQUIREMENTS

Microscope
Mammalian liver, TS
Electron micrograph of liver cell

Note: *A set of electron micrographs with explanatory notes, entitled* The Cell, *is available from Philip Harris Education. The set includes a micrograph of part of a liver cell.*

For consideration

1 What are the advantages and disadvantages of examining cells with an electron microscope?
2 The detail revealed by the electron microscope is due to its *resolving power*. Explain.

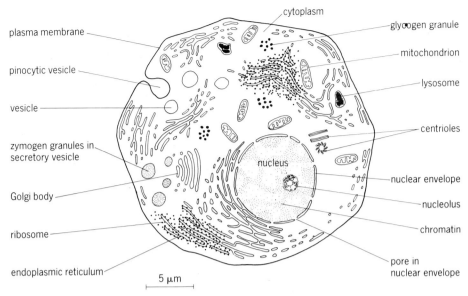

Figure 5.6 Drawing of a generalised animal cell as seen with the transmission electron microscope.

BOX 5.2 ## Getting the best out of your microscope

An immense amount of information can be obtained from the light microscope, but only if it is used properly. Its parts are shown in the illustration. However, different types of microscope differ in their features. For example, some have built-in illumination and lack a mirror and/or condenser.

When setting up your microscope, start by cleaning the lenses. *Then* focus the object with correct illumination under low power. *Then* focus the object with

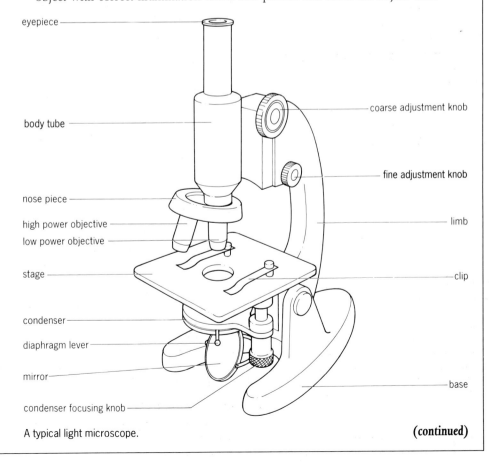

A typical light microscope.

(continued)

correct illumination under high power. Practise using your microscope by examining a prepared slide of e.g. epithelial tissue. Proceed as follows:

Cleaning the lenses

A common reason why students fail to see things clearly under the microscope is that the lenses are dirty. So make sure that both the eyepiece and objective lenses are clean. Dirt and moisture should be removed by gently wiping them with lens paper. If necessary remove the eyepiece and objectives from the microscope first, and moisten them if they are very dirty. The condenser lens should also be clean, as should the slide that you are going to examine.

Low power

Focusing

1 Rotate the coarse adjustment knob until the objective lenses are about 20 mm above the stage. Rotate the nosepiece so that the low power objective lens is in line with the body tube. It should click into place.
2 Put the slide to be examined on the stage. Ensure that the slide is clean and that the object to be viewed is in the centre of the aperture in the stage, immediately beneath the objective lens. Clip the slide in position with both clips.
3 Looking at the microscope from the side, rack down the coarse adjustment until the low power objective is about 5 mm above the slide.
4 Now look down the microscope and rack the coarse adjustment upwards until the object is in focus.

When looking down the microscope never rack downwards to focus an object unless you know for certain that by focusing downwards only a very short distance the image will come into view. If you rack downwards, you run the risk of hitting the coverslip with the objective lens.

Adjusting the illumination

The following instructions are based on microscopes which have a mirror and condenser and an external source of illumination.
1 Decide what source of light to use. The best source is natural daylight or a diffuse bulb. The whole field of view should be evenly illuminated. If a filament lamp is used, interpose a thin sheet of paper between the bulb and the microscope.
2 The mirror has a flat side and a concave side. Using the flat side, adjust the angle of the mirror so that light from the source is transmitted through the microscope.
3 Focus the condenser. The purpose of the condenser is to bring rays of light from a wide angle to bear on the object. To focus the condenser, adjust its height until an object such as a pencil placed in front of the source of light, reflected by the mirror, is seen in focus at the same time as the object on the microscope slide.
4 If your microscope does not have a condenser, or if the condenser is not in use, use the concave side of the mirror to focus the light.
5 Open or close the diaphragm to the right extent. The condenser should be used with the diaphragm as wide open as possible, without admitting too great an intensity of light. The definition of the image will then be at its best. If it is not possible to open the diaphragm widely without admitting too much light, place a sheet of paper between the microscope and the lamp.

Always use the condenser focused. Never use the condenser with the concave mirror. The condenser lenses are designed to give optimum illumination only when focused with the flat mirror.

A common cause of poor definition is that the object is over-illuminated. Better definition is often obtained by cutting down the light, not increasing it.

High power

1 Once the object is well defined under low power, move the slide so that the area which you want to observe in detail is in the centre of the field of view.
2 Rotate the nosepiece until the high power objective clicks into place. The object should automatically come into focus, at least approximately. If it is not in focus, look at the microscope from the side and rack the fine adjustment

(continued)

downwards until the lens is about one millimetre from the slide. Then look down the microscope and focus by racking up.

3   With the object in view down the microscope, adjust the mirror and diaphragm until the illumination is correct and maximum clarity is obtained.

Magnification

The total magnification is the magnification of the eyepiece lens multiplied by the magnification of the objective lens. By using different combinations of lenses, four different magnifications can be obtained as shown in the table alongside.

Don't use a higher power than is necessary. More can be made out under low power with good illumination than under high power with poor illumination. Also the larger the region of the object viewed, the easier it is to interpret what you see.

Eyepiece	Objective	Magnification	Power
×6	×10	60	Low
×10	×10	100	Medium
×6	×40	240	Medium
×10	×40	400	High

Identifying faults

If good definition is not obtained:
*   Is the slide clean?
*   Is the objective centred?
*   Are the lenses clean?
*   Is the source of illumination satisfactory?
*   Is the condenser focused?
*   Is the diaphragm adjusted correctly?

Special techniques in microscopy

Oil immersion

If you require a particularly high magnification, **oil immersion** may be used. Fluid with the same refractive index as the objective lens is placed between a special objective lens and the coverslip so that it touches both. The fluid permits a larger cone of light rays to enter the objective from the specimen, and this increases the resolving power obtainable.

The fluid is usually cedar wood oil. Place a drop of oil on the coverslip above the specimen, then lower the objective until the lens comes into contact with the oil. View the object with appropriate illumination in the usual way.

Dark ground illumination

For small transparent objects it is often best to view the specimen as a bright object against a dark background. This involves using **dark ground illumination**. In this technique the light illuminating the object must not enter the objective lens; the only light rays entering the microscope must be those which have been reflected or scattered by the object itself.

Dark ground illumination can be achieved by illuminating the object obliquely from above and/or by interposing an opaque stop in the centre of the condenser.

Try looking at live unicellular organisms with dark ground illumination.

Phase contrast

Transparent structures, because of slight differences in their density or refractive index, produce invisible changes of phase in the light that passes through them. In **phase contrast microscopy** these changes in phase are converted into corresponding changes of amplitude, resulting in a high-contrast image in which the distribution of light rays is related to the changes in phase. As no staining is necessary, this technique can be used for showing up transparent structures in living material that would otherwise be difficult or impossible to see.

Examining an object with phase contrast involves having a special annular disc beneath the condenser and an objective fitted with a phase plate. Microscopes with built-in phase contrast equipment are available.

REQUIREMENTS

Microscope
Phase contrast microscope, if available
Lamp
Slide and coverslip
Thin sheet of paper
Lens paper
Oil immersion objective
Cedar wood oil
Prepared slide of e.g. epithelial tissue
Unicellular organisms, live in mixed culture

Note: *The phase contrast microscope is best set up as a demonstration.*

Structure and function of mitochondria

Mitochondria are a basic feature of all eukaryotic cells. Their function is to transfer energy from organic molecules to **adenosine triphosphate (ATP)**. In this investigation we shall look at the detailed structure of mitochondria and carry out a simple experiment to investigate how they work.

Guidance
Structure of mitochondria

Examine electron micrographs of mitochondria which have been sectioned in various planes (transverse, longitudinal and oblique). From the appearance of the sections, reconstruct the three-dimensional structure of a single mitochondrion. Build a model of a mitochondrion out of plasticine and cut it in various planes. Does the appearance of the cut surfaces agree with what you can see in electron micrographs? Pay particular attention to the cristae. The cristae increase the internal surface area of the mitochondrion. Why is this necessary?

Function of mitochondria

Examine living cells under the light microscope and try to find mitochondria. Suitable cells may be obtained from celery tissue (Figure 5.7). Even under high power the mitochondria will appear only as very small cigar-shaped granules in the cytoplasm. Confirm that such granules are mitochondria by irrigating with Janus green. Any mitochondria present should stain blue and then gradually become decolorised.

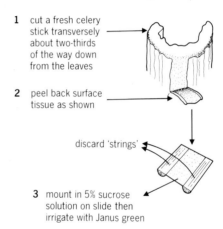

1 cut a fresh celery stick transversely about two-thirds of the way down from the leaves

2 peel back surface tissue as shown

discard 'strings'

3 mount in 5% sucrose solution on slide then irrigate with Janus green

Figure 5.7 How to obtain and treat celery tissue for studying mitochondria.

REQUIREMENTS

Microscope
Slides and coverslips
Teat pipette
Knife
Plasticine
Janus green B stain
Electron micrograph(s) of cells showing mitochondria cut in various planes

Note: The set of electron micrographs of the cell, available from Philip Harris Education, includes several showing mitochondria.

For consideration

1 Janus green is an oxidation-reduction indicator. Normally in aerobic respiration oxygen is reduced by hydrogen atoms to form water. However, in the presence of Janus green, the dye is reduced and changes from blue to colourless. What conclusion would you draw about the functioning of mitochondria from the way they stain with Janus green?
2 Mitochondria appear to occur in all eukaryotic cells. What conclusions, if any, would you draw from this observation?

BOX 5.3 Measuring the size of an object under the microscope

Objects can be measured under the microscope by means of an **eyepiece graticule**. This is a transparent scale mounted in the focal plane of the eyepiece, so it can be seen in the field of view at the same time as an object is being examined under the microscope.

Obviously to be of any use the eyepiece graticule scale must be calibrated.

(continued)

This can be done by placing a **stage micrometer** under the microscope. This is a glass slide on which is etched a series of vertical lines separated by distances of 1.0 mm, 0.1 mm and 0.01 mm – rather like a miniature transparent ruler. By superimposing the images of the eyepiece graticule and stage micrometer scales, the graticule can be calibrated so that the size of a given object viewed under the microscope can be estimated.

When calibrating, adopt the following procedure. Place the stage micrometer on the stage of the microscope, and bring its lines into focus. Move the stage micrometer until one of its lines coincides with one of the numbered lines on the eyepiece graticule. Count the number of lines on the eyepiece graticule which fill the space between the line that you have selected on the stage micrometer and the next one.

If the distance between the two lines on the stage micrometer is 100 µm, and it is found that x divisions on the eyepiece graticule scale exactly fill this space, then the value of one eyepiece division is $\frac{100}{x}$ µm.

You won't always have time to measure the sizes of objects that you look at under the microscope. However, it is a good idea to get into the habit of doing so when possible, and to indicate the scale of any drawings you make. For example, if you draw a cell 500 times its natural size, the scale of drawing is × 500 and this should be written by the drawing.

Another way of indicating the size of an object in a drawing is to put a line by the drawing corresponding to a particular length. This is called a scale bar and an example is shown in Figure 5.6.

5.5 PRACTICAL EXERCISE

Examination of animal tissues

The main purpose of this practical is to look at different types of animal tissue and relate their structure to the functions they perform. A secondary purpose is to learn how to recognise different types of animal tissue.

To recognise a tissue, five main features need to be considered:
- The type(s) of cell making up the tissue
- The positions of the cells relative to each other
- The presence of non-cellular inclusions in the tissue
- The position of the tissue in the organ.

As you look at different tissues be aware of the extent to which you depend on these five features in learning to recognise them.

Procedure

Epithelial tissue

Epithelial tissue (epithelium) is found lining the surface of the body and the cavities and tubes within it. Recognition depends mainly on the shapes of the cells.
1 First familiarise yourself with the different types of epithelia that exist (Figure 5.8).
2 Now look at prepared slides of the following organs, here listed in alphabetical order: gall bladder, kidney, peritoneum, rectum, small intestine, thyroid gland, trachea. In each case identify the type(s) of epithelium visible. Indicate if the epithelium has any special features such as cilia, brush border or secretory cells (e.g. mucus-secreting goblet cells). Try to relate these special features to the functions of the organs. To what extent do the epithelia depart from the simple patterns shown in Figure 5.8A?

Connective tissue

Connective tissue fills the spaces between other tissues and connects one tissue with another. It consists of various types of cells and non-living inclusions, and recognising different types of connective tissue depends on identifying these.
1 Examine a slide of **areolar tissue**, the weakest and most basic type of connective tissue. Use Figure 5.9 to help you identify its components. Note in particular the **collagen** and **elastic fibres** which are widely dispersed in the gelatinous **matrix** (ground substance).

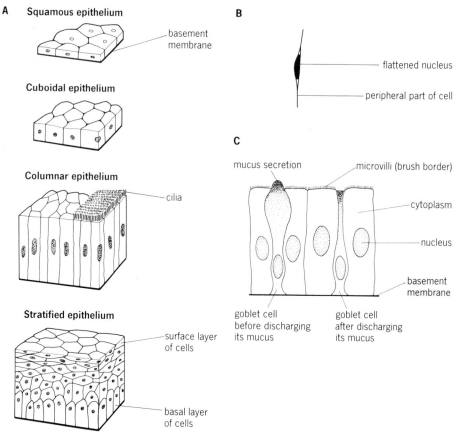

Figure 5.8 Epithelial tissue. **A** Four main types of epithelium found in the human and other mammals. Columnar epithelium is sometimes ciliated, as shown on the right hand side of the drawing.
B A squamous epithelial cell as it may appear in the wall of a capillary: the cells are so flat that, except in the region of the nucleus, they appear as no more than a thin line. **C** Detail of typical columnar epithelium showing microvilli and goblet cells. The microvilli appear as a fuzzy line on the outer surface of the cells, the brush border. A brush border may also be visible on the surface of cuboidal epithelium. Goblet cells, so called because of their shape, secrete mucus.

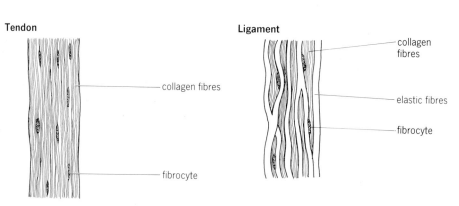

Figure 5.10 Longitudinal sections of tendon and ligament.

Figure 5.9 Areolar connective tissue as it appears in a typical microscopic preparation.

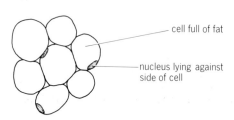

Figure 5.11 Fat cells as they appear in a typical section of adipose tissue.

2   Examine longitudinal sections of a tendon and a ligament (Figure 5.10). In both cases the fibres are more densely packed than in areolar tissue and they lie parallel with one another. Tendons contain mainly collagen fibres, ligaments mainly elastic fibres. Relate this to the functions which tendons and ligaments perform in the human body.

3   Examine a section of **adipose tissue**. It consists almost entirely of densely packed fat cells (Figure 5.11). Whereabouts in the human body is this sort of tissue found and what are its functions there?

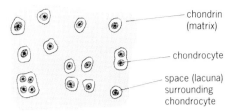

Figure 5.12 Hyaline cartilage as it appears in a typical microscopic section.

chondrin (matrix)

chondrocyte

space (lacuna) surrounding chondrocyte

Cartilage

Cartilage is associated mainly with the skeleton. It consists of **cartilage cells (chondrocytes)** embedded in a matrix. You can recognise cartilage tissue from the characteristic pattern of cartilage cells within the matrix (Figure 5.12).

1 Examine a section of hyaline cartilage, the most basic and softest type of cartilage. Notice how the cells are arranged in the matrix. Does their grouping give any clues as to how they have been formed and what their function is?

2 In some places cartilage contains variable numbers of collagen or elastic fibres, making it tougher. Examine a section of **fibro-cartilage** from e.g. an intervertebral disc, and a section of **elastic cartilage** from e.g. the ear (pinna). What is the function of the cartilage in each of these situations?

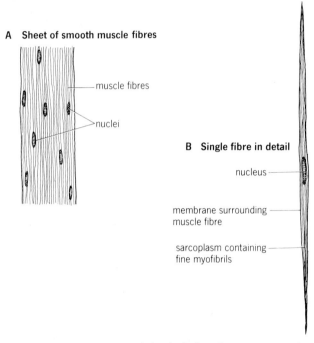

A   **Sheet of smooth muscle fibres**

muscle fibres

nuclei

B   **Single fibre in detail**

nucleus

membrane surrounding muscle fibre

sarcoplasm containing fine myofibrils

Figure 5.13 Smooth muscle tissue as seen in longitudinal section.

Smooth muscle

Smooth muscle is present in the walls of various organs and structures which move or change shape. Recognition depends mainly on the shapes of the cells which are extremely long and spindly and have elongated nuclei (Figure 5.13).

1 Examine smooth muscle in the wall of the bladder and notice the shapes of the cells and their nuclei. What is the function of smooth muscle here?

2 Examine a section of the small intestine and try to locate smooth muscle in its wall. What is the function of the muscle in this situation?

Putting it all together

1 Look again at the organs you used for examining epithelia. In each case see if you can recognise any connective tissue, cartilage or smooth muscle. If present, explain their function(s) in the organ.

2 Examine sections of other organs of your own choice. See how many different tissues you can recognise in each one.

For consideration

1 To what extent does a knowledge of the function of a tissue enable you to make predictions about its structure? Give one example to illustrate your answer.

2 Now consider question 1 the other way round: to what extent does a knowledge of the *structure* of a tissue enable you to make predictions about its *function*? Again, give one example to illustrate your answer.

3 Think of the tissues that you have examined. Which features of each tissue do you consider to be particularly important in enabling you to recognise it?

Reference

Freeman, W.H. and Bracegirdle, B. *An Advanced Atlas of Histology*, Heinemann, 1976. This book contains photomicrographs and explanatory drawings, an excellent aid to accurate identification and interpretation of tissues.

Examination of plant tissues

The object of this practical is to introduce you to some plant tissues which you will encounter repeatedly in later microscopic studies.

As with animal tissues, plant tissues can be investigated by examining prepared slides. However, in this practical we suggest that you make your own temporary slides.

Procedure

Epidermis

Epidermis lines the surface of leaves, stems and other parts of plants. It provides protection against physical damage and water loss.

1   Strip off a piece of epidermis from the lower side of a leaf of ivy-leaved toadflax (*Glechoma hederacea*), and mount it in a drop of water or dilute iodine solution. Examine the epidermal cells, noting their shape and how they fit together. In passing notice **stomata**, each one bordered by a pair of **guard cells**. They are dealt with in detail on page 97.

2   Examine epidermal tissue obtained from other plants, stems as well as leaves, to gain some idea of how this tissue can vary.

Parenchyma (packing tissue)

Parenchyma fills up spaces inside stems, roots and leaves. Provided its cells are turgid, it provides strength and support.

1   Remove a small amount of the pulpy tissue from just beneath the skin of a tomato or grape. Place it in a drop of water on a slide and spread it out with needles. Add a coverslip and examine the parenchyma cells. Irrigate with fresh Schultz solution. What effect does this stain have on what you can see?

2   Mount a small piece of the pulp of a potato tuber in Schultz solution. What does the staining reaction suggest about one function of parenchyma tissue? (Hint: Schultz' solution is otherwise known as chlor-zinc-iodine.)

3   How would you describe the shape of the potato cells? Make a plasticine model to show in three dimensions how the cells fit together.

Chlorenchyma (photosynthetic tissue)

This is a modified form of parenchyma in which the cells contain **chloroplasts** and can therefore undergo photosynthesis. It is found mainly in leaves.

Mount a small leaf of Canadian pondweed (*Elodea canadensis*) in a drop of water on a slide and examine the cells packed with chloroplasts.

Collenchyma

This is a type of strengthening tissue. Strength is derived from ribs of cellulose at the thickened corners of the elongated collenchyma cells.

A good place to see this type of tissue is in the stem of deadnettle (*Lamium* sp.) (Figure 5.14). Cut transverse and longitudinal sections of a deadnettle stem (see Box on page 79). Mount the sections in Schultz solution and make out as much as you can of the collenchyma tissue.

Sclerenchyma

This is another type of strengthening tissue. However, in this case the cell walls are impregnated with **lignin** and the cells are dead. Most of the cells are elongated and are referred to as 'fibres'.

Mount a small quantity of macerated woody tissue in acidified phloroglucinol which stains lignin red. Look for slender sclerenchyma fibres with tapering ends.

In passing, also notice lignified tubular elements. These are **vessels** and/or **tracheids**. They have various sorts of thickening in their walls, which you may be able to see. They contribute mechanical strength to plants and also conduct water and mineral salts from roots to leaves (see Chapter 7).

5.6 PRACTICAL EXERCISE

REQUIREMENTS

Microscope
Slides and coverslips
Razor blade with covered edge
Small paint brush
Petri dish
Watch glass
Plasticine
Dilute iodine solution
Schultz's solution
Phloroglucinol, acidified
Ivy-leaved toadflax (*Glechoma hederacea*)
Tomato or grape
Potato tuber
Canadian pondweed (*Elodea canadensis*)
Stem of deadnettle (*Lamium album*), fresh or preserved
Macerated woody twig

Note: *Woody twigs can be macerated by prolonged immersion in a macerating fluid. Macerating fluids are available from suppliers.*

Corrosive
Schultz's
solution

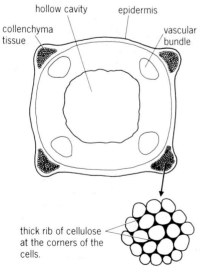

Figure 5.14 Collenchyma tissue in a transverse section of the stem of deadnettle (*Lamium* sp.).

For consideration

1 Relate the structure of the various plant tissues which you have looked at to the functions they perform within the plant.

2 Compare the epidermal tissue of plants with the epithelial tissue of animals from both a structural and functional point of view.

Reference

C.J. Clegg and Gene Cox, *Anatomy and Activities of Plants*, John Murray, 1978. Photomicrographs with text and explanatory diagrams allow quick identification of plant tissues with an understanding of their functions.

BOX 5.4 How to cut and stain plant sections

If you want to examine the internal structure of a plant it is usually necessary to cut thin sections and stain them. The stained sections can then be examined under the light microscope. The details depend on which part of the plant you wish to investigate.

Stems

1 With a sharp scapel, remove a short length of stem from between two nodes (Illustration 1).

2 With a new razor blade, cut thin transverse sections of the stem (Illustration 2A). Hold the piece of stem in one hand and the blade in the other. *Keep the hand that you are holding the stem with well away from the cutting edge of the blade.* Cut smoothly and rapidly, constantly wetting the blade and surface of the stem with water. As the sections accumulate on the surface of the blade, transfer them to a Petri dish of water with a small paint brush.

3 Select your thinnest sections and transfer them to a watch glass of water. A section need not necessarily go right across the stem; often a thin wedge-shaped sliver is more useful than a complete section. Stain the sections in an appropriate stain for ten minutes, then mount them in dilute glycerine. Alternatively the sections can be mounted in the stain itself.

4 Try using different stains to see their effects. Each stain shows up a specific structure. Don't mix the stains: use a different one for each section.

The main stains used are:

- **Dilute iodine solution** which stains starch grains blue-black
- **Schultz's solution** which stains cellulose purple
- **Acidified phloroglucinol** which stains lignin red.

Danger
Razor blade

Eye protection must be worn

Corrosive
Schultz's solution

Corrosive
Acidified phloroglucinol

Irritant
phloroglucinol
Iodine solution

REQUIREMENTS

Scalpel
Razor blade, new
Petri dish
Paint brush, small
Watch glass
Scissors, small
Elder pith and/or carrot tuber
Dilute glycerine
Dilute iodine solution
Schultz's solution
Phloroglucinol, acidified
Fabil stain

Note: *Slides made as described above cannot be kept indefinitely. They are only temporary preparations. To make permanent preparations see Box on page 81.*

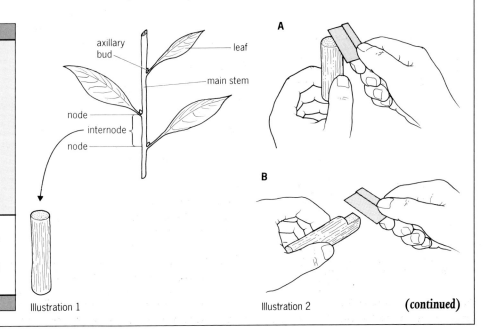

Illustration 1

Illustration 2

(continued)

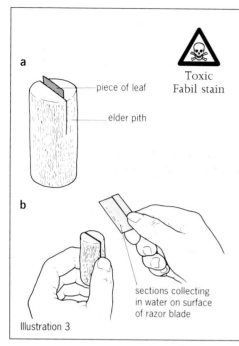

a

piece of leaf

elder pith

b

sections collecting
in water on surface
of razor blade

Illustration 3

Toxic
Fabil stain

In addition **Fabil stain** can be used to distinguish different tissues in one and the same section. It is toxic and messy to use and gives variable results. However, it generally stains xylem elements brown, sclerenchyma pink, cellulose pale blue, cytoplasm and nuclei darker blue, starch black.

5   To build up a complete picture of the three-dimensional structure of the stem and its constituent cells, cut longitudinal sections as well as transverse sections (Illustration 2B). Longitudinal sections can be stained and mounted in the same way as transverse sections. Oblique sections are often useful too.

Leaves

1   With small scissors cut out the part of the leaf that you wish to investigate.
2   As the leaf is thin and flexible it must be mounted in a firm position while the sections are being cut. Do this by inserting it into a vertical slit made down the centre of a piece of moistened elder pith or carrot tuber (Illustration 3).
3   Collect the sections, then stain and mount them as for the stem.

Roots

Roots, like leaves, are flexible, so they too must be mounted in elder pith or a carrot tuber before they can be sectioned. Proceed as for the leaf above.

5.7 INVESTIGATION

Different kinds of structural organisation in organisms

Here are ten different ways of describing an organism:
- Unicellular (single-celled)
- Multicellular (many-celled) with undifferentiated cells (cells all of one type)
- Multicellular with differentiated cells (cells of more than one type)
- Solitary (separate from other individuals)
- Modular (made up of numerous identical parts)
- Colonial (linked to other individuals)
- Asymmetrical
- Radially symmetrical
- Bilaterally symmetrical
- Cephalised (possesses a head).

The purpose of this investigation is to look at a series of organisms and decide which descriptions apply to each one.

REQUIREMENTS

Microscope
Slides and coverslips
Teat pipette
Dissecting instruments
Amoeba, WM
Creeping buttercup (*Ranunculus repens*),
    entire with runners
Earthworm (*Lumbricus terrestris*), live,
    freshly killed and TS
Flatworm (*Planaria* or *Dendrocoelum*), live
    and TS
Hydra, live and TS
Iris, entire with rhizome
Obelia, preserved and whole mount
Paramecium, live and whole mount
Pleurococcus, live
Spirogyra, live

Guidance

First make sure that you understand the meaning of all the terms. Then try to decide which terms apply to each of the following organisms, listed in alphabetical order: *Amoeba*, creeping buttercup (*Ranunculus repens*), earthworm (*Lumbricus*), flatworm (*Planaria* or *Dendrocoelum*), *Hydra*, *Iris*, *Obelia*, *Paramecium*, *Pleurococcus*, *Spirogyra*.

In each case you will need to consider the whole organism and its microscopic structure. In the case of the earthworm you will need to examine the inside of the animal by means of dissection and/or looking at a prepared transverse section.

Extend the list to include other organisms if you wish. Present your conclusions in the form of a table.

For consideration

1   What other ways are there of describing the structure of organisms besides those considered in this investigation?
2   Can you think of any non-structural ways of describing organisms, for instance according to their behaviour? Illustrate your answer by giving two contrasting examples.

BOX 5.5 Making permanent preparations

Making **permanent preparations** of tissues, organs and other microscopic material is often desirable, particularly if you are doing a project. The processes involved, particularly staining, can make the study of cell detail much easier, and the slides can be kept for years.

The making of a permanent preparation involves the following processes:

- **Fixing.** The purpose of this is to kill the living tissues with minimum distortion, so as to permit subsequent staining and mounting of the preparation. A suitable fixative for most purposes is **70% ethanol**.
- **Staining.** The purpose of this is to colour structures that otherwise would be difficult or impossible to see under the microscope. Staining is normally carried out at the appropriate stage during the dehydration process. This will vary with the stain used: aqueous stains should be used before dehydration; stains in 50% ethanol after dehydration in 50% ethanol, and so on. Be careful not to leave the material in the stain for too long: many a preparation has been ruined by overstaining.
- **Differentiating.** The purpose of this is to remove excess stain from the material and sharpen the contrast between e.g. nuclei and cytoplasm. **Acidified ethanol** is often used as a differentiating agent. It is advisable to examine the material under the microscope during the differentiation process. When you do this, make sure that the underside of the slide or watchglass is dry.
- **Dehydrating.** The purpose of this is to remove all traces of water from the material. It is carried out by passing the material through a series of ethanols of gradually increasing concentration. The appropriate stain is inserted into the series at the correct point.
- **Clearing.** The purpose of this is to remove the ethanol and make the material transparent. Suitable clearing agents include **xylene** and **clove oil**. If dehydration is not complete, a milky precipitate may be formed in the clearing agent. If that happens, the material must be returned to absolute ethanol until dehydration is complete. The material must not be mounted until completely cleared.
- **Mounting.** The purpose of this is to embed the material in a transparent medium, which subsequently hardens, on a microscope slide. A much used mountant is **Canada balsam**. A drop is placed over the tissue on the slide, and a coverslip added. The slide is left on a hotplate. The balsam is dissolved in xylene; as the xylene evaporates, the balsam sets hard and the coverslip remains fixed in position.

The above notes apply in general to the making of any permanent preparation. However, the details vary according to the material and the stain which is to be used.

The manipulations may be carried out in one of two ways:

- For complete organisms or pieces of tissue, transfer the specimen from one reagent to another in a series of watchglasses. The mounted material is referred to as a **whole mount**.
- For smears and sections, immerse the slide, with the smear or section attached to it, in a series of **dipping jars**, each containing the appropriate reagent. After clearing, cover the smear or section with the mountant and put on a coverslip.

Four useful staining techniques

Borax carmine

Specially suitable for whole mounts of animal material, this technique involves the use of a single stain.

1   Place the material in 50% ethanol, if not already in it.
2   Stain in **borax carmine** until the specimen is just thoroughly penetrated (about 10 minutes).
3   Differentiate in acidified ethanol until the material is pale pink. While differentiating, examine under low power. Nuclei should be red against a pink background. If understained return the specimen to borax carmine; if overstained leave it in acidified ethanol.

REQUIREMENTS

Microscope
Slides and coverslips
Watchglasses
Dipping jars
Ethanol, 50%, 70%, 90%, absolute
Acidified ethanol (4 drops concentrated hydrochloric acid to 100 cm³ 70% ethanol)
Xylene
Clove oil
Canada balsam
Borax carmine, in 50% ethanol
Haematoxylin, in 30% or 50% ethanol
Eosin, in 90% ethanol
Safranin
Fast green
Cellosolve (2-ethoxyethanol)
Safranin and fast green in cellosolve

Note: *Ready-cut sections of animal and plant tissues and organs are available from suppliers.*

Highly flammable
Ethanol
Borax carmine

(continued)

4   Dehydrate in 70% ethanol (5 minutes), 90% ethanol (5 minutes), and two successive lots of absolute ethanol (5–30 minutes each, depending on the thickness of the specimen).

5   Clear in xylene.

6   Mount in Canada balsam, supporting the coverslip with strips of paper or card if necessary. Leave the slide on a hotplate until the mountant hardens.

On viewing under the microscope, the nuclei should be red (or dark pink) and the cytoplasm pale pink.

Haematoxylin and eosin

This is a double staining technique in which the material is treated with two stains in succession. The second stain is called a **counterstain**. It is specially suitable for sections of animal material, and for smears.

1   Place the material in ethanol of the same concentration as that in which the haematoxylin is dissolved (i.e. 30% or 50%).

2   Stain in **haematoxylin** until the specimen is dark blue (2–5 minutes).

3   'Blue' in tap water. While blueing, examine under low power. Nuclei should be dark blue, the cytoplasm light blue or colourless. If understained, return the specimen to haematoxylin; if overstained, differentiate in acidified ethanol.

4   Dehydrate in 50%, 70%, then 90% ethanol (about 3 minutes each).

5   Counterstain in **eosin** for 2–5 minutes.

6   Replace in 90% ethanol. The specimen may be examined again under low power. If understained, return the specimen to eosin; if overstained leave it in the ethanol.

7   Complete the dehydration process in absolute ethanol for about 5 minutes. Don't leave the specimen in absolute ethanol for too long or you will remove all the eosin.

8   Clear in xylene and mount in Canada balsam. Leave the slide on a hotplate until the balsam hardens.

On viewing under the microscope, the nuclei should be blue and the cytoplasm pink.

Safranin and fast green

This double staining technique is suitable for plant tissues, including sections.

1   Stain in **safranin** (about 10 minutes).

2   Dehydrate in 50%, 70% and 90% ethanol (1 minute in each).

3   Complete dehydration in two successive lots of absolute ethanol (3–5 minutes each).

4   Counterstain in **fast green** in clove oil (1 minute).

5   Clear in clove oil (5 minutes).

6   Mount in Canada balsam and leave the slide on a hotplate.

On viewing under the microscope, cytoplasm and cell walls should be green, lignified tissues and nuclei red, and chloroplasts pink.

Safranin and fast green in cellosolve

It is possible to dehydrate and double-stain in a single solution, as follows:

1   Stain and dehydrate in safranin and fast green in cellosolve (5–10 minutes).

2   Wash in cellosolve. The cellosolve slowly removes the stain; watch under the microscope until the required intensity of staining is achieved.

3   Transfer the material to a mixture of equal volumes of cellosolve and xylene.

4   Clear in pure xylene (two changes).

5   Mount in Canada balsam and leave the slide on a hotplate.

Corrosive
Acidified
ethanol

flammable
Haemotoxylin
Acidified
ethanol

Harmful
Safranin
Canada
balsam

Eye protection
must be worn

Flammable
Xylene

Harmful
Xylene
safranin and
fast green
in cellosolve

5.8 PRACTICAL EXERCISE

Water potential of potato tuber cells; the weighing method

When a plant cell is bathed in a solution of the same water potential, its mass and volume remain the same, because water enters and leaves it at the same rate.

  If samples of a tissue are immersed in a range of solutions of different concentrations (molarities), the cells will gain water, and mass, in solutions of higher water potential

Table 5.1 Relationship between molarity and solute potential of sucrose solutions.

Molarity (mol dm^{-3})	Solute potential (kPa)
0.05	−130
0.10	−260
0.15	−410
0.20	−540
0.25	−680
0.30	−860
0.35	−970
0.40	−1120
0.45	−1280
0.50	−1450
0.55	−1620
0.60	−1800
0.65	−1980
0.70	−2180
0.75	−2370
0.80	−2580
0.85	−2790
0.90	−3000
0.95	−3250
1.00	−3500

⚠️ Danger Razor blade

```
REQUIREMENTS
Boiling tubes with stoppers ×6
Boiling tube rack
Wax pencil
Cork borer about 10 mm diameter
Razor blade
Filter papers
Forceps
Balance weighing in intervals of 0.01 g or
    smaller
Distilled water
Sucrose solutions (0.2, 0.4, 0.6, 0.8, 1.0
    mol dm⁻³)
Potato tuber (large)
```

and lose water, and mass, in solutions of lower water potential. The water potential of the tissue is equal to that of the solution in which it neither gains nor loses mass. The purpose of this practical is to estimate the water potential of potato tuber cells by this method.

In practice, none of the experimental solutions is likely to have *exactly* the same water potential as the cells, but the solution in which there would have been no gain or loss in mass can be estimated from a graph.

Potato tuber cells are widely available in bulk but in principle this technique can be applied to any plant tissue.

Procedure

1 Label six boiling tubes: DW (distilled water), 0.2, 0.4, 0.6, 0.8 and 1.0 mol dm⁻³. Place about half a tube-full of distilled water in the first tube and the appropriate sucrose solution in each of the other tubes. Firmly stopper each tube (why?).

2 Using a cork borer and razor blade, prepare six potato cylinders, each about 10 mm in diameter and 50 mm long. Place each on a separate sheet of filter paper which you have labelled in pencil with the figures 0, 0.2, 0.4, 0.6, 0.8, 1.0 respectively.

3 Take the cylinders and the boiling tube rack to a balance. For each cylinder, record its mass on the filter paper, transfer it to one of the boiling tubes with forceps, make a note of which tube it is in, stopper the tube and record the mass of the filter paper on its own. Calculate the initial mass of each cylinder once you have transferred them all to the tubes. Note the time.

4 After at least 25 minutes remove the cylinders from the tubes in turn, in the same order that you inserted them. Remove any *surplus* fluid quickly and gently with filter paper, using a standardised procedure. Do not squeeze the cylinders, or they will *all* lose water! Then reweigh each cylinder and record its mass.

5 Work out the percentage change in mass of each cylinder (change in mass multiplied by 100 divided by the original mass). Plot this against the molarity of the sucrose solutions. Your vertical axis will have increases in mass at the top, no change in mass in the middle and decreases in mass at the bottom. Join adjacent points with straight lines.

6 Calculate the water potential of the potato cells as follows. Find where your line crosses the place on the vertical axis corresponding to no change in mass. Read off the horizontal axis the molarity of sucrose at this point. From Table 5.1 find the water potential of a sucrose solution of that molarity. That is the water potential of your sample of potato cells. Express your result in kiloPascals (kPa).

For consideration

1 Account for any anomalous results. How could your experimental procedure have been improved?

2 Can you devise a method to determine the water potential of a plant tissue which is based on changes in volume rather than mass?

3 The value of the water potential differs from the solute potential of the solution in the vacuoles of the cells. Why?

4 What factors affect the water potentials of potato tuber cells in the soil? In what way is the water potential of the potato cells relevant to the role of a potato tuber in the life cycle of a potato plant?

5.9 PRACTICAL EXERCISE

Water potential of potato tuber cells; the density method

Suppose that we suspend some plant tissue in a sucrose solution for some time. Then we deposit beneath the surface a coloured drop of sucrose solution of equal concentration (molarity). If this drop neither rises nor falls, its water potential is equivalent to that of the solution *and the tissue suspended in it*. If, however, the tissue had previously gained water from the surrounding sucrose solution, making the solution more dense, the coloured drop would rise. If the tissue had previously lost water to the solution, making the solution less dense, the coloured drop, being denser, would fall.

Suppose, therefore, that we suspend samples of a tissue in solutions of various strengths. We later add to each solution a coloured drop of the same concentration as the original solution. The original strength of the solution in which the drop shows least tendency to rise or fall corresponds most closely to the original water potential of the tissue.

Procedure

1 Arrange two rows of seven test-tubes, one directly behind the other. Label the front row of test-tubes in order 10, 15, 20, 25, 30, 50 and 70. Using a separate graduated syringe in each case, place 5 cm³ of the appropriate sucrose solution in each of the front tubes – 0.10, 0.15, 0.20, 0.25, 0.30, 0.5 and 0.7 mol dm⁻³ of sucrose.

2 From the test-tube containing 0.1 mol dm⁻³ sucrose and labelled '10', pipette 3 cm³ into the tube behind, leaving 2 cm³ in the original front tube. Repeat the procedure with all the other sucrose solutions in turn, *using a different pipette in each case*. You will now have two rows of seven labelled test-tubes, with the front ones containing 2 cm³ of solution each and the back ones containing 3 cm³ each of the same solution.

3 Place *one drop* of methylene blue into each of the front test-tubes. This will colour the solution but will not significantly alter its water potential.

4 Using a cork borer and a razor blade, prepare a cylinder of potato tuber tissue about 7 mm diameter and 60 mm long. Slice the cylinder into thirty discs of approximately equal (2 mm) thickness.

5 Place four of the potato discs into each of the test-tubes in the back row (those containing 3 cm³ of solution). Manipulate the discs so that they are all covered with sucrose solution in each tube. Note the time.

6 After at least 25 minutes, pour off into a clean test-tube the fluid from the tube containing potato discs in the 0.10 mol dm⁻³ solution This tube of decanted solution should be placed in the test-tube rack in the position previously occupied by the tube containing the potato discs immersed in 3 cm³ of 0.10 mol dm⁻³ sucrose.

7 Use a teat pipette to collect a small quantity of blue sucrose solution from the 0.10 mol dm⁻³ solution tube, labelled '10', at the front. Now, *with great care*, introduce a *single* drop of this blue fluid into the tube behind it, that is, the tube containing the decanted fluid which had been in contact with the potato slices. The drop should be released into the centre of the liquid about 5 mm below the surface.

8 Watch the drop. Note whether it remains in the same place, or rises, or sinks. Release another drop into the same solution and continue until you are certain that you have made the correct observation about the behaviour of the drop.

9 Repeat steps 6, 7 and 8 with the other six sets of tubes, using a clean pipette for each sucrose concentration.

10 Present your results in the form of a table.

For consideration

1 From your understanding of the factors which cause water to leave or enter plant cells, explain what has been happening in each of the sucrose concentrations. In each case account for the behaviour of the blue drops.

2 A 1.0 mol dm⁻³ solution of sucrose has a water potential of -3500 kPa. From your results, estimate the approximate water potential of the potato tissue.

3 Were you estimating the water potentials of the potato cells, or the water potentials of the solutions in their vacuoles? Explain your answer.

4 Consider very critically the instructions given for this practical exercise. Suggest how they might be improved.

Danger
Razor
blade

REQUIREMENTS

One double-row test-tube rack or two
   single-row test-tube racks
Test-tubes ×21
Marker for writing on glass
Graduated syringes (5 cm³ or 10 cm³) ×7
Graduated pipettes (3–5 cm³) ×7
Teat pipettes ×7
Cork borer (c. 7 mm diameter)
Razor blade
Ceramic tile
Sucrose solutions (at least 5 cm³ each of
   0.10, 0.15, 0.20, 0.25, 0.30, 0.50 and
   0.70 mol dm⁻³)
Methylene blue solution
Potato tubers

5.10 PRACTICAL EXERCISE

Solute potential of cell sap of plant epidermal cells

Water and other energy potentials in cells are given the symbol ψ, the Greek letter psi. The water potential of a plant cell (ψ_{cell}) is related to the solute potential of the sap (ψ_s) and the pressure potential (ψ_p) by the equation:

$$\psi_{cell} = \psi_s + \psi_p$$

The solute potential is the reduction in the water potential of the solution in the cell which can be attributed to the particles dissolved in the solution.

When a plant cell is surrounded by a solution of lower water potential it **plasmolyses**, that is, its cytoplasm loses water and contracts, gradually separating the plasma

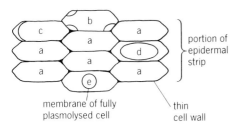

membrane of fully plasmolysed cell

thin cell wall

portion of epidermal strip

Figure 5.15 The appearance of onion epidermal cells at various stages of plasmolysis. Cells **a** are unplasmolysed, cells **b** and **c** exhibit incipient plasmolysis, and cells **d** and **e** show progressive plasmolysis as their plasma membranes separate from their cell walls.

⚠️ Danger Razor blade

REQUIREMENTS
Microscope
Slides and coverslips
Razor blade
Forceps
Specimen tubes with stoppers x6
Marking pen
Graph paper
Filter paper
Distilled water
Sucrose solutions (0.3, 0.4, 0.5, 0.6, 0.7, 1.0 mol dm^{-3}, 10cm^3 of each)
Iodine solution
Onion scale leaf or alternative (see note below)

Note: *Suitable alternatives to onion include the pigmented epidermis of red cabbage, rhubarb or Rhoeo. The experiment may also be performed on the filamentous alga Cladophora: see Rouan, C. Plasmolysis experiments with Cladophora. Journal of Biological Education* **15** *(2), 100 (1981).*

membrane from the cell wall until it rounds off in the centre. When plant cells are placed in a range of solutions of different concentrations, the solution just strong enough to make the plasma membrane separate from the cell wall in places ('incipient plasmolysis') can be regarded as having the same solute potential as the cell sap. This is because, in the equation above, if no inward pressure is exerted by the cell wall ($\psi_p = 0$), the water potential of the cell (ψ_{cell}) equals the solute potential (ψ_s). This provides us with a way of estimating the solute potential of a plant tissue, which is the aim of this practical.

In practice, the cells in a piece of plant tissue plasmolyse at different rates. We can regard 'incipient plasmolysis' as taking place when half the cells in the tissue exhibit visible plasmolysis.

Procedure

1 Into each of six specimen tubes, place about 10 cm^3 of a different sucrose solution; 0.3, 0.4. 0.5, 0.6, 0.7 and 1.0 mol dm^{-3}; and label each tube appropriately.

2 Remove one of the fleshy scale leaves of an onion. With a razor blade, cut the inner epidermis (the outer epidermis is more suitable but less easy to obtain) into twelve squares of side about 5 mm. The best results are obtained with epidermal strips one cell thick. Place two pieces of epidermis into each of the specimen tubes, stopper the tubes and gently shake the contents to submerge the tissue. Note the time.

3 After 20 minutes, remove one piece of epidermis from each tube and mount it on a labelled microscope slide, beneath a coverslip, in a drop of the solution in which it has been immersed. Observe under low power. Look for plasmolysed cells (Figure 5.15). If plasmolysed cells are not clearly visible in the more concentrated sucrose solutions, irrigate with dilute iodine solution to stain the cytoplasm, or view the second epidermal strips.

4 Count all the cells visible within the low power field of view. Now count all those which are plasmolysed. Include those which show a visible separation of the cell contents from the cell wall, however slight. If any reading is markedly at variance with the others, repeat the estimate with the second piece of epidermis.

5 Record the results in a table. Plot a graph of percentage plasmolysis against molarity of sucrose solution and join the points by straight lines.

6 Read off your graph the molarity of sucrose which corresponds to 50 per cent plasmolysis. This solution may be regarded as having the same solute potential as the cell sap of the tissue. Use Table 5.1 to estimate the corresponding solute potential in kiloPascals. Now you can breathe a psi of relief!

7 Finally, looking down the microscope as you do so, irrigate with distilled water a piece of epidermis which had been mounted in concentrated sucrose. Use filter paper to draw the water beneath the coverslip. Observe what happens and interpret the results.

For consideration

1 If you used the epidermis of rhubarb or red cabbage, can you suggest where the red pigment is located within the cell?

2 Explain the shape of your graph.

3 What are the major sources of inaccuracy in this method?

4 Why do not all the cells in the tissue have the same solute potential, and what might be the consequences of this?

5.11 INVESTIGATION

The influence of water potential on dandelion scapes

The hollow scapes (flower stalks) of dandelion (*Taraxacum officinale*) exhibit various degrees of curvature when placed in sucrose or salt solutions of different water potential. The aim of this investigation is to quantify the effects of this, and suggest explanations, in terms of the anatomy of dandelion scapes and the differences in water potential between tissue and solution.

⚠️ Danger Razor blade

Guidance

To obtain the material for your investigation, split a scape longitudinally into six portions of length 5 cm. The strips immediately bend outwards. Immerse the strips in

Microscope
Ruler
Razor blade
Botanical razor
Pith or carrot tap root
Slides and coverslips
Large beakers
Supply of salt or sucrose solutions of
    various water potentials
Scapes (hollow peduncles) of dandelions
    (*Taraxacum* spp.)

Note: *The upper parts of bluebell scapes
are also suitable: see Freeland, P.W.
Problems in Practical Advanced Level
Biology,* Hodder & Stoughton *(1985).*

solutions of different water potentials for fifteen minutes and record the results. If possible, devise a quantitative measure of curvature which takes the initial bending into account. You may also need to replicate your experiments, and to consider if you are justified in comparing strips from different scapes.

Why do the strips bend outwards as soon as they have been separated from one another? Investigate this by cutting thin sections of a scape by hand (see page 000) and examining the anatomy of the stem. You may wish to separate parts of the scape and determine the water potential of each one on its own, or you may be able to assess the degrees of curvature obtained when the inside layers or the outside layers of the scapes are exposed to various solutions on their own.

For consideration

Put your findings together to produce a full explanation of the degrees of curvature of the strips in the different solutions, using water potential terminology throughout.

PROJECTS

Before starting a project, discuss your intended procedure with your teacher.

1 Variation within a cell type. Take one particular type of cell, e.g. onion epidermal cells, and analyse how much variation there is in the visible features of the cells. Features that you might investigate include shape, position of the nucleus, and the number of nucleoli.

2 The variety of cells. To what extent do cells depart from the basic features which you have studied in the practicals and investigations presented here? Try to answer this question using prepared slides and/or fresh material treated in whatever way you think appropriate. One approach would be to identify different cell types in different parts of a whole plant, e.g. a broad bean plant, rhubarb plant or celery plant, by macerating the various parts or making temporary preparations. The project would be made even more interesting by studying the cell types present at different stages of the plant's development.

3 Investigate the epidermis of the leaves of different species of flowering plants. Include stomata, hairs, spines and any other epidermal structures you come across. Relate your findings to the environments of the plants.

4 The stems and/or flower stalks of certain herbaceous plants, e.g. paeonies, readily bend under the weight of the flowers, particularly when it rains. Can this be related to the amount and/or distribution of the strengthening tissue?

5 Water is much denser than air. Amongst plants growing in water there might be less selection pressure for support tissue than amongst plants on land, since water plants may be supported by the water itself. Test this hypothesis by comparing the quantity and arrangement of support tissue in transverse sections of stems, petioles and leaves of (a) plants submerged in water and closely related species growing on land, and (b) parts of plants submerged beneath the water surface and similar parts in the air. To what extent do you think the presence and distribution of support tissues is genetically determined and environmentally determined?

6 The unicellular organism *Paramecium* is delightful to watch under the microscope. Obtain a *Paramecium* culture and observe live specimens under the microscope. In the course of making observations you will doubtless discover all sorts of phenomena worthy of investigation. For example, you might test the hypothesis that *Paramecium* moves towards favourable stimuli and away from unfavourable stimuli.

7 Compare the water potentials of the innermost and outermost tissues of a potato tuber. After investigating the structure and permeability of the outermost layers of the potato suggest how water moves within, and out of, a tuber, i.e. from cell to cell and also across the 'skin'. Water movement across the skin could be related to the structure of the skin.

8 Compare the water potentials of potato tubers with those of the submerged stems or roots of aquatic plants (e.g. Canadian pond weed, *Elodea canadensis*), and/or with those of salt marsh plants (e.g. samphire, *Salicornia* spp. and sea lavender, *Limonium* spp.) and/or seaweeds. Relate the differences to the habitats, water relations and tissue structures of the plants. If you have to remove parts of a plant from the wild, keep damage to the bare minimum, and under no circumstances uproot any complete plants.

9 Determine the solute potential of red blood cells in blood from an abbatoir or HIV-free heat-treated human blood from a hospital. Compare the effects on plant and animal cells of altering the water potentials of the surrounding solution.

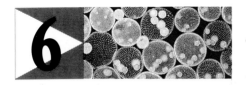

Autotrophic and heterotrophic nutrition

Human teeth

In most vertebrates other than mammals the teeth are all alike. However, in mammals the teeth are differentiated into specialised types, each with a specific function. Typically there are cutting **incisors**, piercing **canines**, and grinding **premolars** and **molars**. In this practical we shall look at the structure and arrangement of human teeth.

Procedure

Study the external features of human teeth by (a) observing your own teeth in a mirror, (b) feeling the surface of your teeth with the tip of your tongue, and (c) examining teeth that have been extracted by a dentist.

1   Notice that all the teeth have a **crown** which projects from the gum, and one or more **roots** which are embedded in the jaw bone.

2   Observe how the different types of teeth differ: incisors are more or less chisel-shaped with single roots, canines are pointed with single roots, whilst the pre-molars and molars have two or more **cusps** on the surface of the crown and are multi-rooted. Can you suggest different functions for these teeth in the human?

3   Make outline drawings of all the teeth on one side of the upper and lower jaws, using Figure 6.1 to help you.

4   Examine a vertical section of a tooth under the microscope. There is a layer of hard **enamel** on the outside, then a layer of slightly less hard **dentine**, and in the centre a **pulp cavity** containing blood vessels and nerve fibres. The roots are covered with a layer of **cement** and attached to the jaw bone by fibres.

5   For convenience we can summarise a mammal's complement of teeth by the **dental formula.** This is explained in Box 6.1. Do your own teeth agree with the formula given for the human? If not, why not?

6   If your teeth do not agree with the formula, it could be that you have not yet acquired a full set of teeth. Humans have two sets of teeth in the course of life. First there are the **milk teeth** consisting of incisors, canines and premolars, but no molars; these are later replaced by the **permanent teeth** characteristic of the adult. At what ages were your milk teeth replaced by your permanent teeth, and is the permanent dentition complete yet?

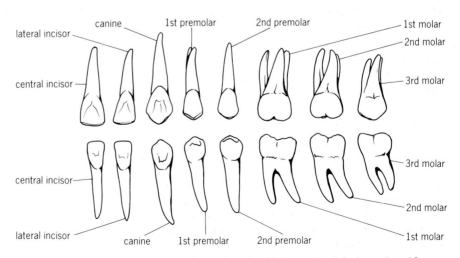

Figure 6.1 Permanent teeth of an adult human from the right hand side of the jaws, viewed from inside the mouth.

BOX 6.1 Dental formulae

It is conventional to summarise a mammal's complement of teeth in the form of a **dental formula**. The number of teeth of each type on one side of the upper jaw is written above the number of teeth of each type on one side of the lower jaw.

Here are the dental formulae of three mammalian species:

Human

$$i\frac{2}{2}, c\frac{1}{1}, pm\frac{2}{2}, m\frac{3}{3} = \frac{8\times2}{8\times2} = 32$$

Dog

$$i\frac{3}{3}, c\frac{1}{1}, pm\frac{4}{4}, m\frac{2}{3} = \frac{10\times2}{11\times2} = 42$$

Rat

$$i\frac{1}{1}, c\frac{0}{0}, pm\frac{0}{0}, m\frac{3}{3} = \frac{4\times2}{4\times2} = 16$$

key: i, incisors; c, canines; pm, premolars; m, molars.

To think about

1   Do you think there is any functional significance in the differences between the dental formulae of these species?
2   What may have been the dental formula of the ancestral mammal from which present-day mammals are believed to have evolved?

For consideration

1   Why are human babies born with no teeth?
2   Next time you eat a meal, consider the action of your teeth on the food. Do you think the differentiation of your teeth into incisors, canines, premolars and molars is a useful adaptation?
3   You may have had some of your teeth filled or extracted by a dentist. Which of your teeth have been filled or extracted, and why? (You may like to discuss this with your dentist next time you see him or her.)

REQUIREMENTS

Microscope
VS mammalian tooth
Human teeth

6.2 INVESTIGATION

The teeth of various vertebrates

The aim of this investigation is to look at the skulls of a selection of vertebrates, noting the way the teeth are adapted to deal with particular kinds of diet.

Guidance

To build up a complete picture of how the teeth are adapted you will need to observe the action of the jaws. For example, do the jaws move up and down, or from side to side, or backwards and forwards? These questions can be answered by watching the animals eating, and by observing the mode of articulation of the lower jaw (mandible) with the back of the skull.

You will also need to know what sort of food the animal eats. In general, vertebrates can be divided into **carnivores** (meat eaters), **herbivores** (plant eaters) and **omnivores** which eat meat and plants. You would expect the teeth and their actions to be related to the diet.

Procedure

1   Examine the skulls and teeth of a dog (carnivore), pig (omnivore) and sheep (herbivore). In each case describe the functions of the different types of teeth, and explain how the animal's dentition is related to its diet.
2   Humans are omnivores, like the pig. Compare the teeth of the pig with those of the human. Do both have the same dental formula?

3   Compare the teeth and jaw actions of a sheep and a horse. Is the detailed structure of the teeth related to the action of the jaws?

4   If available examine the skulls and teeth, or photographs thereof, of specialised feeders such as rat, rabbit or beaver (which gnaw their food), elephant (which eats large plants), hedgehog, mole or shrew (which feed on insects and other invertebrates), dolphin (which feeds on squid and fish), walrus (which feeds on clams) and sloth (which feeds on soft fruit). In each case try to relate the structure of the teeth to the diet.

5   Examine the skulls and teeth of other vertebrates such as a fish, a frog (amphibian) and a lizard (reptile). How do their teeth differ from mammalian teeth, and how are they related to their diets?

For consideration

1   In carnivorous vertebrates, what part do the teeth play in obtaining food?

2   What functions are performed by chewing (mastication), what sort of mammals chew their food, and what might be the consequences if they did not do it?

3   The serrated surface of the premolars and molars of herbivores such as sheep and horses results from the the wearing down of the crowns with constant use. Explain how this produces a serrated surface.

REQUIREMENTS

Skulls, or photographs of skulls, of:
  dog
  pig
  sheep
  horse
  hedgehog, mole or shrew
  rat, rabbit or beaver
  elephant
  dolphin
  walrus
  sloth
  fish, e.g. cod
  frog
  lizard

BOX 6.2 **Dissection**

The object of dissection is to reveal the anatomy, not to destroy it. Here are ten golden rules of dissection:

1   Keep your dissecting instruments in good condition; always clean and dry them after use.

2   Pin the specimen to a dissecting board or to the bottom of a dissecting dish so that the body wall is stretched.

3   When appropriate dissect the animal under water; the water supports the organs and will help you to separate the tissues.

4   If you are not dissecting in water, keep your dissection moist at all times. If you need to leave it for a while, cover it with a damp cloth.

5   Before making a cut, consider what organ you are looking for and where it is likely to be. *Never cut or remove anything without knowing what it is.*

6   When dissecting such structures as nerves and blood vessels, work along – not across – their course.

7   When following nerves and blood vessels, avoid damaging them by cutting upwards away from them rather than downwards towards them.

8   Remove only those structures which, if left in position, would obscure the structures you want to expose.

9   In the final stage of your dissection make sure all the structures that you wish to show are clearly displayed.

10 In displaying your dissection make judicious use of pins and thread to separate structures from each other.

CAUTION

In the interests of hygiene, wear a laboratory coat while you are dissecting, and wash your hands thoroughly afterwards. When dissecting tissue such as bone or cartilage wear eye protection to guard against flying splinters.

6.3 PRACTICAL EXERCISE

Dissection of the mammalian alimentary canal

The **alimentary canal**, or **gut**, is essentially a tube running from the **mouth** to the **anus**. Its function is to digest food physically and chemically, absorb the soluble products of digestion and get rid of indigestible waste. To this end it is differentiated into a series of distinct regions, and various glands open into it.

Procedure

1   Pin the rat to a dissecting board, ventral surface upwards and head pointing away from you. Make a mid-ventral incision through the skin (but not through the underlying body wall) and cut forward as far as the lower jaw (mandible), and backwards to the anus. Cut either side of the urinogenital openings as shown in Figure 6.2.

CAUTION

In the interests of hygiene, wear a laboratory coat while you are dissecting, and wash your hands thoroughly afterwards.

Male

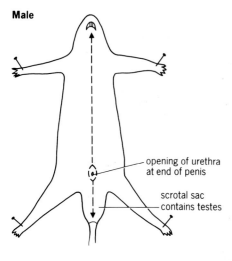

opening of urethra
at end of penis

scrotal sac
contains testes

Female

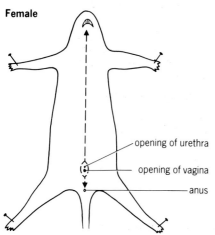

opening of urethra

opening of vagina

anus

Figure 6.2 Opening up the rat. Cut through the skin as indicated by the dotted line.

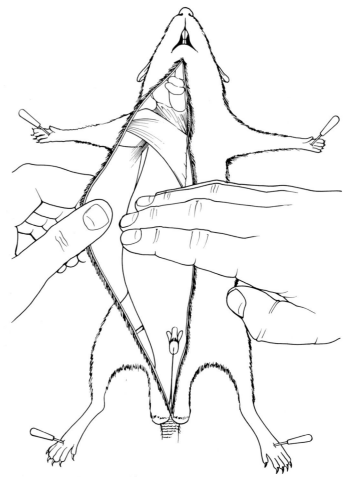

Figure 6.3 How to deflect the skin.

2 Free the skin from the underlying body wall, using your fingers or the handle of a scalpel (Figure 6.3), then pin back the skin as shown in Figure 6.4.

3 With scissors cut through the body wall so as to expose the contents of the abdomen (Figure 6.4). Identify the structures shown in Figure 6.4.

4 Wet your fingers under a tap so that they slide easily between the organs. Look between the **stomach** and **liver** and find the lower end of the **oesophagus** where it joins the top of the stomach. Using your fingers to move the organs this way and that, and *without cutting the mesentery by which the gut is suspended in the abdominal cavity*, follow the alimentary canal all the way back to the **rectum**.

5 Still without breaking the mesentery, push the liver forward and spread out the small intestine to your left as shown in Figure 6.5. Identify its two main parts: **duodenum** and **ileum**. Notice the **pancreas** in the loop of the duodenum and identify the **bile duct** and **pancreatic ducts**. Finally observe the numerous branches of the hepatic portal vein and follow them back to where they unite to form the main trunk of the hepatic portal vein to the liver.

6 With the liver still pushed forward, deflect the whole of the stomach and intestine to your left and stretch the mesentery. Running in the mesentery are three arteries to the gut (Figure 6.6): **coeliac**, **anterior mesenteric** and **posterior mesenteric arteries**. All three are branches of the dorsal aorta, the first two arising at about the level of the left kidney, the last where the aorta splits into the iliac arteries to the legs.

7 Pluck away the fat clinging to the three arteries to show their origin from the dorsal aorta. Then trace them to their destinations. What organs do they supply?

8 Arrange the contents of the abdomen so as to display *in one view* as much as possible of the gut and its blood supply. This will require some ingenuity since various organs lie on top of each other.

9 Either draw your dissection and label it, or flag-label it and take a photograph.

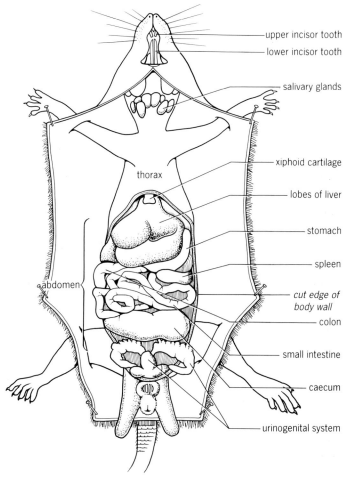

Figure 6.4 Contents of the abdominal cavity of a male rat in their normal positions.

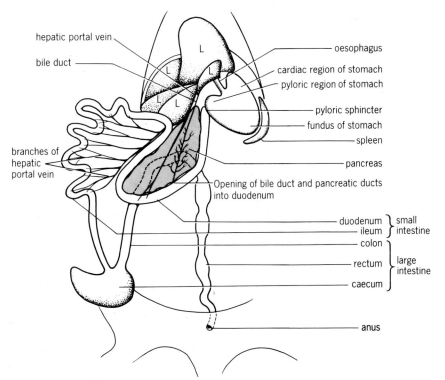

Figure 6.5 Alimentary canal of the rat as seen with the duodenum deflected downwards, the stomach pushed to the observer's right, and the ileum spread out to the observer's left. The branches of the hepatic portal vein may not be visible from above because they are covered by lymph nodes; however, they are usually visible from beneath. L, lobes of liver.

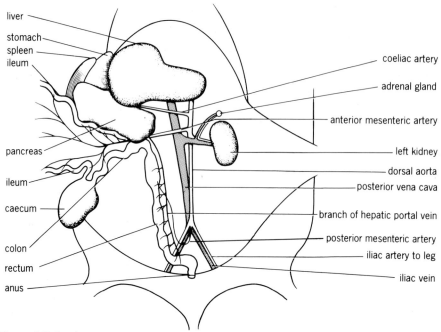

Figure 6.6 Arteries supplying the alimentary canal and associated structures of the rat.

10 Remove the gut as follows. Ligature the main trunk of the hepatic portal vein, cut through the oesophagus where it enters the stomach, and cut through the rectum where it disappears under the urinogenital organs. Cut through the mesentery so as to lift out the whole of the gut, spleen and pancreas (keep a piece of ileum for 6.4 Practical Exercise). Be careful not to cut any major blood vessels beneath the gut. Leave the liver. The rat can now be used again later for dissecting other systems.

For consideration

1 The veins serving most organs take blood straight to the heart. However, the vein serving the gut (the hepatic portal vein) takes blood to the liver from which it then flows to the heart. Why is there this difference between the venous supply of the gut and other organs?

2 In what ways is the gut, as you have observed it in your dissection, adapted to carry out its functions?

References
Rowett, H.G.Q. *Dissection Guides, III The Rat*, John Murray, 1951.
A video of a rat dissection, produced by the Institute of Biology in conjunction with the TV Centre of the University of Portsmouth, is available from the Institute of Biology, 20–22 Queensberry Place, London SW7 2DZ.

REQUIREMENTS

Dissecting instruments
Dissecting board
Dissecting pins
Rubber gloves
Camera (optional)
Rat, for dissection

Note: *Embalmed rats with blood vessels triple-injected (arteries red, veins blue, hepatic portal vein yellow) are available from Philip Harris Education.*

6.4 PRACTICAL EXERCISE

Microscopic structure of the mammalian gut wall

Although the gut is differentiated into regions, its wall always consists of the layers shown in Figure 6.7:

• **Epithelium.** Inner layer of cells showing various degress of folding; its functions are protective, secretory and/or absorptive.
• **Mucosa.** Connective tissue, blood vessels etc.
• **Muscularis mucosa.** Two thin layers of smooth muscle, an inner circular layer and an outer longitudinal layer.
• **Submucosa.** More connective tissue, blood vessels etc like the mucosa.
• **External muscle coat.** Smooth muscle differentiated into an inner circular layer and an outer longitudinal layer.
• **Serosa.** Connective tissue continuous with the mesentery by which the gut is attached to the body wall.

The aim of this practical exercise is to identify these layers in certain regions of the gut, and to relate their detailed structure to their functions.

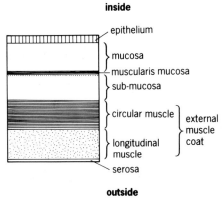

inside

- epithelium
- mucosa
- muscularis mucosa
- sub-mucosa
- circular muscle ⎫
- longitudinal muscle ⎭ external muscle coat
- serosa

outside

Figure 6.7 The principal layers in the wall of the mammalian alimentary canal.

Procedure
Small intestine

1 Examine a section of the ileum under low power. Without getting immersed in the details, identify the different layers of the wall using Figure 6.7 to help you. In what ways does your section depart from the simple diagrammatic pattern shown in Figure 6.7?

2 Now look at your section in detail, still under low power, and identify the parts shown on the left hand side of Figure 6.8. Notice in particular the **villi** and **crypts of Lieberkühn**.

3 Go over to high power and carefully examine the individual parts shown in Figure 6.8. Try to answer these questions:

  a What sort of cells occur in the epithelium lining the villi and crypts of Lieberkuhn and what are their functions?

  b In what ways is the epithelium adapted to carry out its functions?

  c What functions are performed by the muscle tissue visible in your section?

4 Examine a section of the wall of the duodenum. Identify its parts, using the right hand side of Figure 6.8 to help you. How does the wall of the duodenum differ from that of the ileum?

5 Open up a short length of the ileum of a dissected rat. Pin it, inner surface uppermost, to a piece of cork and wash it thoroughly under a tap. Examine it with a binocular microscope. Can you see the villi?

A Sections of the wall of ileum and duodenum

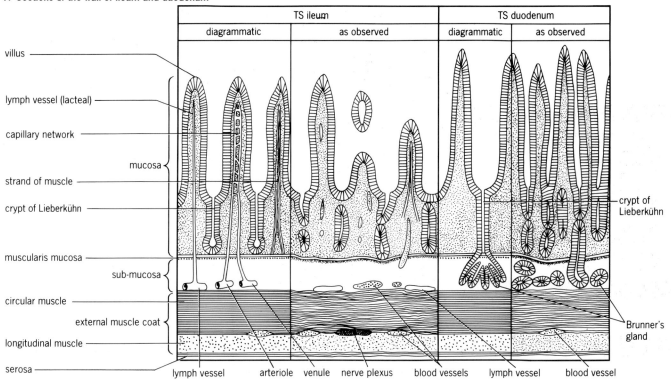

TS ileum — diagrammatic — as observed
TS duodenum — diagrammatic — as observed

villus
lymph vessel (lacteal)
capillary network
mucosa
strand of muscle
crypt of Lieberkühn
muscularis mucosa
sub-mucosa
circular muscle
external muscle coat
longitudinal muscle
serosa

crypt of Lieberkühn
Brunner's gland

lymph vessel   arteriole   venule   nerve plexus   blood vessels   lymph vessel   blood vessel

B Epithelial lining of villus

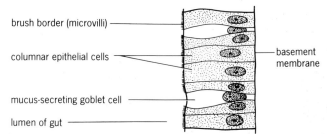

- brush border (microvilli)
- columnar epithelial cells
- mucus-secreting goblet cell
- lumen of gut
- basement membrane

Figure 6.8 Microscopic structure of the wall of the mammalian small intestine.

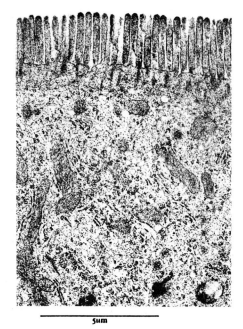

Figure 6.9 Electron micrograph of a section through an epithelial cell lining a villus in the wall of the small intestine of a mouse.

6 Look at the electron micrograph in Figure 6.9. This is a section through an individual epithelial cell lining a villus. Notice the numerous **microvilli** projecting from the free surface of the cell. Did you see these microvilli in the sections of the small intestine which you examined under the light microscope? They may have shown up as a **brush border**. If necessary re-examine the sections to see if you can detect a brush border.

Stomach

1 Examine a vertical section of the wall of the stomach. Identify the various layers of the wall and relate them to Figure 6.10.

A Vertical section of stomach wall

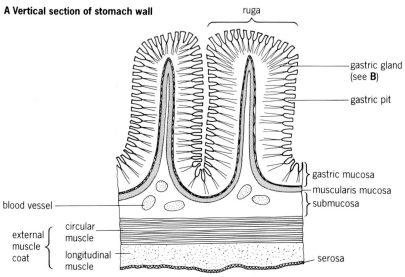

B Gastric glands in mucosa of stomach wall

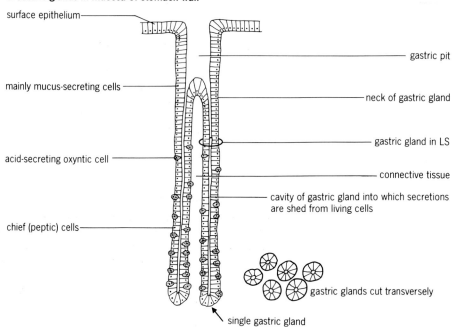

C Lining of gastric gland in detail

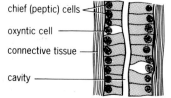

Figure 6.10 Microscopic structure of the wall of the mammalian stomach.

2 Identify the detailed parts of the stomach wall as shown in Figure 6.10A. In particular notice the numerous **gastric glands**.

3 Examine a gastric gland in detail and identify the different types of cells in its epithelial lining (Figure 6.10B). Towards the surface where it opens into a gastric pit, the gastric gland will have been cut longitudinally, but deeper down where the gland twists and turns it will have been cut transversely and obliquely.

4 Using high power, examine an individual **mucus-secreting cell**, **oxyntic cell** and **chief (peptic) cell**. What are the functions of these three types of cell?

Other regions of the gut

Obtain sections or photomicrographs of the tongue, oesophagus, colon, rectum and recto-anal junction. Before examining them, think what each of these parts of the gut has to do and from this *predict* the kinds of cells and tissues which you would expect to find in it. Then examine the sections and see if your predictions are correct. Here are some notes to help you:

1 **Tongue.** Look out for taste buds (flask-shaped bundles of sensory and supporting cells) and for striated muscle. Why should the tongue contain *striated* muscle?

2 **Oesophagus.** The external muscle coat consists mainly of circular muscle in which striated fibres are present, particularly in the upper part of the oesophagus. Functional reason?

3 **Colon.** One of its functions is to reabsorb water. Can you detect any obvious adaptations for this?

4 **Rectum.** Faeces are stored here before being expelled through the anus. Numerous goblet cells secrete mucus to lubricate the passage of the faeces. Can you see any other adaptations?

5 **Recto-anal junction.** Here the rectal tissue gradually gives way to the thicker, more muscular anal tissue. Examining a section through this region provides an excellent opportunity to identify tissues and relate structure to function.

Reference

Newman, M. Inside the intestine, *School Science Review*, Vol. 70, No. 252, March 1989. Describes the technique for viewing the intestinal villi under a binocular microscope.

REQUIREMENTS

Microscopes, monocular and binocular
Cork, approximately 1 cm square
Pins
Ileum, TS
Duodenum, TS
Stomach wall, VS
Tongue, VS
Oesophagus, TS
Colon, TS
Rectum, TS
Recto-anal junction, LS
Ileum of dissected rat

6.5 PRACTICAL EXERCISE

Eye protection
must be worn

Irritant   Corrosive
Iodine   Hydrochloric
solution   acid

Digestion of starch

Normally when we ask you to carry out a practical exercise we make its aims clear. This practical exercise is different. Here you will be presented with a set of instructions for investigating the action of the enzyme **amylase** on starch. The detailed aims will be considered afterwards.

Samples of starch will be mixed with the enzyme under various conditions, and after a given time the mixture will be tested for starch with dilute iodine solution and for reducing sugar with Benedict's solution. Details of these tests are given on page 49.

Procedure

1 Obtain 20 cm³ of amylase solution. Transfer ¼ of the amylase to a test-tube and place this in a boiling water bath for 15 minutes. Transfer a further ¼ of the amylase solution to another test-tube and add four drops of hydrochloric acid, mix well and leave for at least 15 minutes. Keep the rest of the amylase solution untreated at room temperature.

2 Set up six pairs of test-tubes as follows. Label each test-tube with its code number: A1, A2 etc.

Pair A
1   4 cm³ reducing sugar
2   4 cm³ reducing sugar

Pair B
3   4 cm³ starch
4   4 cm³ starch

Pair C
5   4 cm³ untreated amylase
6   4 cm³ untreated amylase

Pair D
7   4 cm³ starch plus 2 cm³ untreated amylase
8   4 cm³ starch plus 2 cm³ untreated amylase

Pair E
9   4 cm³ starch plus 2 cm³ preheated amylase
10 4 cm³ starch plus 2 cm³ preheated amylase

Pair F
11 4 cm³ starch plus 2 cm³ acidified amylase
12 4 cm³ starch plus 2 cm³ acidified amylase

3 Place the test-tubes in a rack in numerical order and leave them for at least 10 minutes.
4 Test the contents of each pair of test-tubes (a) for starch by adding two drops of dilute iodine solution, and (b) for reducing sugar by adding $\frac{1}{8}$ test-tube of Benedict's solution and heating in a water bath (Box 4.1). Do the starch test on the first of each pair of test-tubes, and the sugar test on the second.
5 Record your results in a table, indicating which test-tubes give a positive and which ones a negative result for starch and reducing sugar. It is possible that some may give a result in between; if so, say so.

For consideration

1 Three different, but related, hypotheses are tested by this experiment. What are they?
2 Are the hypotheses supported by your results? Would you say they were *proved*?
3 What were the controls in this experiment?
4 Identify the dependent and independent variables in the experiment. The independent variables are discrete (i.e. non-continuous). How would the experiment have to be altered to make the independent variables *continuous*?
5 Can you suggest any ways of improving the instructions given for this practical exercise?

6.6 INVESTIGATION

This investigation requires more than one practical session.

Digestion of protein

In the gut proteins are hydrolysed by two main enzymes, **pepsin** and **trypsin**. Pepsin is present in the the stomach where conditions are markedly acidic; trypsin is present in the small intestine where conditions are usually slightly alkaline. We may predict that these two enzymes work optimally at acidic and alkaline pH respectively. In this investigation you will test this hypothesis.

Guidance

Set up a series of large test-tubes each containing a sample of protein together with a solution of the enzyme at the required pH. Then find out whether or not the enzyme succeeds in hydrolysing the protein. Use a solid protein such as boiled egg white: a small piece, approximately 1 cm³, is sufficient. You can tell if it has been hydrolysed by seeing if it dissolves in the enzyme solution.

Make sure that in each test-tube the egg white is completely covered by the enzyme solution and that the pH is appropriate. It is suggested that for acidic conditions the pH should be 2.0, and for alkaline conditions 9.0. The pH can be adjusted by adding acid or alkali to the enzyme solution, and tested by means of pH indicator paper. Don't forget to include any necessary controls.

When you have set up the test-tubes, incubate the protein-enzyme mixtures at 37 °C for at least 24 hours before assessing the results.

For consideration

1 Do your results support the hypothesis that pepsin and trypsin work optimally in acid and alkaline conditions respectively?
2 What controls did you set up, and why?
3 Suppose you were to use a *soluble* protein for this experiment. How would you assess whether or not the protein had been hydrolysed?
4 How could you find out the exact pH at which each of these enzymes works optimally?

6.7 INVESTIGATION

Digestion of fat

In the human gut fats are acted upon by **bile salts** from the liver and by **lipase** from the pancreas. The aim of this investigation is to explore the action of these two agents and assess their roles in digestion.

Guidance

When fats are hydrolysed, glycerol and fatty acids are released. The presence of acid, creating a relatively low pH, may therefore be used as an indication that hydrolysis has

Highly
flammable
Phenolpthalein

occurred. You can demonstrate the formation of acid by using the pH indicator phenolphthalein: at a pH above 10, phenolphthalein is pink, but below pH 8.4 it is colourless. If phenolphthalein is added to a test-tube in which an alkaline solution of fat is being hydrolysed, the colour of the contents should change gradually from pink to colourless as fatty acids accumulate. Sodium carbonate may be added to the mixture beforehand to ensure that the pH is well above 10 to start off with.

Procedure

With phenolphthalein as your indicator, design and carry out experiments to test some or all of the following hypotheses:
1   Lipase can hydrolyse fat.
2   Bile salts can hydrolyse fat.
3   Lipase is more effective if the fat has been acted on by bile salts beforehand.
4   Lipase is inactivated by excessive heat.
   You are provided with the basic requirements for testing these hypotheses, but if you need any other items you should ask for them.

For consideration

1   Do you think that using phenolphthalein is a satisfactory way of showing that fat has been hydrolysed? Can you suggest a better way?
2   What do you conclude about the roles of lipase and bile salts in the digestion of fats?
3   Consider your conclusions very critically. Which conclusions, if any, can you really be sure about? What further experiments should be carried out?

REQUIREMENTS

Water bath
Stopclock
Test-tubes
Pipette (for delivering up to 5 cm³
   quantities)
Beaker (for washing pipette)
Bile salts (5%)
Lipase solution (5%, fresh)
Phenolphthalein
Sodium carbonate solution
   (0.2 mol dm⁻³)
Fat (e.g. butter)
Other items may be requested by
   individual students

6.8 INVESTIGATION

Structure of leaves

The leaf is the plant's photosynthetic organ. In what ways is its design suited to this function? One would expect abundant chloroplasts, an efficient water supply, a large surface area for the uptake of scarce carbon dioxide (0.04 % of the atmosphere) and the capacity to remove rapidly the photosynthetic products and distribute them around the plant. In this investigation we shall see if these expectations are realised.

Guidance

Firstly, look at the external features of the leaf of a representative dicotyledon such as privet or holly (Figure 6.11) and note the terminology. Suggest why the upper side of the leaf is more shiny and a darker green than the lower side. What are the functions of the midrib and veins?

   Compare the pattern of veins in your dicotyledonous leaf with the leaf of a monocotyledon such as a grass or iris.

   Examine carefully under the microscope a transverse section of the leaf of privet. First try to find, under low power, examples of all the tissues shown in Figure 6.12,

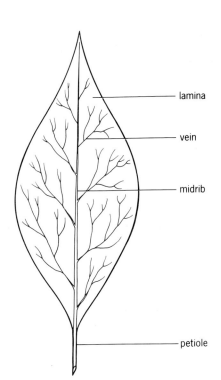

Figure 6.11 The external features of a generalised dicotyledonous leaf.

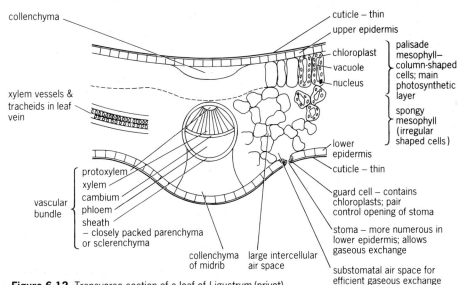

Figure 6.12 Transverse section of a leaf of *Ligustrum* (privet).

noting their relative positions. You may have to search hard before you find, on the lower surface, stomata (small holes) and the guard cells on either side. What part of the cross section makes the leaf shiny? Which tissues prevent it from collapsing in wind or under its own weight?

Next, concentrate on an area of leaf blade about four cells wide, and, examine it under medium and high power. Draw a large labelled diagram, including if visible a vein and a stoma.

Now answer the question posed in the introduction. Where are the most abundant chloroplasts and in which tissue does photosynthesis mainly take place? Through which tissue is water supplied to the leaf? How are the products of photosynthesis removed from the leaf and distributed to the rest of the plant? By what route does carbon dioxide enter the leaf and where is the predicted large surface area for the uptake of this gas? Write down in *detail* the parts of the leaf and the parts of the indi-vidual cells through which a molecule of carbon dioxide might move on its journey to a chloroplast in the upper layers of the leaf.

For consideration

Write down as many ways as you can think of in which the structure of a leaf equips it to be an efficient photosynthetic organ. Aim for fifteen points – your teacher will fill in the gaps!

REQUIREMENTS

Microscope

TS leaf of privet (*Ligustrum*)
Leaf of dicotyledon such as privet or holly (*Ilex aquifolium*)
Leaf of a monocotyledon such as a grass or *Iris*

6.9 PRACTICAL EXERCISE

Separation of photosynthetic pigments by chromatography

The photosynthetic pigments can be separated and identified by chromatography. A piece of absorptive paper or a thin layer plate (silica gel on an aluminium backing), with a concentrated spot of leaf extract on it, is dipped into a suitable organic solvent. As the solvent ascends the porous paper or silica, it carries the pigments with it at different rates. In this way they become separated from one another and can be iden-tified by their different colours and positions.

The relative distances travelled by the various pigments depend on which solvent and separation medium (type of paper or thin layer plate) is used. Thin layer plates usually provide a quicker and cleaner separation than chromatography paper or filter paper. A well-established paper chromatography method is described here, but a thin layer plate can be used instead and there is plenty of scope for devising your own variation.

Highly flammable Propanone   Harmful Propanone

Procedure

1 Cut a strip of chromatography paper (filter paper will do) sufficiently long to almost reach the bottom of a boiling tube and narrow enough so that the edges will not touch the sides of the tube.
2 Rule a pencil line across the strip of paper 30 mm from one end. Fold the other end through 90° and attach it to the stopper with a pin (as shown in Figure 6.13). Check that the strip almost touches the base of the tube and the edges do not touch the sides.
3 Grind up fresh healthy nettle leaves in pure propanone, producing as concentrated a pigment solution as possible. Filter this through muslin into a small beaker.
4 Remove the paper from the boiling tube and, using the head of a small pin as a dropper, place a drop of the pigment solution at the centre of the pencil line. Let the drop dry, then place a second small drop on the first. Repeat this process several times, building up a small area of concentrated pigment (and carry out step 5 simultaneously).
5 While preparing your pigment spot, pour some solvent into the boiling tube to a depth of not more than 15 mm. Seal the tube with a stopper for about 10 minutes so that the atmosphere inside becomes saturated with vapour.
6 Now suspend the strip of paper in the boiling tube. The bottom edge of the paper should dip into the solvent, but make sure that the pigment spot is not immersed.
7 The solvent front will rise rapidly and the pigments will separate in about ten minutes. When the solvent is close to the top of the paper, remove the strip, rule a pencil line to mark the solvent front, and dry the paper.
8 Identify the pigments. If all has gone well you should be able to detect the five

---

REQUIREMENTS

Pestle and mortar
Filter funnel
Muslin
Beaker (100 cm³)
Boiling tube rack
Boiling tube
Stopper
Pin
Chromatography paper, filter paper or thin layer plate
Scissors
Propanone
Solvent (1 part 90% propanone (acetone) to 9 parts petroleum ether (b.p. 80–100 °C)

Fresh leaves, e.g. of nettle (*Urtica dioica*)

Table 6.1 Colours and R_f values for the pigments in a typical leaf, separated in a propanone/ether mixture.

Name	Colour	R_f
Carotene	Yellow	0.95
Phaeophytin	Yellow–grey	0.83
Xanythophyll	Yellow–brown	0.71
Chlorophyll a	Blue–green	0.65
Chlorophyll b	Green	0.45

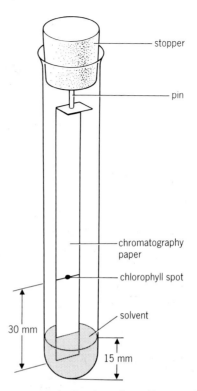

Figure 6.13 One possible arrangement for the chromatographic separation of photosynthetic pigments.

pigments listed in Table 6.1 (phaeophytin is a breakdown product of one of the chlorophylls). They can be identified by their colours and R_f values.

9   Measure the distance from the original pencil line (step 2) to the leading edge of each clearly detectable pigment, and work out the R_f value for each one: $R_f = a/b$, where a is the distance moved by the pigment from its original position and b is the distance moved by the solvent from the same position. Compare your results with the information in Table 6.1.

For consideration

1   What is the possible functional significance of the fact that there are several pigments, not just one?

2   How could you ascertain if there are more pigments present in the leaf than the ones you have identified?

6.10 PRACTICAL EXERCISE

Effect of light intensity on the rate of photosynthesis

A convenient way to investigate the effect of light intensity on the rate of photosynthesis is to compare the volume of oxygen produced by an aquatic plant at different levels of illumination. You will use the Canadian pondweed, *Elodea canadensis*, from whose stem and leaves gas may be seen emerging as a stream of bubbles.

It is more accurate to collect the bubbles evolved by the plant in a given time, and to measure their volume, than merely to count bubbles (why?). The bubble-collecting apparatus is known as a **photosynthometer**.

Procedure

Danger
Razor blade

1   Choose a piece of well-illuminated *Elodea* about 10 cm long which already has bubbles emerging from it. Make a clean oblique cut with a sharp razor blade near the end of the stem, under water. You may have to cut the end of the stem several times until bubbles emerge rapidly. Place the plant, bubbling end upwards, in a test-tube containing the same water that the pondweed has been kept in.

2   Add a pinch of hydrogencarbonate powder to the water. *Elodea* can use hydrogen-carbonate ions as well as carbon dioxide as a substrate for photosynthesis. If

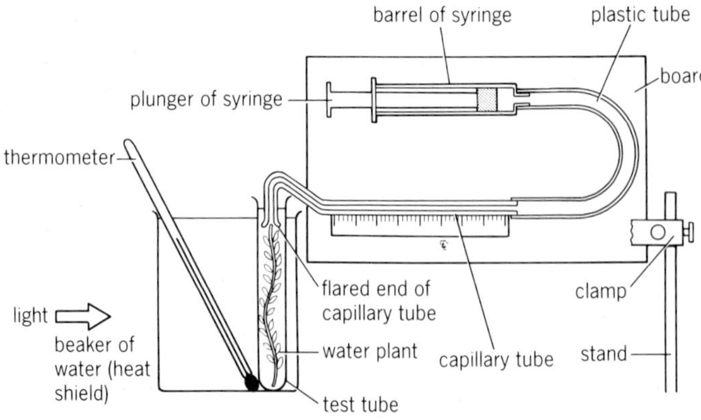

Figure 6.14 Apparatus suitable for investigating the effect of light intensity on the rate of photosynthesis of a water plant such as *Elodea*. The plastic tube is where the gas produced by the plant is deposited after it has been collected and measured in the capillary tube. Commercial versions of this apparatus often have a screw for pulling the gas through.

A simple piece of apparatus for determining the rate of photosynthesis of a water plant is shown in Figure 6.16 on p. 103.

hydrogencarbonate powder is added to the water there is less chance that lack of carbon dioxide will limit the rate of photosynthesis at high light intensities.

3 Stand the test tube in a beaker of water to reduce temperature fluctuations during the experiment; check the temperature from time to time.

4 The apparatus (Figure 6.14) consists of a capillary tube, flared at one end for collecting the gas, and connected at the other end, via a plastic tube, to a 2 cm^3 syringe.

Fill it with water as follows. Remove the plunger of the syringe, and run water from a tap into the syringe barrel until the whole of the syringe and plastic tube are full of water. Then replace the plunger and gently expel water from the flared end of the capillary tube until the plunger is deep inside the syringe barrel. Make sure that the whole apparatus is full of water and that there are no air bubbles in the capillary tube.

5 With the room darkened (why?), position a light source 5 cm from the plant. A bench lamp with a 40 W bulb is suitable but a lantern slide projector with a heat shield is better.

6 Wait for the plant to produce bubbles at a steady rate. Then collect the gas which the plant produces in a given period of time (five minutes is usually sufficient but some specimens of *Elodea* produce a large volume in one minute). Draw the gas bubble into the capillary tube by gently pulling the plunger of the syringe. Measure its length against the scale and record it, together with the distance of the plant from the light source. Then gently pull out the syringe plunger and deposit the gas in the plastic tube.

7 Repeat stages 4, 5 and 6 with the light source at increasing distances from the plant, say 10, 20, 40 and 80 cm.

8 Then take a second reading at each distance, moving the lamp gradually *closer* to the plant.

9 The relationship between the distance of the light from the plant and the light intensity is described by the '**inverse square law**'; The light intensity is inversely proportional to the square of the distance, $I \propto 1/d^2$, where I is the light intensity and d is the distance between the light source and the object. Thus, if the distance (d) between the light and the plant is doubled, the light intensity falls to a quarter of its previous value. For each distance, work out the relative light intensity as $10\ 000/d^2$, where d is the distance between the light source and the plant in cm; this produces whole numbers to plot.

10 Plot a graph of the volume of oxygen evolved in a standard time against the light intensity. Take care over the horizontal axis. Not only do the points where the lamp was closest to the plant appear at the right hand end, but the points will not be equidistant!

Analysis of the gas in the bubble

At the end of the experiment some of the collected gas may be analysed for oxygen and carbon dioxide by the same method that is used to analyse the gases in inspired and expired air (see page 133).

Eye protection must be worn

Corrosive
Potassium hydroxide
Pyrogallol

Harmful
Pyrogallol

REQUIREMENTS

Photosynthometer (Figure 6.14).
The capillary tube bore should be not more than 1 mm. The rubber plunger of the syringe should be greased so that it moves easily inside the barrel.
Safety razor blade
Test-tube
Beaker (400 cm³)
Thermometer
Lamp with 40 W bulb (or other suitable light source)
Metre rule
Safety goggles
Potassium hydroxide solution (40%)
Pyrogallol, pyrogallic acid (benzene 1,2, 3-triol)
Sodium or potassium hydrogencarbonate powder
Canadian pondweed (*Elodea canadensis*) or similar pondweed (healthy, illuminated, bubbling)

11 Place the light as close as possible to the plant and collect a sample of the gas several millimetres long. Measure the length of this bubble in millimetres in the usual way (do not hold the capillary tube in your hand or the rise in temperature will cause the gas to expand).

12 Gently push in the syringe plunger until the bubble is about 1 cm from the flared open end of the capillary tube. Quickly put the open end into a solution of potassium hydroxide and, keeping the open end in this solution, gently pull out the syringe plunger until the bubble reaches the other end of the capillary tube. Still holding the open end in the potassium hydroxide solution, slowly shunt the bubble back and forth along the length of the tube at least six times.

13 Put the end of the capillary tube back in water for 5 minutes. Then measure the length of the bubble. Any decrease in length is due to the absorption of carbon dioxide by the potassium hydroxide solution.

14 Now repeat steps 12 and 13 with pyrogallol instead of potassium hydroxide. The pyrogallol reacts with any potassium hydroxide still in the tube to form potassium pyrogallate which then absorbs the oxygen. Record the final length of the bubble in the capillary tube. The further decrease in the length of the bubble is due to the absorption of oxygen by the pyrogallate.

15 Calculate the percentages of carbon dioxide and oxygen in the original sample of gas. Interpret your results. Are they what you expected?

For consideration

1 What relationship between gas production and light intensity is demonstrated by the results of your experiment?

2 What factors may limit the rate of photosynthesis at (i) the lower light intensities, (ii) the higher light intensities?

3 How might the procedure be modified to investigate the influence of carbon dioxide concentration on the rate of photosynthesis?

4 What effect did respiration have on your results? Were you measuring the rate of photosynthesis, or merely the extent to which photosynthesis exceeded respiration (i.e. net rate of photosynthesis)?

5 If, say, oxygen makes up 66% of the volume of the gas produced and carbon dioxide is another 1%, what does the rest consist of and why?

6.11 PRACTICAL EXERCISE

Compensation point of a plant

At the **compensation point**, the rate of photosynthesis of a plant equals its rate of respiration. Its carbon dioxide input and output are equal. The *light* compensation point of a plant is the light intensity at which the plant is in 'carbon balance', or equivalently, in oxygen balance, because for every molecule of carbon dioxide absorbed in photosynthesis a molecule of oxygen is evolved.

One way to determine the compensation point of a plant is to measure a plant's oxygen output at a range of light intensities from zero to bright light. The light intensity at which there is no net oxygen input or output is the light compensation point.

With appropriate sensors and software available, the most elegant way to determine the light compensation point is to use a computer to record and analyse the data.

Procedure

1 Obtain a potted *Pelargonium* plant and set it up as shown in Figure 6.15. Make sure that the polythene bag is tightly secured around the pot.

2 Switch on a lamp with a 100 W bulb close to the plant. Wait for five minutes. Then record the pattern of oxygen concentration in the closed jar for ten minutes.

3 Obtain a graph of the oxygen output over time and use the software to work out the total oxygen output of the plant over the ten minutes. Use a photographic light meter or a light probe to determine the average light intensity which reached the plant. Record both these values.

4 Repeat these measurements with the lamp at distances of 20, 40 and 80 cm from the bell jar containing the plant. If the experiment gives consistent results you may be able to shorten the measurement period.

5 Switch off the light, wait for five minutes, and determine the net oxygen exchange of the plant in the dark over ten minutes.

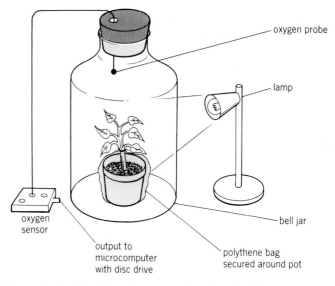

Figure 6.15 Apparatus for determining the compensation point of a *Pelargonium* plant. The microcomputer must be programmed with the appropriate program disc. This will allow it to store and display the observations. If the microcomputer is linked to a printer, the stored data can be printed out in the form of a table or graph.

6   If you have time you may be able to alter the distance of the lamp from the bell jar until there is no net oxygen exchange.

7   Plot a graph of the net oxygen input or output over ten minutes (vertical axis) against the light intensity (horizontal axis). Read off the graph, and record, the light intensity at which there is no net oxygen exchange. This is the compensation point of the *Pelargonium* plant under these conditions.

For consideration

1   Which wavelengths of light does your light sensor measure? Are they the same as the optimal wavelengths which a plant uses in photosynthesis?

2   Why was the soil beneath the *Pelargonium* plant enclosed in a polythene bag?

3   Is it strictly true that for every molecule of carbon dioxide absorbed in photosynthesis a molecule of oxygen is evolved? Explain your answer.

4   Explain how you could determine the *carbon dioxide* compensation point of a plant.

5   Predict how the light compensation point of a 'shade' plant would differ from that of a 'sun' plant. Give your reasons.

PROJECTS

Before starting a project, discuss your intended procedure with your teacher.

1   Test the hypothesis that a given part of the gut of an animal contains an enzyme which hydrolyses a particular substrate. You will need to extract the contents of different parts of the gut (or gut wall) of the animal that you choose to investigate, and test them for enzymatic activity. Animals suitable for examination include the locust (*Locusta*), cockroach (*Periplaneta*), earthworm (*Lumbricus*) and garden snail (*Helix*). (See Hui Tat-Keung and Tang Tsui Sau-mei, Digestive enzymes in the grasshopper, *School Science Review*, Vol. 70, No. 253, June 1989; and G.S. Preece, To demonstrate the distribution of invertase in the gut system of *Periplaneta americana*, *School Science Review*, Vol. 69, No. 249, June 1988.)

2   Test the hypothesis that pepsin and/or trypsin act only on protein and have no effect on other substrates such as starch and fat, whatever the conditions.

3   Investigate the enzymatic efficiency of trypsin at a series of different pHs. At what pH does trypsin work optimally? How does this relate to the normal range of pH found in the small intestine of a mammal?

4   It has been suggested that trypsin hydrolyses protein more rapidly in the presence of intestinal tissue than when intestinal tissue is absent. Test this hypothesis using duodenal tissue from a freshly-killed rat or mouse, and present a possible explanation. This project requires careful planning, and the conditions in which experiments are carried out need to be carefully controlled.

5   Investigate the action of human saliva. There are several things you might do here. For example, you could find out how long a sample of starch has to remain in the mouth (with and without chewing) for salivary amylase to hydrolyse the starch to sugar. This would enable you to assess how effective *in practice* your salivary amylase is in the normal digestion of starchy foods.

6 It has been suggested that the saliva produced just before a meal is more potent than the saliva produced after a meal. Test the truth of this suggestion.

N.B. *Experiments on saliva should be done on your own saliva, not on anyone else's. Clean all glassware thoroughly afterwards, using laboratory disinfectant.*

7 Investigate how the garden snail (*Helix aspersa*) feeds. With the animal on a sheet of glass, observe the mouth from underneath. How is food drawn in and eaten? Examine prepared sections of the head under the microscope and find out as much as you can about the feeding apparatus. Relate the structures observed to the animal's feeding behaviour.

8 Use the data-logging apparatus in Practical Exercise 6.11 to compare the light compensation points of a species habitually found growing in shade (e.g. bluebell (*Hyacinthoides non-scripta*), wood anemone (*Anemone nemorosa*)) with one characteristic of full sunlight.

9 Compare the leaves of the same plant growing in sun (at the top of the leaf mosaic) and shade (at the bottom of the leaf mosaic). Suggest how the differences between them might allow the plant to photosynthesise more efficiently. Compare the leaves at different levels of the same tree in area, thickness, number of palisade layers, chloroplast number, pigment concentration, cuticle thickness, stomatal frequency and if possible, photosynthetic rate.

10 An alternative design for a photosynthometer is shown in Figure 6.16. Adapt this to investigate the effect of limiting factors such as temperature, light intensity and hydrogencarbonate concentration on photosynthesis. Can you design a more efficient apparatus and compare it with the others? See Freeland P.W. *Problems in Practical Advanced Level Biology*, Hodder & Stoughton, 1985.

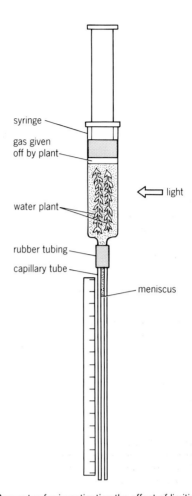

Figure 6.16 Apparatus for investigating the effect of limiting factors on the rate of photosynthesis of a water plant such as *Elodea* (after Freeland). Gas given off by the plant accumulates under the plunger in the barrel of the syringe and forces the water down the capillary tube. The rate of photosynthesis is estimated by measuring the rate of movement of the meniscus.

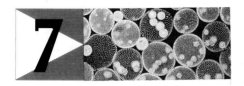

7 Transport and exchange

Problems of transport

Oxygen and soluble food substances have to be transported, either passively or actively, to all parts of an organism's body. Organisms may have one or more of the following features which help with this transport function:

- The organism is small enough for diffusion alone to distribute oxygen and dissolved food substances throughout its body.
- The organism is flat with the result that oxygen which has been absorbed across the surface readily diffuses to its innermost parts.
- The inside of the organism is folded into thin membranes which come into direct contact with oxygen and soluble food substances.
- Ciliated water-filled canals carry oxygen and dissolved food substances to all parts of the body.
- The gut has numerous blindly-ending branches through which soluble food substances can reach all parts of the body.
- Oxygen diffuses through pores in the surface after which it diffuses between and through the cells.
- Oxygen diffuses through pores in the surface and then to the tissues via narrow air-filled tubes.
- Oxygen and soluble food substances are carried to all parts of the body by a blood-filled circulatory system.

Procedure

1 Try to fit the above descriptions to each of the following organisms, here listed in alphabetical order:
   Amoeba, earthworm(Lumbricus), flowering plant, Hydra, insect, jelly fish (Aurelia), liver fluke (Fasciola hepatica), sea anemone (Anemonia and/or Actinia).
   In each case examine the intact organism first, live or preserved, then prepared slides. In some cases you may wish to carry out a dissection.
2 Write a brief account of how the tissues of each organism *probably* obtain oxygen and soluble food substances. In each case relate your suggestion to the structure of the organism as *you yourself have observed* it. Where you are doubtful about a suggestion, say what further observations you would need to make to test it.

For consideration

1 Can you relate an organism's transport system, or lack of it, to (a) the size of the organism, and (b) how active it is?
2 Place each of the organisms which you have studied in this investigation in its correct phylum and class. Does this give you any clues as to the approximate sequence in which transport systems may have arisen in evolution?

REQUIREMENTS

Microscope
Dissecting instruments
Dissecting dish
Amoeba, live and WM
Earthworm (Lumbricus), live, TS and whole animal for dissection
Flowering plant, dicotyledonous, leafy shoot and TS leaf
Hydra, live, WM and LS
Insect, WM of small species (e.g. flea) showing tracheal system
Jelly fish (e.g. Aurelia aurita), preserved and/or WM
Liver fluke (Fasciola hepatica), preserved and WM showing gut
Sea anemone (e.g. Anemonia or Actinia), live, preserved and TS

Transport through a flowering plant

It is well known that water enters a flowering plant through the roots and flows up the stem to the leaves. But even today many unanswered questions remain as to *how* water rises up stems, particularly of tall plants. The purpose of this investigation is to find out which components of the plant are necessary for this transport process to take place.

Plan, and carry out, experiments to find out if (a) roots, (b) leaves and (c) stomata are necessary for water to rise up a stem.

Guidance

When faced with the task of finding out if a particular structure is needed for a process to take place, one approach is to remove the structure and observe any effect the process. Appropriate controls must be set up, and all variables should be kept constant except the one you are trying to investigate. Precautions should be taken to eliminate effects caused by manipulating the plants.

You will need some way of telling whether or not water is rising up the stem. There are various ways of doing this, some more direct than others. One way is to use Busy Lizzie (*Impatiens*): its stems are semi-transparent and when the plant is stood in a suitable aqueous stain, the stain may be seen moving up the stem.

Using Busy Lizzie plants and the stain provided, carry out the experiments and draw conclusions.

For consideration

1   Why did an *aqueous* stain have to be used for this investigation?
2   Suppose you used a plant with a *non*-transparent stem for this investigation. How could you tell whether or not water had risen up the stem?
3   How could you find out if a source of metabolic energy within the stem itself is necessary for water to rise up the stem?

7.3 PRACTICAL EXERCISE

Looking at red blood cells

Red blood cells (**erythrocytes**) are amongst the simplest of cells. They lack a nucleus and their cytoplasm appears to be less elaborate than that of other cells. Yet at the chemical level they perform the specialised job of taking up oxygen in the lungs and transporting it to the tissues. They are also involved in the transport of carbon dioxide from the tissues to the lungs. Bear these functions in mind as you examine red blood cells.

Procedure

1   You will be provided with a specimen tube containing a sample of mammalian blood. With a dropping pipette place a drop of the blood towards one end of a slide. Then smear the blood over the slide using the technique shown in Figure 7.1.
2   Let the blood smear dry, then examine it under the microscope, low power first then high power. You will see large numbers of red blood cells. What colour are they, and why?
3   Examine a single red blood cell in as much detail as possible. Can you get any clues as to its shape from its appearance under the microscope? What can you say about its internal structure?

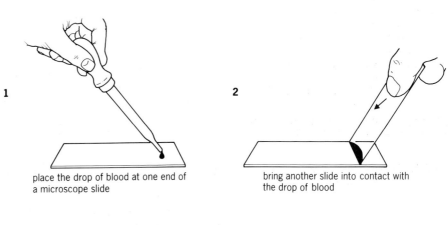

1   place the drop of blood at one end of a microscope slide

2   bring another slide into contact with the drop of blood

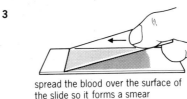

3   spread the blood over the surface of the slide so it forms a smear

Figure 7.1 How to make a blood smear for examination under the microscope.

4 Using a micrometer scale (see page 000), measure the diameter of a red blood cell. How does this compare with the width of most animal cells? What limits the size of the red blood cells?

5 Examine a prepared slide of frog's blood under the microscope. How do the red blood cells differ from those of the mammal? Which do you think might be more efficient at carrying oxygen, and why?

6 Examine a scanning electron micrograph of mammalian red blood cells. What information does the micrograph provide about the shape of the cells?

7 Examine a transmission electron micrograph of a mammalian red blood cell in section. What does it tell you about its internal structure?

For consideration

1 A human red blood cell has a life span of approximately 120 days. What do you think limits its life span, and how are new red blood cells formed?

2 It has been said that a mammalian red blood cell is the ideal shape for performing its function of carrying oxygen. Comment.

3 Suppose you wanted to calculate the number of oxygen molecules supplied to the tissues each day. List all the information you would require and the assumptions you would need to make. (If you have access to the necessary information, carry out this calculation.)

7.4 PRACTICAL EXERCISE

How many red blood cells?

It is obviously impossible to count all the blood cells present in a circulatory system, so we resort to *sampling* – that is, we count the cells in a representative volume.

A device for sampling cells is the **haemocytometer.** A measured volume of blood is diluted a known number of times. The red blood cells are then counted in a known volume of the diluted blood, from which the number of cells per mm^3 of undiluted blood can be calculated.

Procedure

1 First examine the haemocytometer and understand how it works (see Box 7.1, page 113).

2 You will be provided with a specimen tube containing a sample of diluted mammalian blood. The blood has been diluted one 100-fold with 0.75% sodium chloride solution, so the concentration of the blood is 1 in 100.

3 Place the coverslip in the centre of the haemocytometer slide. Using a teat pipette, place one drop of the diluted blood onto the slide, alongside the coverslip, in the area between the two deep grooves. The blood should be drawn under the coverslip. If the blood flows into the grooves, clean the slide and coverslip and start again.

4 Place the slide under the microscope and adjust the illumination so that the grid and the red blood cells can be clearly seen. If the cells are very unevenly distributed, clean the slide and coverslip and start again.

5 Count the red blood cells in 96 of the smallest (i.e. Type C) squares. (96 is a convenient number because the small squares are in blocks of 16, and 96 is 6 × 16.) Record your results by ruling out a grid and writing the number of cells in each square.

   Note – In each square count all the cells which lie entirely within it, plus those which touch or overlap the top and left hand sides. Do not include those which touch or overlap the bottom and right hand sides.

6 Clean the slide and coverslip when you have finished counting.

7 Calculate the average number of red blood cells in a Type C square. Knowing the volume of a Type C square, and the dilution factor, calculate the number of cells per mm^3.

For consideration

1 A typical human red blood cell count might be 5 million per mm^3. Assuming that the total volume of blood in the body is 5 litres, calculate the number of red blood cells in the entire circulation of a human.

2 Under what circumstances might a person's red blood cell count be (a) unusually high, and (b) unusually low?

Harmful
Propanone

Highly
flammable
Propanone

REQUIREMENTS

Microscope
Haemocytometer
Lens paper
Distilled water
Propanone (acetone)
Pig or sheep blood, diluted 1 in 100 with 0.75% sodium chloride solution, in specimen tube

Note: *Mammalian blood, treated to prevent clotting, is available from biological suppliers. It can be stored for up to one week in a refrigerator.*

Dissection of the circulatory system of the rat

This practical exercise has two aims:
• To dissect the rat so as to show the heart and the arteries and veins that are attached to it;
• To trace the arteries and veins to their destinations.

Procedure

Use the rat which you have already used for dissecting the alimentary canal. The alimentary canal should have been removed, the thorax opened up and the thymus gland removed (see page 89).

Observing the heart and vessels attached to it

1 Observe the **heart** and pluck away the fat from around the vessels that are attached to it. Be careful not to damage the **ductus arteriosus**, a slender strand linking the **pulmonary artery** and **aorta**. It is a relic of a vessel which was present in the foetus.
2 Push the heart to your left and identify the structures shown in Figure 7.2.

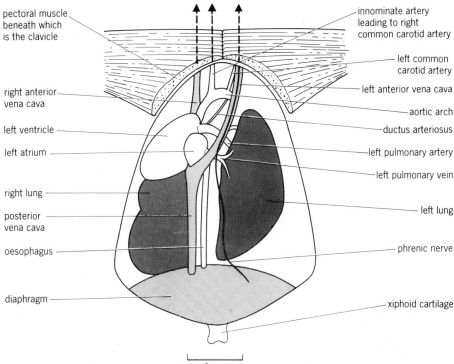

Figure 7.2 The heart and major blood vessels of the rat as seen in a ventral view of the thorax with the heart deflected to your left.

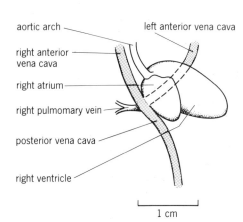

Figure 7.3 The heart and major blood vessels of the rat as seen in a ventral view of the thorax with the heart deflected to your right.

Do not use a dissection guide for this part of the dissection. Try to follow the arteries and veins to their destinations in a truly exploratory way. Bear in mind that William Harvey, who did much of the early work on the circulation, did not have a dissection guide.

3 Push the heart to your right and identify the point where the **venae cavae** enter the right atrium (Figure 7.3).
4 Mentally reconstruct the flow of blood into, through, and out of the heart, identifying all the blood vessels along which it flows *en route*.

Tracing the vessels to their destinations

1 Carefully trace the **anterior venae cavae** and the branches of the **aortic arch** from the thorax into the neck (the dotted arrows in Figure 7.2). This will necessitate removing the **pectoral muscle** and **clavicle** ('collar bone'). Be careful in the armpit region when you remove the clavicle because the anterior venae cavae are immediately underneath.

REQUIREMENTS

Dissecting instruments
Dissecting board
Dissecting pins
Rubber gloves
Rat, embalmed

Note: *Rats, triple injected (arteries red, veins blue, hepatic portal vein yellow) are available from Phiiip Harris Education.*

2 Continue tracing the veins and arteries forward towards the jaws, cutting away the neck muscles as necessary. Watch out for the branches of the arteries•and veins. What structures are served by the various vessels?

3 Now trace the **posterior vena cava** and **aorta** from the thorax into the abdomen. What structures are served by these vessels? Recall the **hepatic portal vein** and the arteries supplying the alimentary canal which you have already dissected (page 89).

4 Towards the posterior end of the abdomen the aorta and posterior vena cava split into vessels which go to the hind legs. Follow these vessels into the legs, noting their branches.

5 Check your dissection against Figures 7.4 and 7.5. Can you identify all the vessels shown in these diagrams? To what extent, if any, do the blood vessels in your rat differ from those in the diagram?

6 Draw and label your dissection, showing the arteries and veins in the same view.

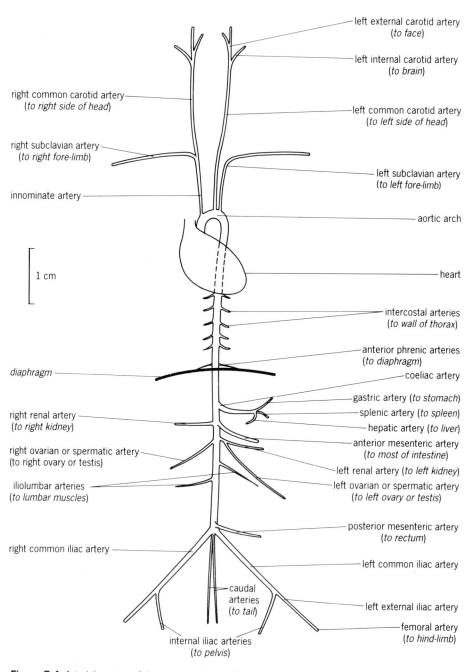

Figure 7.4 Arterial system of the rat, ventral view. Only the major arteries are shown.

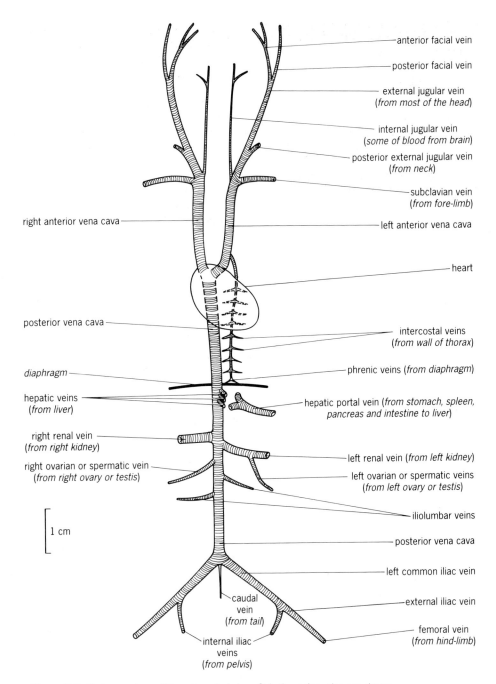

Figure 7.5 Venous system of the rat, ventral view. Only the major veins are shown.

anterior facial vein

posterior facial vein

external jugular vein
(*from most of the head*)

internal jugular vein
(*some of blood from brain*)

posterior external jugular vein
(*from neck*)

subclavian vein
(*from fore-limb*)

left anterior vena cava

heart

intercostal veins
(*from wall of thorax*)

phrenic veins (*from diaphragm*)

hepatic portal vein (*from stomach, spleen, pancreas and intestine to liver*)

left renal vein (*from left kidney*)

left ovarian or spermatic veins
(*from left ovary or testis*)

iliolumbar veins

posterior vena cava

left common iliac vein

external iliac vein

femoral vein
(*from hind-limb*)

right anterior vena cava

posterior vena cava

diaphragm

hepatic veins
(*from liver*)

right renal vein
(*from right kidney*)

right ovarian or spermatic vein
(*from right ovary or testis*)

1 cm

caudal vein
(*from tail*)

internal iliac veins
(*from pelvis*)

For consideration

1   In your dissection you will have noticed that the veins generally have a wider diameter and a darker colour than the arteries. Explain the reason for the difference.

2   To what extent is the circulatory system of the rat not bilaterally symmetrical? How would you explain the lack of bilateral symmetry?

3   Through what series of vessels does blood flow from the heart to (a) the brain, (b) the right forelimb, (c) the liver, (d) the left kidney, (e) the left hindlimb?

4   Through what series of vessels does blood flow to the heart from (a) the sides of the head, (b) the left forelimb, (c) the lungs, (d) the intercostal muscles, (e) the small intestine?

Reference

Rowett, H.G.Q. *Dissection Guides, III The Rat*, Murray, 1970.

Structure and action of the mammalian heart

The purpose of this practical work is to study the anatomy of the heart and to relate this to its job of pumping blood round the body. You will be given detailed instructions on how to proceed, but first draw up a plan of your own based on the following preliminary considerations.

Preliminary considerations

First recall your theoretical knowledge of the heart, using Figure 7.6 to help you. Notice the direction in which blood flows through the heart, as indicated by the arrows.

One of the most interesting questions about the heart is: how does it keep blood flowing in one direction and prevent it flowing backwards? In this the valves play a crucial part, and one aim of this practical is to see how the valves work.

With this in mind, draw up a detailed plan of how you might investigate the heart. Then read through the following procedure and see to what extent your plan coincides with the instructions given here.

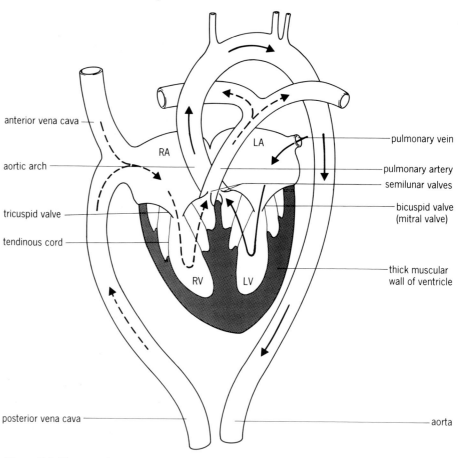

Figure 7.6 Diagram of a generalised mammalian heart, ventral (front) view. RA, right atrium; LA, left atrium; RV, right ventricle; LV, left ventricle. Deoxygenated blood, broken arrows; oxygenated blood, solid arrows.

Procedure

You will be provided with the heart of a sheep or pig.

1 Distinguish between the ventral (front) and dorsal (back) sides of the heart. The ventral side is the more rounded (convex) side, and the thick walled arteries arise from this side. The veins open into the heart on the more concave dorsal side.
2 Identify the parts of the heart shown in Figure 7.7. Observe the **coronary vessels** ramifying over the surface of the heart. Can you distinguish between the main coronary artery and coronary vein? What are their functions? Observe the pattern of their branching.
3 Attach a rubber tube to a water tap and insert the other end into the anterior vena cava. Clamp the posterior vena cava. Run water into the anterior vena cava and

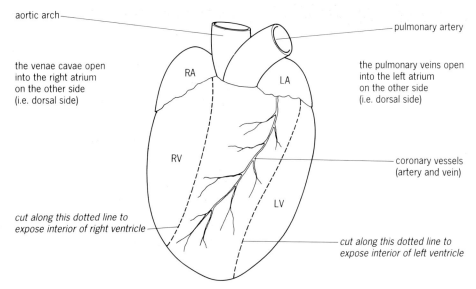

Figure 7.7 Ventral aspect of the mammalian heart showing the attachment of the aorta and pulmonary artery to the ventricles. The veins are on the other side. RA, right atrium; LA, left atrium; RV, right ventricle; LV, left ventricle.

note its flow through the heart. From which blood vessel does the water emerge? This is the pulmonary artery. Now run water into the pulmonary vein and note the vessel from which it emerges. This is the aorta.

4 Expose the interior of the left and right ventricles by making two longitudinal cuts on the ventral side of the heart along the course of the broken lines in Figure 7.7. Notice how thick the walls of the ventricles are. Significance?

5 Peer into the right ventricle. Notice the valve between the atrium and ventricle. It consists of three flaps, for which reason it is called the **tricuspid valve**. Examine the entrance to the pulmonary artery and notice that it is guarded by semilunar valves. Why are they described as *semilunar*?

6 Now peer into the left ventricle. In this case the valve between the atrium and ventricle consists of two flaps, for which reason it is called the **bicuspid valve**. It is also called the **mitral valve** because of its resemblance to a bishop's mitre. To help his students remember which side of the heart has the mitral valve, T.H. Huxley (a well known agnostic) used to say: 'The mitre's on the left because bishops are never right'!

7 Notice the semilunar valves guarding the entrance to the aorta. They are similar to the valves at the entrance to the pulmonary artery on the other side of the heart.

8 Observe the **tendinous cords** by which the flaps of the bicuspid and tricuspid valves are attached to the walls of the ventricles. What sort of tissue do you think they are made of?

9 Turn the heart the other way up and run water into the ventricles through the slits that you have cut. What happens to the bicuspid and tricuspid valves? What is the function of these valves, and what part do the tendinous cords play?

10 Now turn the heart back the way it was. Run water into the cut ends of the pulmonary artery and aorta and notice the action of the semilunar valves. What is the function of these valves? They are also called *pocket valves* – why?

11 Cut into the atria and examine the bicuspid and tricuspid valves from above. Notice the opening of the coronary vein on the left hand side of the right atrium (the right hand side as you view it from the ventral side).

12 Cut into the pulmonary artery and/or aorta and examine the semilunar valves from above. Notice the opening into the coronary artery from the aorta just above the semilunar valves.

13 Examine the openings of the venae cavae and pulmonary veins into their respective atria. Are there any valves guarding these openings? If there are, what do they achieve? If there are not, how does the heart manage without them?

14 Finally notice the relative sizes of the four chambers of the heart and the relative thickness of their walls. Which is the largest chamber, and which one has the thickest wall? Explain the reasons for any differences observed.

For consideration

1 In what ways might the valves of the heart show malfunctions, and what would the consequences be?
2 What would be the result of a blockage in the coronary artery or one of its branches? How might such a block arise?
3 Suggest a *functional* reason why the tricuspid valve has three flaps but the bicuspid valve has only two.
4 Looking back over this practical, how might the instructions given above be improved?

Reference

Rouan, C. The heart – a different approach, *Journal of Biological Education*, Vol. 15, No. 3, 1981.
Sheffield Bioscience Physiology Programs include a computer simulation of experiments performed on the heart of a pithed frog. Sheffield Bioscience Programs, 11 Robinson Drive, Harrogate, North Yorkshire HG2 9DN, UK.

7.7 INVESTIGATION

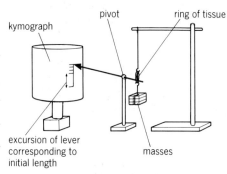

Figure 7.8 Technique for recording and measuring changes in length of a ring of tissue with increasing load. The lever amplifies the changes in length which can be recorded by manually rotating the kymograph.

Properties and structure of blood vessels

Pumped by the heart, blood is propelled round the body in tubular **blood vessels**. The blood vessels include **arteries** and **veins**. The arteries carry blood from the heart to the tissues, and the veins carry the blood back to the heart. Knowing their functions, can you *predict* the physical properties of the walls of the arteries and veins, and the kinds of tissues which each is likely to possess? The purpose of this investigation is to test your predictions.

Guidance
Properties of the vessels

You will be provided with a short length of an artery and a vein, each in the form of a ring. Using the apparatus provided, compare the elastic properties of the artery and vein rings. Figure 7.8 shows one way of carrying out the experiment, but you may be able to devise a better way. Make your investigation quantitative. The data you obtain should provide information on the stretchability of the artery and vein and their ability to return to their original length after being stretched.

Consider carefully how to express your results. For example, should you express a change in length of the artery or vein in absolute terms or as a percentage of the initial length?

Structure of the vessels

From the results of your experiment on the artery and vein, try to predict the kinds of tissues which each is likely to possess in its wall.

After you have made your predictions, examine a transverse section of an artery and vein under the microscope. How do they differ in the thickness of their walls and the tissues in the walls? Both contain elastic fibres, collagen fibres and smooth muscle but these three types of tissue differ in their relative amounts and distribution.

Try to relate differences in the structure of the artery and vein to their elastic properties.

For consideration

1 How do the elastic properties and microscopic structure of the artery and vein relate to the stresses and strains which these vessels are likely to experience in life?
2 Find out as much as you can about varicose veins. Can you relate this condition to the structure and properties of veins?
3 In an experiment masses were hung on blood vessel rings until they broke. Here are the results for three specific vessels: dorsal aorta 5000 g, pulmonary artery 3500 g, vena cava 800 g. Comment.
4 Why do veins not transmit a pulse?

Reference

For the microscopic structure of arteries and veins see Freeman, W.H. and Bracegirdle, B. *An Advanced Atlas of Histology*, Heinemann, 1976.

REQUIREMENTS

Kymograph
Stands and clamps ×2
Recording lever
Cotton thread
Hooks ×2
Masses, 10 g
Ring of large artery
Ring of large vein

BOX 7.1 How to use a haemocytometer

Although the haemocytometer is designed for sampling blood cells, it can be used for sampling any cells that are uniformly distributed on the surface of the slide. For example, yeast cells can be sampled in this way (see page 36).

The haemocytometer consists of a special slide with a ruled area in the centre, together with a coverslip (Illustration).

The haemocytometer slide

Examine the slide under the low power of the microscope and locate the ruled area in the centre. The middle of the ruled area consists of a grid with an area of 1 mm², i.e. its sides are 1 mm long. We shall call this the Type A square. If you use the ×10 objective and ×10 eye piece, the Type A square should just about fill the field of view.

Notice that the Type A square is subdivided by triple lines into 25 Type B squares, each of which has an area 1/25 mm². Each Type B square is further subdivided by single lines into 16 Type C squares, each of which has an area of 1/400 mm².

Now observe the two deep grooves that cross the slide on either side of the grid. The surface of the slide between these two grooves is 0.1 mm lower than the rest of the slide on either side of the grooves. So when the coverslip is put on, its lower surface clears the ruled surface of the slide by 0.1 mm. The volume represented by the Type A square is therefore 0.1 mm³; the volume represented by a Type B square is 0.004 mm³; and the volume represented by a Type C square is 0.00025 mm³.

To do a blood count you place a sample of diluted blood under the coverslip. You then count the cells in, say, 96 Type C squares and work out the average. Knowing the volume represented by a type C square, and the degree to which the blood has been diluted, you can calculate the number of cells per mm³.

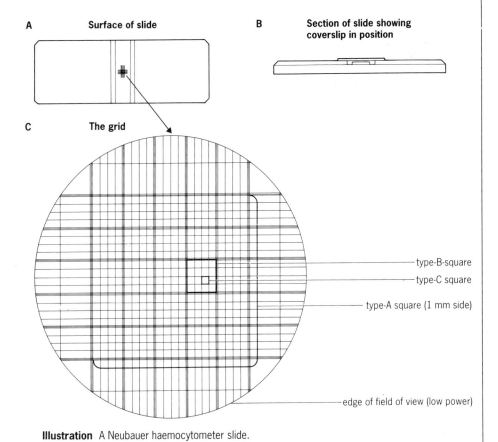

A   Surface of slide

B   Section of slide showing coverslip in position

C   The grid

— type-B-square
— type-C square
— type-A square (1 mm side)
— edge of field of view (low power)

Illustration A Neubauer haemocytometer slide.

Diluting the blood

If you looked at normal undiluted blood on a haemocytometer slide, the red blood cells would be far too close together for you to be able to count them satisfactorily. So the blood has to be diluted. A known volume of blood is mixed with a known volume of isotonic sodium chloride solution (saline), and a drop of the mixture is then pipetted onto the haemocytometer slide.

The blood is diluted either by mixing small samples of the blood and saline in a special pipette supplied with the haemocytometer, or by measuring out samples of the blood and saline with standard pipettes and mixing them in a beaker.

In the practical exercise on blood counting (page 106), the blood has been diluted for you.

Cleaning the haemocytometer slide and coverslip

The haemocytometer slide is a delicate piece of equipment. Be careful not to scratch it. Ensure that both the slide and coverslip are cleaned after use. Wash them with distilled water followed by propanone; when the propanone has evaporated, rub them with lens paper.

REQUIREMENTS
Microscope
Haemocytometer (slide and coverslip)
Lens paper
Distilled water
Propanone (acetone)

Harmful
Propanone

Highly flammable
Propanone

7.8 PRACTICAL EXERCISE

Effect of fitness on the pulse rate

Your **pulse rate** tells you the number of times your heart beats per minute, that is the **cardiac frequency**. The purpose of this practical is to measure your pulse rate under different conditions and, from this, assess your fitness.

Work singly or in pairs. If you work in a pair, one of you should act as the subject, the other as the experimenter.

How to measure the pulse rate

You can feel the pulse by placing a finger immediately over the radial artery on the lateral side of the wrist (Figure 7.9). Practise taking the pulse rate by counting the number of throbs in a one minute period.

To measure changes in the pulse rate continuously over a short period, count the number of pulses every ten seconds and convert to pulses per minute.

As an alternative to feeling the pulse, a **pulse monitor** or **sensor** may be used. If the output of a pulse sensor is fed into a computer, a graph can be obtained to show variations in the pulse rate in different conditions.

Procedure

We shall use a modified version of the **Harvard Step Test** which involves finding the effect of posture and exercise on the pulse rate.

Effect of posture

1 Lie down quietly for five minutes, then measure the pulse rate.
2 Stand up for a further three minutes, then measure the pulse rate again.
3 Calculate the increase in the pulse rate on standing.

Effect of exercise

1 Engage in a standard bout of exercise by stepping onto a stool 45 cm high and then down again, once every three seconds. Do this five times, thus taking 15 seconds in all.
2 Immediately after the exercise measure the pulse rate at ten second intervals until it returns to the normal standing rate. Record how long this takes.
3 Calculate the increase in the pulse rate immediately after the exercise compared with the standing rate.

Assessing fitness

Convert your pulse rates into scores, using the following tables.

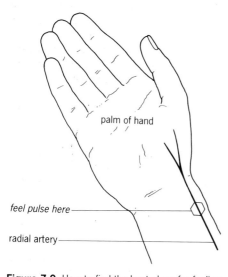

palm of hand

feel pulse here

radial artery

Figure 7.9 How to find the best place for feeling the pulse.

A Pulse rate lying down ('reclining pulse')

Rate	Points
50–60	3
61–70	3
71–80	2
81–90	1

B Pulse rate standing up ('standing pulse')

Rate	Points
60–70	3
71–80	3
81–90	2
91–100	1
101–110	1

C Increase in pulse rate on standing

Reclining pulse rate (A)	Increase in pulse rate on standing		
	0–10 beats	11–18 beats	19–26 beats
50–60	3	3	2
61–70	3	2	1
71–80	3	2	0
81–90	2	1	–1

D Time taken for pulse to return to standing rate after exercise

Seconds	Points
0–30	4
31–60	3
61–90	2
91–120	1

E Increase in pulse rate immediately after exercise compared with standing rate

Standing pulse rate (B)	Increase in pulse rate immediately after exercise		
	0–10 beats	11–20 beats	21–30 beats
60–70	3	3	2
71–80	3	2	1
81–90	3	2	1
91–100	2	1	0
101–110	1	0	–1

Calculate the total score:

Table	Points
A	
B	
C	
D	
E	
Total	

Assess fitness as follows:
Excellent   16 points
Good   12–15   "
Fair   8–11   "
Poor   less than 8 "

REQUIREMENTS

Stool, 45 cm high
Facilities for taking vigorous exercise, e.g. running track or field for performing 100 metre sprint.
Pulse monitor or sensor if available
Bicycle ergometer if available

Note: *Sheffield Bioscience Physiology Programs include a computer program of data on a range of subjects (male and female, trained and untrained) who have worked through a standard exercise regime on a bicycle ergometer. The data include oxygen consumption.*

Danger

Further experiments

1   Perform a bout of light exercise (e.g. running on the spot for 10 seconds), then measure the pulse rate at ten second intervals until it returns to the normal standing rate. Now perform a bout of vigorous exercise (e.g. 100 metre sprint), then measure the pulse rate at ten second intervals until it returns to the normal standing rate. Graph both sets of results on the same sheet of graph paper, putting pulse rate on the vertical axis and time on the horizontal axis. Compare the slopes of the curves. Draw conclusions . (As an alternative to running on the spot and sprinting, a bicycle ergometer capable of measuring the work done may be used.)

2   Investigate the effect of **forced breathing** on the pulse rate. In forced breathing you should sit comfortably and breathe as deeply and as frequently as possible with the minimum of muscular effort to the body as a whole. Suggest an explanation of your results .

Do not engage in forced breathing for more than 30 seconds and only do it when a teacher is present.

For consideration

1   Do you think the Harvard Step Test, as used in this practical exercise, is a valid way of assessing a person's fitness? Can you suggest a better method?

2   To what extent might your result have been influenced by your life style? For example, do you take regular exercise, smoke etc.?

Reference

Reiss, M.J. Monitoring human blood pressure and pulse rate, *Journal of Biological Education*, Vol. 23, No. 2, Summer 1989. Reviews various electronic devices currently available.

7.9 PRACTICAL EXERCISE

Structure of stems

The primary tissues of the stem are formed from the dividing cells at the apex of the growing shoot (see 12.6 Investigation, page 219). The three main functions of the stem are to lift the leaves and flowers into an elevated position, to convey water and mineral salts from roots to leaves and to transport synthesised food materials from the leaves to other parts of the plant. The stem needs strengthening tissues to support the aerial parts and to resist the sideways forces of the wind, and it requires conducting tissues for transport.

The aim of this practical exercise is to examine the structures of the various tissues inside stems, and to relate their positions to their functions.

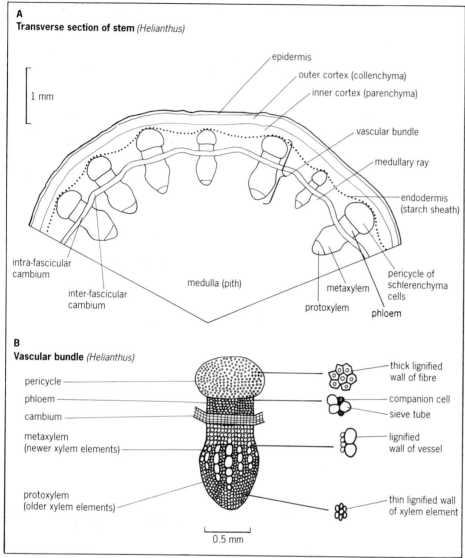

A
Transverse section of stem (*Helianthus*)

1 mm

epidermis
outer cortex (collenchyma)
inner cortex (parenchyma)
vascular bundle
medullary ray
endodermis (starch sheath)
pericycle of schlerenchyma cells
phloem
protoxylem
metaxylem
medulla (pith)
inter-fascicular cambium
intra-fascicular cambium

B
Vascular bundle (*Helianthus*)

pericycle
phloem
cambium
metaxylem (newer xylem elements)
protoxylem (older xylem elements)

thick lignified wall of fibre
companion cell
sieve tube
lignified wall of vessel
thin lignified wall of xylem element

0.5 mm

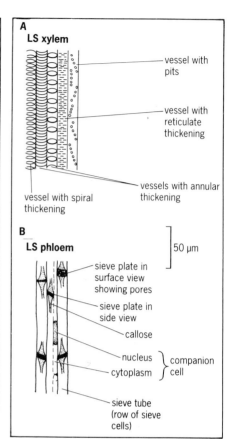

A
LS xylem

vessel with pits
vessel with reticulate thickening
vessels with annular thickening
vessel with spiral thickening

B
LS phloem

50 μm

sieve plate in surface view showing pores
sieve plate in side view
callose
nucleus
cytoplasm
companion cell
sieve tube (row of sieve cells)

Figure 7.11 Vascular tissues as seen in longitudinal section of a dicotyledonous stem, based on *Cucurbita*.

Figure 7.10 Structure of the stem of a dicotyledon, based mainly on the sunflower *Helianthus*. This particular plant is unusual in having an endodermis (starch sheath) in its stem.

Procedure

Harmful
Iodine
solution
Phloroglucinol

Corrosive Acidified
phloroglucinol
Schultz's solution

1   Investigate the internal structure of the stem of a dicotyledonous plant such as sunflower (Figure 7.10) by cutting thin cross and longitudinal sections and staining in acidified phoroglucinol, iodine solution or Schultz's solution (see Box 5.4, page 79).

2   Using Figure 7.10 to help you, look at prepared slides of cross and longitudinal sections of a dicotyledonous stem (*Helianthus* or *Cucurbita*) and identify the following tissues, arranged here roughly from outside to inside:

   • **Epidermis**: single layer of cuboidal cells covering the surface of the stem.
   • **Collenchyma**: see Practical 5.6; several layers of living thick-walled cells immediately beneath epidermis, cells vertically elongated and cellulose walls thickened at the corners; constitute outer part of cortex.
   • **Parenchyma**: see Practical 5.6; living thin-walled packing and storage cells, usually more or less circular in cross-section, making up the bulk of the cortex, pith and medullary rays.
   • **Sclerenchyma**: see Practical 5.6; dead, empty, thick-walled vertically-elongated fibres on the immediate outside of each vascular bundle, which together, in a large group, constitute the **pericycle.**
   • **Phloem**: vertically-elongated sieve tubes, companion cells and parenchyma on the immediate inside of the pericycle; sieve tube elements are living but lack

nuclei (Figure 7.11B) and have sieve plates with pores; each sieve tube element is associated with a smaller nucleate companion cell.

- **Cambium**: several layers of small living rectangular cells wedged between xylem and phloem in each vascular bundle; cambium tissue continuous (in *Helianthus*) between vascular bundles (**interfascicular cambium**). Cambium cells can divide to produce secondary tissues such as the annual rings of woody plant stems.
- **Xylem**: mainly composed of dead, vertically elongated, empty lignified tube-like cells (Figure 7.11A); small cells in inner parts of vascular bundle, formed first, known as **protoxylem**; larger cells nearer cambium, formed later, known as **metaxylem**.

3 Now examine macerated tissue (see 5.6 Practical Exercise) mounted in safranin and light green and see if you can distinguish between the various types of cells.

4 Cut, stain and mount transverse sections of the stem of a typical monotyledon such as maize, iris or lily. Alternatively, examine prepared slides. Under low power, note that the arrangement of vascular bundles differs from that in the dicotyledon. How would you explain the difference?

5 Examine under high power an individual vascular bundle of a monocotyledonous stem. Identify phloem and xylem, but cambium is absent.

For consideration

1 List the functions of each of the visible tissues in the cross-section.
2 What advantages might there be to a dicotyledon in having the vascular bundles arranged in a ring towards the outside of the stem, instead of in a central cylinder, as in the root?

Reference

Clegg, C.J. and Cox, G. *Anatomy and Activities of Plants*, John Murray, 1978.

REQUIREMENTS

Microscope
Microscope slides
Coverslips
Dish for sections
Fine brush
Safety razor blade
Iodine solution
Acidified phoroglucinol
Safranin
Light green
Schultz's solution
Dilute glycerol (25%, aqueous, for mounting)
Prepared microscope slides of TS and LS *Helianthus* or *Cucurbita* stems, and TS monocotyledon stem
Stems of sunflower (*Helianthus*) or marrow (*Cucurbita*), fresh or in 70% alcohol
Stem of monocotyledon e.g. maize, *Iris*
Macerated stem tissue (see 5.6 Practical Exercise on examination of plant tissues)

7.10 PRACTICAL EXERCISE

Structure of roots

Roots absorb water and mineral salts from the soil, and transport these to the stem. They expose to the soil a large surface area for absorption and contain xylem and phloem, vascular tissues which link up with those in the stem. Roots also store food reserves and anchor the plant in the soil. As you examine each tissue, ask yourself how it contributes to these functions.

The tissues are derived from cell divisions in the root apex (see 11.1 Investigation to find out how the mature tissues develop).

Procedure

External structure

1 Examine the radicle of a seedling such as mustard, cress or pea. Notice that the root hairs (functions?) are confined to a particular zone just behind the apex. The radicle develops into the taproot, or main root, from which lateral roots sprout. Are any lateral roots visible in your seedling?

2 Compare your seedling with that of a grass such as maize or wheat. Notice that instead of one main root, grasses produce several fibrous roots of equal importance.

3 Mount a radicle in iodine solution without crushing it. Examine it under the microscope. Note that each root hair is a single cell.

Internal structure

4 Cut cross-sections of a young primary root, such as broad bean or buttercup. Insert the root into a vertical slit in a piece of moistened elder pith or carrot tap root (see Box 11.1, page 203), and cut thin sections with a safety razor blade into a dish of water.

5 Using a brush, transfer two or three of the thinnest sections to a microscope slide. Add a drop of iodine solution and examine your sections under the microscope. To highlight the vascular tissue, stain with acidified phloroglucinol (eight drops phloroglucinol plus three drops of concentrated HCl) which stains lignin red.

Harmful
Iodine
solution

Irritant
Acidified
phloroglucinol

Danger
Razor
blade

Corrosive
Acidified
phloroglucinol
Hydrochloric
acid

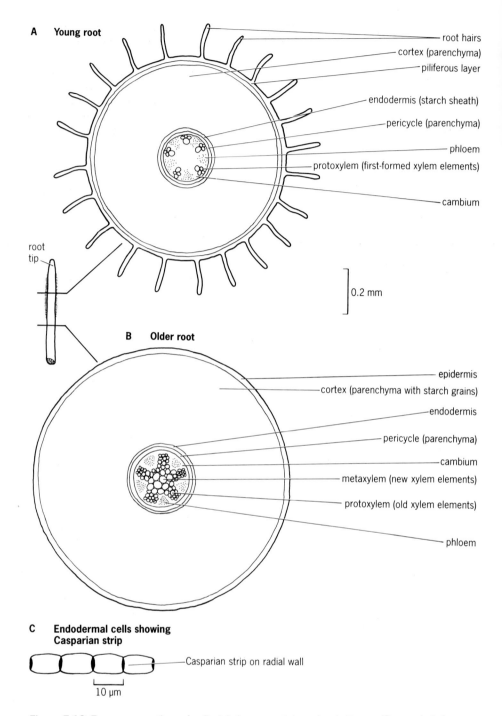

Figure 7.12 Transverse sections of a dicotyledonous root, based on buttercup (*Ranunculus*). **A** young part of root in the root hair zone just behind the tip. **B** older part of root, just behind the tip. **C** endodermal cells from above, showing suberised thickenings (Casparian strips) on the radial walls. In a monocotyledonous root (e.g. *Iris*) there are more (up to twenty) points on the xylem star.

Corrosive Hydrochloric acid

6 Using Figure 7.12 as a guide, and supplementing your observations with the use of prepared slides of transverse sections of roots, identify the following tissues:
- **Outer cell layer**: in the younger parts of the root this is the epidermis (in the root hair zone known as the **piliferous layer**). This is one cell wide and is sloughed off in the older part of the root. There the outer layer of cortex cells may become suberised (corky), constituting the **exodermis**.
- **Cortex**: extensive volume of parenchyma cells which present a massive area to soil water (which saturates their cell walls) for water and mineral ion uptake. Also stores starch; can you see the grains, which stain blue-black with iodine solution?

- **Endodermis**: single layer of prominent cuboidal cells (inner layer of cortex). Notice the suberised radial walls, containing the Casparian strips (function?) (Figure 7.12)
- **Pericycle**: indistinct layer of parenchyma cells immediately inside endodermis; may become lignified in older roots. Lateral roots originate here.
- **Vascular tissues**: within the endodermis and pericycle, the water-conducting xylem tissue is generally star-shaped in older roots, with sucrose-conducting phloem between the spokes of the star (Figure 7.12). Xylem (protoxylem) first forms at the points of the star (Figure 7.12). The xylem elements in the centre of the star (metaxylem) develop later.
- **Cambium**: small cells are wedged between xylem and phloem and divide in older roots to produce secondary xylem and phloem.

For consideration

1   List the ways in which each of the tissues in the root cross-section contributes to the uptake and transport of water taken up from the soil.
2   Why do roots have an endodermis?
3   Stems are generally stiff and erect, but roots are flexible. Explain this difference in terms of their internal structure.

7.11 PRACTICAL EXERCISE

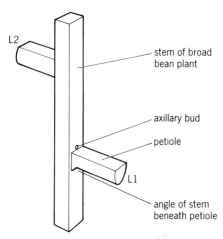

L2

stem of broad
bean plant

axillary bud

petiole

L1

angle of stem
beneath petiole

Figure 7.13 Diagram of part of a stem of broad bean (*Vicia faba*) showing the distance over which vascular bundles should be dissected.

Supply of water to the leaves of broad bean

The water which evaporates from the leaves of a plant is replaced by uptake from the vascular bundles of the **petioles** (leaf stalks). The vascular bundles in the stem must branch to provide bundles which run up the petioles of the leaves to the leaf blades. The pattern of bundles can be investigated by dissecting part of a leafy stem after its vascular bundles have taken up a stain.

Procedure

1   Fill a beaker with water. Select two healthy shoots of broad bean. Cut them off at soil level and immediately plunge the cut ends into the water.
2   Pour the eosin/Rose Bengal stain into two separate test-tubes, until each is filled to about 2 cm from the rim. Place them in a rack.
3   Cut the base of each stem under water, obliquely, about 5 cm from the base of the lowest expanded leaf. Immediately transfer each shoot to a test-tube containing stain and make sure that the cut surface is fully immersed.
4   Leave the shoots in the stain in a light and well-ventilated place for at least thirty minutes. The stain will stain the xylem tissue in the vascular bundles.
5   Remove one of the shoots from its test-tube. The other plant is an emergency reserve.
6   Cut a cross-section of the shoot near the base and examine with a lens the pattern of stained bundles. Immortalise the pattern in a labelled diagram.
7   Examine and draw in a similar manner a cross-section across a leaf petiole.
8   Using a fairly blunt scalpel or razor blade, begin to scrape gently on one of the angles of the stem just below a fully expanded leaf (Figure 7.13). The stained xylem of a major vascular bundle should soon become visible.
9   Now use further scraping and dissection to investigate the arrangement of the stained xylem. Begin your investigation about 1 cm below a fully expanded leaf (L1 in Figure 7.13) and complete it 1 cm above the top leaf (L2), which will be on the opposite side of the stem from L1. Aim to find the courses of all the stained bundles in the stem between the start and finish points. Pay particular attention to the junctions of bundles.
10   Follow vascular bundles as far as you can along the petiole and into the leaf.

For consideration

1   If water is continually taken up by the cells between the vascular bundles, why is the dye restricted to the vascular bundles in your sections?
2   Speculate on the internal factors which determine the pattern of vascular bundles in the leaf petiole and the stem during leaf and shoot development.

BOX 7.2 **Use of the microbalance**

A microbalance is a sensitive device which can be used to measure small changes in mass, such as when water is lost from a transpiring leaf. A home-made microbalance is shown in the Illustration.

Procedure
Determining the mass of a leaf

1   Suspend the leaf from the hook. Alter the shape of the plasticine, and, if necessary, the position of the fulcrum, until the balance beam is more or less horizontal.
2   Record its position by marking a line on the paper behind the tip of the knitting needle. Then *remove* the leaf, making sure that the plasticine at the other end does not change in shape or position.
3   Slide a wire rider up and down the beam until the tip of the beam reaches the same horizontal position as before. Then measure the distances a and b from the fulcrum (Illustration). By moments, $ax = by$, where
a = distance of leaf from the fulcrum,
b = distance of the rider from the fulcrum (sewing needle),
x = mass of the leaf (as yet unknown)
y = known mass of rider
Since $ax = by$, $x = by/a$. If the rider is measured in grams, the units of x will also be grams.

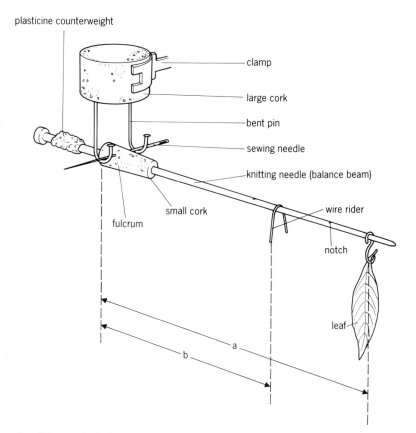

Illustration Using a microbalance to measure the mass of a leaf. Graph paper is clamped behind the apparatus. The microbalance is set up away from air currents, which can seriously upset its equilibrium.
(Based on Grace Monger (Ed.) *Revised Nuffield Biology, Practical Guide 3* , Longmans, 1985)

(continued)

Measuring water loss from a transpiring leaf

4 Attach the leaf to the tip of the horizontal balance beam and mark the position of the tip of the knitting needle on the graph paper behind. Allow the leaf to lose water whilst still suspended from the balance. The tip of the balance beam will rise.

5 After a known time, slide a rider up and down the notched beam until its tip returns to its previous position. Measure the distance (b) of the rider from the fulcrum at equilibrium. The mass of water lost = by/a, as explained above.

Measuring water loss from several leaves in the same experiment

6 Make the plasticine counterweight concave on top. Arrange it in such a position that when you add a leaf to the other end of the knitting needle, it can be counterbalanced exactly by an additional tiny ball of plasticine placed on top of the counterweight. When you hang the leaf up to dry, carefully save its appropriate plasticine ball.

7 Now place other leaves or leaf bundles on the microbalance, and save a balancing plasticine ball for each of them.

8 When you come to reweigh a particular leaf, you must place its appropriate plasticine ball on the counterweight.

REQUIREMENTS

Microbalance (Illustration)
Weighed riders of 10, 20, 50 mg
   made from fuse wire
Plasticine
Clamp stands, bosses and clamps
Graph paper
String
Ruler
Large sheets of cardboard to shelter
   the microbalance from draughts

7.12 INVESTIGATION

Comparing the rates of water loss from leaves

The rate at which leaves transpire depends both on the structural characteristics of the leaves and the environment to which they are exposed. One might expect the number and distribution of stomata, for example, to influence the evaporation rate. The aim of this investigation is to compare water loss from the leaves of different species, or from the upper and lower surfaces of leaves, and relate it to stomatal frequency.

Guidance

Water loss can be measured by weighing groups of detached leaves at intervals. Bundles of leaves can be strung together with thread and hung between readings from 'washing lines' consisting of string between clamp stands. They can be treated in different ways. For example, some bundles can be subjected to turbulent air from a fan, hair dryer or convector heater. Others can have their upper or lower surfaces covered with a thin layer of vaseline. Weigh each bundle at intervals and plot water loss on a graph.

Water loss from individual leaves is best compared with a microbalance (see Box 7.2) or cobalt paper. Anhydrous cobalt paper is blue, but in the hydrated state it is pink. Attach strips of anhydrous cobalt chloride or cobalt thiocyanate paper to both surfaces

---

REQUIREMENTS

Clamp stands
String
Cotton thread
Fuse wire
Electrical top-pan balance
Microbalance (Box 7.2) and accessories,
   such as weights and S-wire
Convector heater, fan or hairdryer
Microscope
Microscope slides
Coverslips
Elastic bands or paper clips
Pin
Forceps
Marking pen
Transparent ruler/scale, or micrometer
   eyepiece graticule and micrometer slide
Vaseline or silicone grease
Anhydrous cobalt chloride or cobalt
   thiocyanate paper
Polystyrene cement or nail varnish
Leaves, e.g. of cherry laurel (*Prunus
laurocerasus*) or *Rhododendron*

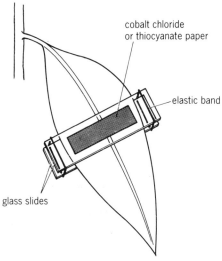

Figure 7.14 The attachment of cobalt chloride or thiocyanate paper to a leaf to compare the rate of water loss from its upper and lower surfaces.

of leaves (Figure 7.14) and compare the time taken for the paper to change colour on the upper and lower surfaces.

The results can be related to stomatal frequency as follows. Place a drop of polystyrene cement or nail varnish on the surface of a leaf and spread it out with a pin. When dry, peel it off with forceps, place it on a microscope slide under a drop of water, add a coverslip and count the numbers of stomata in the field of view. Do at least four counts at different places and take the average.

To express the results on a unit area basis, estimate the diameter of the field of view with either a transparent ruler or an eyepiece graticule with a micrometer slide (Box 5.2). To express the results on a unit leaf basis, trace the outlines of the leaves on graph paper and count squares.

For consideration

1 On the basis of your results, to what extent does stomatal frequency influence the rate of transpiration?
2 What other structural features of leaves, apart from the density of stomata, may influence the rate of transpiration?
3 In what sorts of environment would you expect to find (a) plants with a large number of stomata per unit leaf area and (b) plants with relatively few stomata?

Factors affecting the rate of transpiration

The aim of this investigation is to investigate the influence of various environmental factors on transpiration. This can be determined experimentally with a cut shoot in a potometer (Box 7.3)

Procedure

Attempt some or all of the following investigations:
1 Place the plant in a current of air created by, e.g. an electric fan – does a hot or a cold current make any difference?
2 Put the plant in a humid environment, e.g. by covering the shoot with a large polythene bag. Whether the bag is black or transparent may make a difference (why, in terms of stomata?).
3 Raise the temperature (measure it!) by putting the plant close to a heat source such as a radiator.
4 Smear the upper surfaces of the leaves with vaseline or silicone grease. Measure the rate of water uptake. Then compare the effect of smearing the lower surfaces too.

For consideration

1 What effect might the removal of the roots have had on the flow of water through the plant?
2 How and why might the rate of water uptake be affected by (i) wetting the leaves whilst attaching the shoot to the apparatus and (ii) allowing the end of the stem to be exposed to the air for a long time before attaching it to the potometer?
3 Under what circumstances might the rate of water uptake differ from the rate of water loss?

Rate of translocation of sucrose in a stolon of potato

The products of photosynthesis are transported away from the leaves to the rest of the plant in the phloem sieve tubes. In a potato plant (*Solanum tuberosum*), much of the sucrose is transported along **stolons**, narrow tube-like underground outgrowths from the base of the main stem, and is stored as starch in tubers ('potatoes') at the ends. Since all the dry matter in a tuber has entered through its stolon, you can estimate the rate of phloem transport if you make a few assumptions.

In particular, you need to know (i) the volume of sucrose solution which enters the tuber in a given period of time and (ii) the cross-sectional area occupied by sieve tubes in the stolon. Since volume = length x area, length = volume/area. To calculate the length of phloem sieve tube which empties per hour, divide the volume of sucrose

Table 7.1 Some measured rates of phloem transport in plant organs. The values in the table are figures calculated on the basis that the solutes in the sieve tubes make up to two per cent of the mass of the translocated solution. (Adapted from M.J. Canny, *Biological Reviews*, Vol. 35, 1960.)

Plant and organ	Trans-location rate (cm h^{-1})	Experimenters
Potato tuber stem	225	Dixon & Ball
Potato tuber stem	105	Crafts
Yam tuber stem	220	Mason & Lewin
Bean petiole (*Phaseolus*)	28	Birch-Hirschfield

Danger
Razor blade

Corrosive
Hydrochloric
acid
phloroglucinol

Harmful
phloroglucinol

solution which enters the tuber per hour by the cross-sectional area through which it has travelled. This is the *rate* at which sucrose solution is translocated in the stolon.

Guidance

To estimate the *volume of sucrose* which enters the tuber each hour you need to know the fresh mass of a clean potato, which has probably taken thirty days to form. You can assume that eighty per cent of its mass is water and the rest is derived from sucrose transported into it down the stolon (how could you determine the dry mass of the potato more accurately?). This will allow you to calculate the *mass* of sucrose entering the tuber each hour. You may wish to increase this figure by 25 % to allow for the sucrose which has been used in cellular respiration to keep the potato cells alive.

If you imagine that the sieve tube contents are a 2% sucrose solution, you can calculate the volume of sucrose solution which must have passed down to the tuber each hour.

To determine the *cross-sectional area occupied by sieve tubes* in the stolon, cut several thin cross-sections of a stolon (see Box 11.1, page 203) and stain with acidified phloroglucinol. Examine under a microscope with an eyepiece graticule which has been calibrated with a stage micrometer (see Box 5.2, page 71), and estimate the cross-sectional area of the phloem in a single vascular bundle (see Figure 7.9, page 114) for the structure of a stem). Assume that a fifth of this area consists of the conducting area of the sieve tube elements. Multiply by the number of vascular bundles in the cross-section to obtain the total cross-sectional area of the sieve tubes.

Divide the volume of sucrose by the cross-sectional area of the sieve tubes to estimate the rate of translocation (be careful with your units!).

For consideration

1   Compare your estimate of the rate of translocation with those in Table 7.1. If it is not within the same range, evaluate the accuracy of each of the many assumptions suggested above, alter the figures accordingly and recalculate the result.

2   Outline the various factors which might determine the rate at which a tuber fills up with starch, and its ultimate size.

BOX 7.3   **Use of the potometer**

A potometer is a device for measuring the rate of water uptake by an isolated leafy shoot. The water in the xylem elements in the shoot is continuous with the water filling a capillary tube attached to its cut end. The rate at which a bubble of air moves along the capillary indicates the rate of water uptake.

The major influence on the rate at which water is taken up by a detached shoot is the rate at which water evaporates into the atmosphere from the leaves and stem in **transpiration**. You can alter the conditions around the leaves and assess their influence on water uptake.

Look at the three different patterns of potometer illustrated in the Illustration. It is important, whilst setting up the apparatus, to minimise contact between the air and the cut end of the stem, to exclude air bubbles and to seal potentially leaky joints with vaseline grease.

Setting up the potometer

Using secateurs, cut a leafy shoot of, for example, holly or sycamore, and plunge its base into a bowl, bucket or beaker of water straight away to prevent air bubbles from being trapped in the xylem. Bear in mind when you select the shoot that the base of the shoot will have to fit snugly into the rubber tubing or stopper of the potometer, and that shoots with few leaves often yield inadequate results.

In the laboratory, rapidly transfer your shoot to a large sink or bowl of water so that its stem base (but not any leaves) are immersed. Using a razor blade (secateurs might crush the xylem), cut off the bottom centimetre of the stem obliquely *under water*.

Danger
Razor blade

(continued)

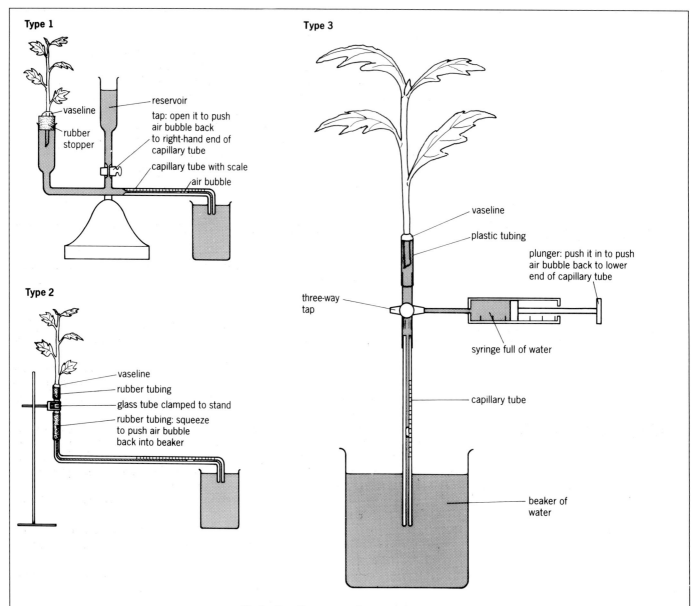

Type 1

vaseline

rubber stopper

reservoir

tap: open it to push air bubble back to right-hand end of capillary tube

capillary tube with scale

air bubble

Type 2

vaseline

rubber tubing

glass tube clamped to stand

rubber tubing: squeeze to push air bubble back into beaker

Type 3

vaseline

plastic tubing

plunger: push it in to push air bubble back to lower end of capillary tube

three-way tap

syringe full of water

capillary tube

beaker of water

Illustration Three types of potometer.

Immerse the potometer in the water and move it around to remove all the air bubbles. Carefully, under water, insert the cut end of the stalk into the rubber tubing or bung, keeping the leaves out of the water as much as possible. Make sure that any reservoir taps are closed before you remove the apparatus. As you take it out of the water, grease the joint between the stem and the potometer.

Set up the apparatus with the end of the capillary tube in a beaker of water. Check it for leaks and expel any air bubbles. Set up a millimetre scale along the capillary tube.

Using the potometer

Perform a trial run with the plant in normal room conditions. Remove the capillary tube from the beaker for a few seconds to allow a bubble of air to enter it. Measure the distance moved by the air bubble in a certain interval of time.

Return the bubble to its original position in the capillary tube, as indicated in the Illustration. Take at least three readings with the plant in each experimental condition and average the results. Allow the plant three minutes to settle down in a new condition before you begin to take readings.

(continued)

Calculation of results

Your initial measurements will be in terms of distance moved by the air bubble in a certain time interval, e.g. in mm per minute. You can convert these results to the volume of water taken up per unit time (e.g. mm^3 per minute) if you can estimate the radius, r, of the capillary tubing (volume = $\pi r^2 h$ where h is the distance travelled by the bubble and π = 3.142).

The best way to compare water loss in different shoots (e.g. of different species) is on the basis of unit leaf area. After the experiment, remove the leaves and lay them on squared paper. Draw outlines of the leaves and count squares to determine their area. Then you can express water loss in terms of volume per unit area per unit time (e.g. mm^3 per m^2 per hour).

7.15 PRACTICAL EXERCISE

CAUTION

In the interests of hygiene wear a laboratory coat while you are dissecting, and wash your hands thoroughly afterwards. Wear eye protection when dissecting tissue such as bone or cartilage.

Dissection of the gaseous exchange system of the rat

The purpose of this dissection is to investigate the pathway by which air passes into and out of the lungs. This pathway, an essential part of the **gaseous exchange system**, can be seen by dissecting a rat.

Procedure

1   If it has not already been done, deflect the skin in the thoracic and neck regions of the rat and pin it back as explained in 6.3 Practical Exercise, page 89. The specimen should look like Figure 7.15.
2   Open up the thorax by cutting along the dotted lines shown in Figure 7.15. Tie a thread round the xiphoid cartilage and pull it back so as to pull the **diaphragm** down (Figure 7.16). Note the **muscles of the diaphragm** and the **intercostal muscles** between the ribs.
3   Remove the thymus gland from the surface of the heart. Be careful not to damage the heart and blood vessels for you may want to explore them in a future dissection (page 107). Note the **phrenic nerve** which innervates the diaphragm.
4   With a scalpel cut along the centre of the neck muscles (arrow 1 in Figure 7.16). Deflect the muscles so as to see the **trachea** underneath.
5   Cut along the angle of the jaws on both sides of the head (arrow 2 in Figure 7.16).
6   Grasp the tongue with forceps and cut along the sides of the **pharynx** as far back as the **glottis**. This is the point where the breathing tract crosses the alimentary canal.
7   Pull back the tongue and floor of the pharynx and notice the **epiglottis** guarding the glottis (Figure 7.17). Insert a seeker into the glottis and confirm that it enters the **larynx** ('voice box') and trachea.
8   Under the trachea, as you look at your dissection, is the **oesophagus**. Insert a seeker into the entrance to the oesophagus. Wiggle the probe from side to side and notice that it distends the wall of the oesophagus.

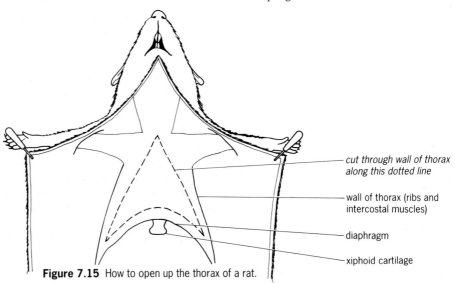

cut through wall of thorax along this dotted line

wall of thorax (ribs and intercostal muscles)

diaphragm

xiphoid cartilage

Figure 7.15 How to open up the thorax of a rat.

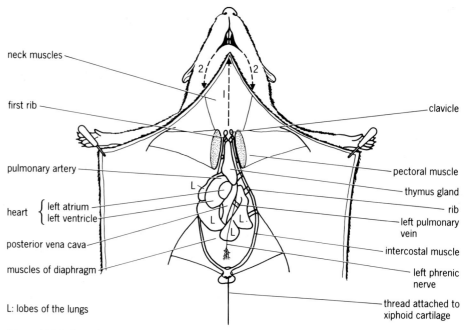

Figure 7.16 Stage in the dissection of the breathing apparatus of the rat.

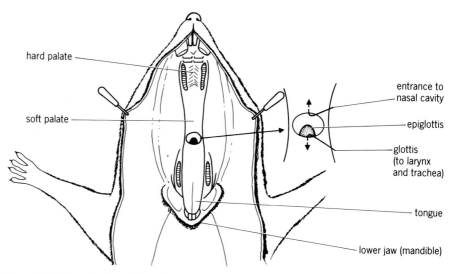

Figure 7.17 The glottis and related structures of the rat.

9 Now identify the soft palate. Beneath this, as you look at your dissection, is the **nasal cavity**. Insert a flexible bristle into the nasal cavity from the glottis and push it upwards. It should come out of one of the **nostrils**.

10 Insert the tip of an air-filled teat pipette into the glottis so that it points down the trachea. Squeeze the rubber bulb. This should have the effect of inflating the **lungs**.

11 Follow the trachea down to the thorax. It passes under the heart, as you look at your dissection, and divides into a pair of **bronchi**, one to each lung. Seeing the connection between the bronchi and the lungs necessitates removing the heart and major blood vessels. Don't do this now if you will be using this rat for dissecting the circulatory system later (Practical Exercise 7.5, page 107).

For consideration

1 Draw a diagram, *based on your dissection*, showing in side view how the breathing tract crosses the alimentary canal in the throat.

2 What are the possible advantages and disadvantages of the fact that the breathing tract crosses the alimentary canal in the throat?

REQUIREMENTS

Dissecting instruments
Dissecting board and pins
Teat pipette
Thread
Flexible bristle
Rat for dissection
Eye protection

3   Trace the path taken by a molecule of oxygen from the air just outside a person's nose to the lungs.

Reference

Rowett, H.G.Q. *Dissection Guides, III The Rat*, John Murray, 1951.

7.16 PRACTICAL EXERCISE

Microscopic structure of the mammalian gaseous exchange system

Functionally the gaseous exchange system consists of two components:
* The surface where gaseous exchange takes place, the **gaseous exchange surface**.
* The pathway through which air is moved to and from the gaseous exchange surface, the **breathing tract**.

In its microscopic structure the **gaseous exchange surface** would be expected to show an intimate relationship between the inspired air and the bloodstream, while the breathing tract should keep the tubes permanently open and prevent anything other than air reaching the gaseous exchange surface. In this practical exercise we shall examine the **trachea** and the **lungs** under the microscope and see if these predictions are true.

Procedure

Trachea

The trachea is a permanently open tube which permits the unimpeded flow of clean air to and from the lungs.

1   Examine a transverse section of trachea under first low and then high power. Use Figure 7.18 to help you identify the various structures in the tracheal wall.
2   Look carefully at the **ciliated epithelium** lining the inner surface of the wall. The ciliated cells are interspersed with mucus-secreting **goblet cells**. What is the function of the cilia and mucus?
3   Look out for **mucous glands** in the submucosa immediately beneath the epithelium. If you are lucky your section may show a duct leading to the surface from one of the glands. (Why do you need to be 'lucky' to see this?)
4   Notice the incomplete ring of **cartilage** embedded in the centre of the wall. What is the function of the cartilage, and why is the ring incomplete?

REQUIREMENTS

Microscope
Oil immersion, if available
Eyepiece graticule and stage micrometer
Trachea, TS
Lung, section
Electron micrograph of alveolus and
  adjacent capillary

Note: *Excellent high magnification electron micrographs of alveoli and adjacent capillaries can be found in* An Atlas of Ultrastructure *by J.A.G. Rhodin (Saunders, 1963).*

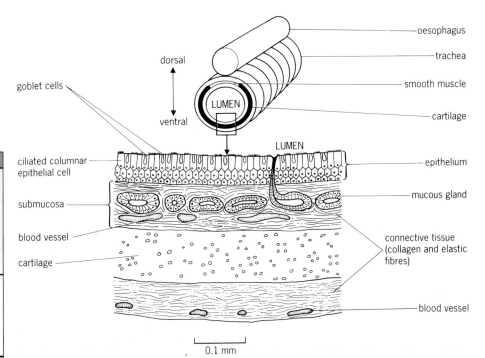

Figure 7.18 Diagram of a transverse section through the wall of the mammalian trachea.

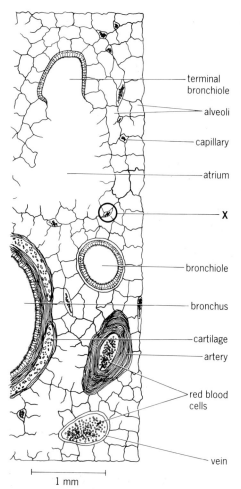

terminal
bronchiole

alveoli

capillary

atrium

X

bronchiole

bronchus

cartilage

artery

red blood
cells

vein

1 mm

Figure 7.19 Semi-diagrammatic drawing of a section of mammalian lung.

Lung

The lung consists of a tree-like system of branching tubes (bronchi and bronchioles) which lead, via cavities called **atria**, to numerous **alveoli**.

1   Examine a section of lung under low or medium power. Use Figure 7.19 to help you identify the structures visible in your section. Here are some tips to help you distinguish between the various structures:
   - **Bronchi** are like smaller versions of the trachea: their inner epithelium is ciliated and their walls contain mucous glands and cartilage.
   - **Bronchioles** are usually ciliated but they are much smaller than bronchi and lack mucous glands and cartilage.
   - **Atria** are relatively large cavities into which terminal bronchioles open; they have very thin walls of squamous epithelium (see page 000).
   - **Alveoli** are much smaller cavities leading from the atria; they too have very thin walls of squamous epithelium.
   - **Blood vessels** can be distinguished from other cavities by the fact that they contain numerous red blood cells. **Arteries** can be distinguished from veins by their thicker walls (see page 112). **Blood capillaries** are very small and are lined with a single layer of squamous epithelium.

2   Notice how numerous the alveoli are in your section. Can you work out their approximate frequency?

3   Using high power, with oil immersion if available, explore the intimate association between an alveolus and an adjacent blood capillary. In Figure 7.19 this would be the region marked X, for example.

4   Carefully observe the barrier between the blood in the capillary and the air in the alveolus? This is called the **alveolar barrier**. What exactly does this barrier consist of? Is it uniformly thick or does it vary in thickness? Explain.

5   If you have an eyepiece graticule and stage micrometer, estimate the minimum thickness of the alveolar barrier in micrometres (μm).

6   Examine an electron micrograph of the alveolar barrier. Try to relate the micrograph to what you have seen under the light microscope. Identify the capillary and alveolar epithelial cells abutting against each other.

7   On the electron micrograph measure the minimum thickness of the alveolar barrier and, from the known scale of the micrograph, calculate its thickness in micrometres.

For consideration

1   Did your two estimates of the minimum thickness of the alveolar barrier agree with each other? Suggest possible reasons for any discrepancy between them.

2   Review the ways in which the mammalian lung is adapted to perform its function of ensuring rapid gaseous exchange between inspired air and the blood.

Reference

Freeman, W.H. and Bracegirdle, B. *An Advanced Atlas of Histology*, Heinemann, 1976.

CAUTION

Experiments involving breathing in and out of a spirometer should be carried out only under close supervision by a teacher. Be sure that the mouthpiece is washed and sterilised thoroughly before use. Work in pairs, one of you acting as the subject, the other as experimenter.

BOX 7.4 **Recording human breathing movements**

The spirometer

A **spirometer** can be used for investigating a person's breathing movements and oxygen consumption.

A type of spirometer commonly used in schools and colleges is shown in the Illustration. It consists of a perspex 'lid', hinged to a tank of water. The lid encloses a chamber which is connected to the subject by a rubber mouthpiece at the end of a flexible breathing tube. As the subject breathes in and out, the lid goes up and down in time with his or her breathing. An inlet tube at the side can be used for filling the chamber with oxygen. A canister of soda lime in the course of the breathing tube ensures that all the carbon dioxide in the subject's expired air is removed before the subject breathes in again.

A two-way tap controls the flow of air into and out of the chamber. By rotating

(continued)

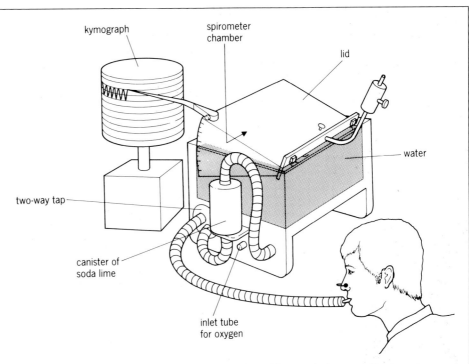

Ilustration A recording spirometer in use. The horizontal lines on the kymograph represent 250 cm³ divisions.

this tap in the appropriate direction the spirometer chamber can be opened to the atmosphere (or to a subject if the breathing tube is connected to the mouth) or closed.

The lid is counterbalanced by a moveable mass whose position should be set so that the lid falls very slowly when the spirometer chamber is open to the atmosphere. When the chamber is closed, the lid should remain stationary; if it falls there is a leak in the system.

Changes in the volume of oxygen in the spirometer chamber can be read off the scale attached to the side of the lid. Movements of the lid can be recorded by a pen writing on a kymograph drum or chart recorder. The recording paper should be calibrated for volume and time. To calibrate for volume make a series of horizontal lines on the paper separated by a distance corresponding to 250 cm³. To calibrate for time you need to know the speed at which the recording paper moves; ideally the speed should be approximately 20 mm per minute. Knowing the speed, you can make a series of vertical lines on the recording paper corresponding to one minute intervals.

Alternatively, the spirometer can be attached to an appropriate transducer and the data logged with a VELA, or a microcomputer programmed with appropriate software.

Using the spirometer
Practise using the spirometer as follows

1   With the two-way tap closed, connect a cylinder of oxygen to the inlet tube. Fill the spirometer chamber with oxygen, then adjust the position of the recording pen so that the writing point is near the top of the paper.
2   Subject: remove the rubber mouthpiece from the antiseptic and rinse it in clean water. Then insert it into your mouth. Clip your nose. With the two-way tap closed, you are connected to the outside atmosphere and should remain so until you have got accustomed to breathing through the mouthpiece.
3   When you are ready to proceed, the experimenter should open the two-way tap so that the subject is connected to the spirometer chamber and breathes in

(continued)

and out of it. Breathe as naturally and as regularly as possible. If necessary read a book or write out a sentence over and over again so as to take your mind off the procedure.

4   Record a few normal breaths then the experimenter closes the two-way tap so that the subject is disconnected from the spirometer and reconnected to the atmosphere.

5   Repeat steps 3 and 4 until you are familiar with the apparatus and can use it competently.

Stethograph

As an alternative to the spirometer, a **stethograph** can be used to record human breathing movements. It consists of a corrugated tube round the chest. The tube can be linked via a tambour or electronic manometer to a kymograph, chart recorder, oscilloscope or microcomputer for recording expansion and contraction of the chest. For details see Roger Lock and Colin Wood-Robinson, Equipment for recording human breathing, *Journal of Biological Education*, Vol. 17, No. 2, Summer 1983.

7.17 PRACTICAL EXERCISE

CAUTION

Always work in pairs, and in the presence of a teacher, when you use a spirometer.

Ventilation of the lungs in the human

How much of our lungs do we use when we breathe, in resting conditions and during exercise? We can answer this question by recording the breathing movements of a human subject with a **spirometer**. This kind of information is particularly relevant to athletes who wish to improve their performance and make best use of their breathing system.

Procedure

The spirometer is explained in Box 7.4, page 128. Study the box carefully and practise using the apparatus before you attempt the experiments outlined below. Work in pairs, one of you acting as subject, the other as experimenter.

Lung volumes at rest

1   Fill the spirometer with oxygen from a cylinder, then connect the subject to the spirometer. Don't forget the nose clip.

2   Record about six normal resting breaths followed by a maximum inspiration and then a maximum expiration. The recordings should look like those in Figure 7.20.

3   From the horizontal lines on the recording paper, determine the **tidal volume**, **inspiratory reserve volume**, **expiratory reserve volume** and **vital capacity**. What percentage of your vital capacity do you use in normal resting breathing?

4   Compare your vital capacity with that of other members of your class. What do you think determines a person's vital capacity?

The effect of exercise on breathing

1   Record the subject's normal resting breaths for one minute, then continue to record for a further three minutes while the subject takes vigorous exercise such as running on the spot or pedalling a stationary bicycle.

2   Compare the volume of air inspired in a single breath at the beginning and end of the bout of exercise. Express each volume as a percentage of the vital capacity. Do the breaths during exercise extend into the inspiratory reserve volume, the expiratory reserve volume, or both?

3   The rate of gaseous exchange may be expressed as the total volume of air inspired per minute. This is the **ventilation rate**. Work out, by whatever means you think fit, the ventilation rate for each minute from the beginning to the end of your set of recordings . Express the ventilation rates in dm^3 min^{-1}.

4   Plot the change in the ventilation rate as a graph with time on the horizontal axis and ventilation rate on the vertical axis.

5   Compare your graph and your recordings with those of other members of your class. How do they differ?

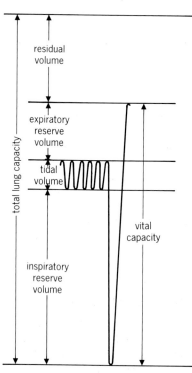

Figure 7.20 Spirometer recordings of the breathing movements of a typical human subject.

For consideration

1   A person may increase his or her ventilation rate by breathing faster and/or more deeply. How do members of your class differ in which of these two alternatives they use? Suggest possible explanations for any differences observed.

2   Why do you think the inspiratory reserve volume is so much greater than the expiratory reserve volume?

3   How might the residual volume of the lungs be measured? What is the significance of this part of the lungs?

7.18 INVESTIGATION

CAUTION

Always work in pairs, and in the presence of a teacher, when you use a spirometer.

Oxygen consumption and the human metabolic rate

A spirometer can be used to measure the volume of oxygen taken into the body in a given time, that is the **oxygen consumption**. From this the amount of energy used per unit time can be calculated. This is the **metabolic rate**. In this session you will investigate the relationship between the metabolic rate and exercise.

Guidance

Be sure you know how to use the spirometer before you start this investigation. Work in pairs, one of you acting as the subject, the other as experimenter.

How to find the metabolic rate

The subject's oxygen consumption can be found by getting the subject to breathe pure oxygen from a spirometer for a longish period (say five minutes) and then noting how far the lid of the spirometer has dropped in a given time. Obviously the canister of soda lime must be in position to absorb the carbon dioxide exhaled. Make sure the initial and final volumes are taken at the same point in the breathing cycle, for example at the end of an expiration.

If you know the subject's body mass you can express the oxygen consumption in dm^3 kg^{-1} h^{-1}.

It has been calculated that for every dm^3 of oxygen consumed by the human body, approximately 20.18 kJ of energy are transferred. This information enables you to express the subject's metabolic rate in kJ kg^{-1} h^{-1}.

Investigating the relationship between metabolic rate and exercise

First determine the metabolic rate with the subject at rest. Then determine the metabolic rate at regular intervals during the performance of a prolonged bout of exercise and at regular intervals during the recovery period afterwards. Continue until the metabolic rate returns to the resting level. Plot your results as a graph.

For consideration

1   How does the oxygen consumption during the exercise and recovery periods compare with the resting metabolic rate? Why should a high metabolic rate continue after muscular exertion has ceased?

2   To what extent does the subject's resting metabolic rate, as measured in this experiment, approximate to his or her *basal* metabolic rate?

3   The energy transferred by a mammal during respiration is more closely related to its surface area than to other parameters such as its body mass or height. Suggest a reason for this.

4   What do you suppose happens to an athlete's metabolic rate during and after the following track events: (a) 100 metres, (b) 10 000 metres? How could your suggestions be tested?

7.19 PRACTICAL EXERCISE

The composition of inhaled and exhaled air

One of the best ways of investigating the general nature of respiration is to compare the percentages of oxygen and carbon dioxide in inspired (i.e. atmospheric) and expired air. This can be done by means of **gas analysis**, which involves using the **J tube** described in Box 7.5, page 133. The experiment is even more interesting if we analyse samples of expired air before and after a bout of exercise. How would you *expect* them to differ, and why?

Eye protection
must be worn

Corrosive
Hydrochloric acid
Pyrogallol
Potassium hydroxide

Procedure

First be sure you are familiar with the J tube and how it works. Then proceed as follows:

1 Draw a sample of atmospheric air into the J tube. Draw water in first, then the air sample, then more water, as described in Box 7.5, page 133. Then analyse the air for carbon dioxide and oxygen.

2 Wearing eye protection, wash out the J tube with dilute hydrochloric acid, followed by water, before continuing further.

3 Collect a sample of expired air in a large test-tube by the method shown in Figure 7.21. Be sure the bent tube has been washed in disinfectant, then rinsed in clean water, before you put it to your mouth. The sample should come from as deep inside your lungs as possible; to ensure this, exhale through the bent tube but don't insert the tip into the test-tube until the end of your exhalation.

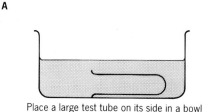 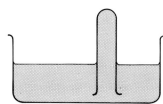

A

Place a large test tube on its side in a bowl of water, and allow it to fill up with water. The water should be at room temperature.

B

Raise the test tube into a vertical position in the bowl.

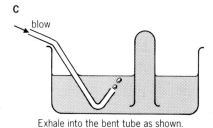

C blow

Exhale into the bent tube as shown.

D blow

Towards the end of the exhalation, insert the tip of the bent tube into the test tube and collect the last lot of expired air in the test tube.

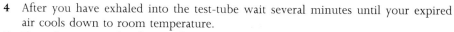

Figure 7.21 A method for collecting a sample of expired air in a test tube.

↑ pull

Figure 7.22 Drawing a sample of expired air into a J tube.

4 After you have exhaled into the test-tube wait several minutes until your expired air cools down to room temperature.

5 Now draw a sample of expired air into the J tube as shown in Figure 7.22. Draw water in first, then the air sample, then more water in the usual way. Then analyse the air for carbon dioxide and oxygen. Wash out the J tube afterwards.

6 Perform a bout of vigorous exercise, then collect a sample of expired air and analyse it as before. Be sure it cools down to room temperature before you start your analysis, and don't forget to wash out the J tube afterwards.

7 Make a table comparing the percentages of carbon dioxide and oxygen in inspired air, expired air at rest and expired air after exercise.

For consideration

1 You will have found it difficult to measure the percentage of carbon dioxide in atmospheric air. Why? How might the J tube method be improved so as to achieve a more accurate result?

2 What sources of error might there be in the way you measured the percentage of oxygen in this experiment? How could you minimise the error?

3 What other gases besides carbon dioxide and oxygen are present in the air we breathe? What is their biological significance, if any?

4 In what circumstances might the percentage of carbon dioxide in atmospheric air be higher than usual?

REQUIREMENTS

J tube (see Box 7.5, page 133)
Bent glass tube (see Figure 7.21)
Large test-tube
Bowl, large enough to accommodate large test tube laid horizontally
Safety goggles
Potassium hydroxide solution, concentrated
Pyrogallic acid (pyrogallol), concentrated
Hydrochloric acid, dilute
Antiseptic (Milton recommended, follow instructions on bottle)
Clean water

BOX 7.5 **Gas analysis**

In biological investigations it is sometimes necessary to find out how much oxygen and carbon dioxide are present in a sample of air. The principle behind **gas analysis** is as follows. A sample of air is drawn into a capillary tube and its volume noted. A reagent which absorbs carbon dioxide is then drawn into the tube, causing the sample of air to decrease in volume. The new volume is noted. Then a reagent which absorbs oxygen is drawn into the tube, causing the sample of air to decrease in volume once more. Again the new volume is noted. From the decrease in volume of the air when the carbon dioxide absorber and oxygen absorber are added, the percentages of carbon dioxide and oxygen in the air sample can be calculated.

Practical details

A type of gas analysis apparatus often used in colleges and schools is called a **J tube**. It consists of a bent capillary tube with a syringe at one end (see Illustration). The syringe is for drawing in the air and reagents. The volume of the air sample is expressed as the length of capillary tube which it occupies. To improve accuracy at least three samples of air should be analysed and the average taken. It is important that the air samples should be at constant temperature. To this end give each air sample time to come to room temperature before its volume is measured.

Technique for carrying out an analysis

The solutions to be used are corrosive; wear eye protection when handling them.

1 Assemble four small beakers containing the following:
   A Water; B Potassium hydroxide (for absorbing carbon dioxide);
   C Pyrogallol (for absorbing oxygen) (see footnote, page 134); D Dilute hydrochloric acid (for cleaning the J tube).

2 Push the plunger of the syringe to the far end of the barrel. Dip the open end of the J tube in the beaker of water, then pull the plunger until a column of water approximately 5 cm long has been drawn into the tube.

3 Remove the tip of the tube from the water, then draw in approximately 10 cm of air. Then draw in water again until the column of air occupies the straight part of the J tube, as shown in the illustration. Wait for at least one minute, and do not handle the straight part of the tube where the air is located (why?). Now measure the length of the air column with a ruler.

4 Expel all but about 1 cm of the water from the open end of the J tube (this forms a seal for the air column), then draw in concentrated potassium hydroxide. Keeping the tip of the tube in the hydroxide, carefully shuttle the potassium hydroxide backwards and forwards about six times so that the air sample comes into repeated contact with the glass lining of the tube which has been wetted with the hydroxide. The hydroxide will absorb carbon dioxide from the air sample. Wait for a further minute, then re-measure the length of the air column.

5 Now expel all but the last 5 cm or so of the hydroxide and draw in pyrogallol. Keeping the tip of the J tube in the pyrogallol, shuttle the pyrogallol backwards and forwards as before but *don't* expel the hydroxide. The pyrogallol will react with the potassium hydroxide still in the tube, forming potassium pyrogallate which then absorbs oxygen from the air sample. Wait a further minute, then measure the length of the air column again.

6 Wash out the J tube thoroughly, first with dilute hydrochloric acid, then with water.

7 Calculate the percentage of carbon dioxide and oxygen in the air sample:

$$\text{Percentage of } CO_2 = \frac{a - b}{a} \times 100 \qquad \text{Percentage of } O_2 = \frac{b - c}{a} \times 100$$

where
   a is the original length before potassium hydroxide was admitted
   b is the new length after potassium hydroxide was admitted
   c is the new length after pyrogallol was admitted

(continued)

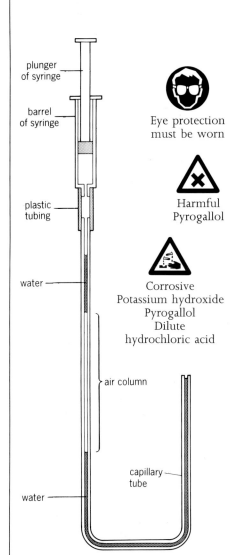

plunger of syringe

barrel of syringe

Eye protection must be worn

plastic tubing

Harmful Pyrogallol

water

Corrosive
Potassium hydroxide
Pyrogallol
Dilute hydrochloric acid

air column

capillary tube

water

Illustration J tube for gas analysis. A column of air has been drawn into the straight part of the tube. Commercial versions of this apparatus have a screw instead of a syringe for admitting air.

Footnote

It is conventional in gas analysis to use previously prepared potassium pyrogallate (alkaline pyrogallol) for absorbing oxygen. Potassium pyrogallate is unstable and must be made up immediately before the practical session by mixing equal quantities of pyrogallol (pyrogallic acid) and potassium hydroxide. The potassium pyrogallate thus formed must be covered immediately with liquid paraffin to prevent it taking up oxygen. When the experiment is performed, the end of the J tube has to be inserted through the liquid paraffin before the potassium pyrogallate is drawn up. This is messy and can be avoided by drawing up pyrogallol instead of potassium pyrogallate and allowing it to react with potassium hydroxide still in the J tube, as described in the instructions here.

7.20 INVESTIGATION

Gaseous exchange in insects

In insects gaseous exchange takes place by means of a system of tubes, the **tracheal system**, via which oxygen reaches all parts of the body and carbon dioxide is expelled. Air enters the tracheal system through openings in the cuticle, called **spiracles**, on either side of the thorax and abdomen. In this session you will investigate the structure and functioning of the tracheal system.

Guidance

This investigation involves a combination of dissection, microscopic examination and experimentation. It is best to use a large insect such as a locust or cockroach. You will be provided with a freshly killed specimen for dissection and removal of tissues for microscopic examination, and a live specimen for observations and experiments. Figure 7.23 shows how you can fix the insect in position for observation under a binocular microscope.

If you carry out an experiment on the insect make sure that you do not hurt it or subject it to undue stress. Discuss your plans with your teacher before you carry out any experiments.

Using the different approaches outlined above, try to answer the following questions:

1   The tracheal tubes are said to penetrate deep into the tissues. Is this true?
2   Do the tracheal tubes have a uniform diameter throughout their length, or do they get narrower towards their ends?
3   What keeps the tracheal tubes permanently open and prevents their walls collapsing?
4   We might predict that muscles would have a richer supply of tracheal tubes than other tissues. Can you find any evidence to support this prediction?
5   Is air pumped through the tracheal system by muscular action, or does it simply diffuse through? If there is a pumping mechanism, how does it appear to work?
6   Are the spiracles permanently open, or can they open and close?
7   Is there any evidence that the rate of gaseous exchange increases if the concentration of carbon dioxide in the air rises?
8   Do the spiracles permit water to evaporate from inside the body? If so, are the spiracles adapted in any way to prevent this?

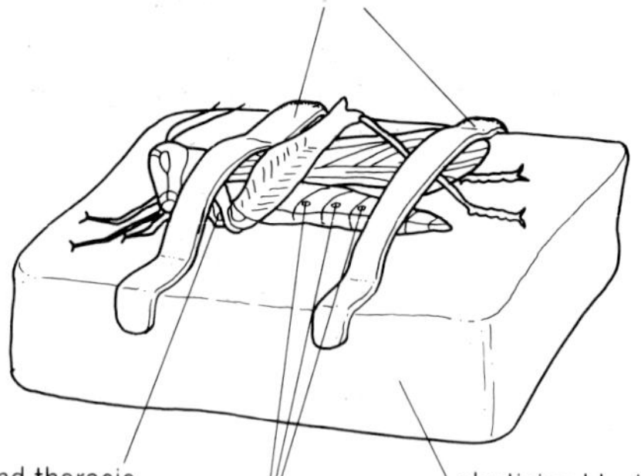

For consideration

1   Insects are generally rather small, and this is said to be due, at least partly, to their method of gaseous exchange. Why should their size be limited by their gaseous exchange system, and what other factors might determine their size?
2   In view of the fact that insects carry out gaseous exchange by means of the tracheal system, what predictions can you make regarding the structure and functions of their blood?

Reference
Clarke, W.M. and Richards, M.M. *The Locust as a Typical Insect*, John Murray, 1976.

Figure 7.23 A live locust fixed in position for viewing under a binocular microscope.

strips of plasticine or blu-tack

2nd thoracic spiracle

abdominal spiracles

plasticine block

REQUIREMENTS

Microscopes, monocular and binocular
Slides and coverslips
Plasticine and blu-tack
Dissecting instruments
Locust or cockroach, freshly killed for dissection
Locust or cockroach, live
Other items may be requested by individual students

PROJECTS

Before starting a project, discuss your intended procedure with your teacher.

1 Investigate the effect of posture and/or exercise on blood pressure. Blood pressure may be measured using a sphygmomanometer or digital blood pressure monitor. Quantify the exercise and graph your results, with exercise as a continuous variable.

2 Test the hypothesis that people's blood pressure and/or pulse rate increase when they tell lies. You could also investigate other mental factors that might increase the blood pressure and/or pulse rate, such as reading an exciting book or receiving a sudden fright. However, be sure that any volunteers you use are not subjected to undue stress.

3 Carry out a fitness test (e.g. the Harvard Step Test) on a wide range of volunteers and ask them to complete a questionnaire on their smoking habits, amount of sleep, exercise regime etc. Using appropriate statistical techniques (see Appendix), test the hypothesis that there is no relationship between fitness and any of these variables.

4 If you are keen on dissection, compare the circulatory systems of different vertebrates, e.g. fish, frog or toad, lizard, snake and bird. Concentrate on specific aspects, such as the way the aorta arises from the heart, whether or not structures other than the lungs receive blood from the pulmonary arteries, and the presence of portal veins other than the hepatic portal. (A portal vein is one which, instead of returning blood to the heart, sends it to another organ first.) *Any animals you plan to dissect must be obtained through your teacher.*

5 Is there a correlation between the mass of water lost from different species of flowering plants, and the stomatal frequency or distribution?

6 Compare the rate of water loss per unit leaf area from the leaves of a mesophyte (a species habitually found in habitats where the water supply is average) and a xerophyte (a species habitually growing where water is scarce).

7 Investigate the effect of hair points on the water relations of mosses. Hair points are prolongations of the midrib vein beyond the leaf blade in some species (e.g. *Tortula muralis, Bryum capillare*). Expose saturated clumps of mosses to dry environments created by silica gel in closed containers and plot decline in mass, first with intact leaves and then with hair-points removed with a razor blade (*care*).

8 When you bend stems, some bend but others snap. Investigate the possible reasons why stems behave in this way. Cut sections to correlate the presence and distribution of different types of mechanical and strengthening tissue with the properties of the stem.

9 Use a stethograph (see Box 7.4, page 128) to investigate the effect on a person's pattern of breathing of any or all of the following: talking, laughing, yawning, gasping, sighing, crying, sobbing, coughing and sneezing. From your recordings assess the relative importance of inspiration and expiration in these actions.

10 Test the hypothesis that during exercise fit people breathe more deeply and at a lower frequency than unfit people. Use a spirometer or stethograph, with kymograph, chart recorder or computer, for recording breathing movements, and, if available, a bicycle ergometer for taking measured amounts of exercise. In selecting volunteers you will need to consider what constitutes a 'fit' as contrasted with an 'unfit' person. You must also consider how to test your results statistically.

11 Investigate the composition of the expired air of people engaged in different types of muscular exertion, e.g. sprinting, long-distance running, walking etc. You will need to collect samples of expired air *during* the exercise period. If available use a Douglas bag. This is an expandable bag fitted with valves which enable you to inhale fresh air from outside but exhale into the bag. A short side tube allows samples of the expired air to be collected and analysed. Alternatively, devise your own way of collecting the air.

12 It has been suggested that, in the locust, air is drawn into the tracheal system through the first four pairs of spiracles and leaves via the remaining spiracles. Test this hypothesis experimentally. If it turns out to be true, suggest an hypothesis to explain the mechanism that ensures this unidirectional flow of air. Then make predictions from your hypothesis and gather as much information as you can to test the predictions.

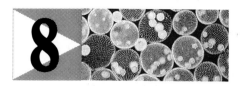

Control of the internal environment

8.1 INVESTIGATION

An artificial feedback system

The effectiveness of a homeostatic feedback process depends on three main things:
*   The sensitivity of the **detector (receptor)**
*   The speed with which the **corrective mechanism** comes into action
*   The time taken for the **effector** to respond.

In this investigation you will explore these aspects of homeostatic mechanisms in an artificial feedback system.

Guidance

The system is shown in Figure 8.1. The idea is to keep the temperature of the aluminium block as constant as possible at a predecided set point, say 60 °C. Proceed as follows:

With the power supply to the heating coil turned full on, switch on the heater until the set point temperature is reached, then switch it off. When the temperature falls below the set point switch the heater on again, and so on.

Once the system settles down into a regular pattern, record the temperature of the block at half-minute intervals. Plot the temperature of the block (vertical axis) against time (horizontal axis). By how much did the temperature deviate from the set point? Calculate the average deviation.

low voltage supply

variable control knob

thermometer

heating coil

aluminium block

Figure 8.1 A homeostatic feedback system for regulating the temperature of an aluminium block.

Reducing the fluctuations

You have probably found that the temperature fluctuated widely on either side of the set point. For example, when the temperature of the block reached the set point it overshot it. How could you reduce the overshoot?

One way would be to switch off the heater *before* the temperature of the block reaches the set point. Try doing this. Run some trials and determine exactly when the heater should be switched off so as to minimise the overshoot.

Now run the system continuously, switching the heater on or off at the appropriate moments, until a regular pattern is given. Then record the temperature of the block at half-minute intervals and plot the results. To what extent have the deviations been reduced? Express the reduction as a percentage.

Refining the system

An even better way of reducing the overshoot might be to gradually reduce the power supply as the temperature of the block approaches the set point. Run trials to test this idea, and plot the results as before.

Continue to refine the system in whatever ways you can think of until the fluctuations are reduced to a minimum and the temperature of the block is as regular as possible.

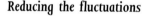

REQUIREMENTS

Aluminium block with heating coil and thermometer
Power supply, 12–16 V with variable control
Switch
Insulated wire
Stop-clock

For consideration

1   In the system which you have been investigating, what constitute the receptor, effector and corrective mechanism?
2   The type of feedback in this system is *negative* feedback. What does *negative* mean in this context? Under what circumstances might the system which you have been investigating show *positive* feedback?
3   Feedback systems can never keep anything absolutely constant. Explain this with reference to the aluminium block experiment.
4   Summarise the potential sources of delay in homeostatic feedback systems.

8.2 PRACTICAL EXERCISE

Microscopic structure of the pancreas

The pancreas has two distinct functions:

- It secretes digestive enzymes (which ones?) into the pancreatic ducts down which they flow to the duodenum. In this capacity the pancreas functions as a ducted **exocrine gland**.
- It secretes the hormones **insulin** and **glucagon** into the bloodstream. In this capacity the pancreas functions as a ductless **endocrine gland**.

The pancreas is both an exocrine and endocrine gland. Knowing this, can you make any predictions about its microscopic structure?

Procedure

1   Examine a transverse section of mammalian pancreas under low power. The bulk of it is made up of groups of enzyme-secreting cells called **acini** (singular: **acinus**). Here and there, amongst the acini, are **islets of Langerhans** which secrete the hormones. A typical section might include about six islets. Use Figure 8.2A to help you locate the acini and islets.

2   Go over to high power and examine an acinus in detail (Figure 8.2B). The term acinus can be applied to any exocrine gland; an acinus is simply a group of secretory cells associated with a branch of a duct, in this case the pancreatic duct. Do the acini in your section fit this description?

3   Now look at an islet of Langerhans in detail (Figure 8.2C). How does the arrangement of the cells differ from that of an acinus? Notice the intimate association between the islet cells and the capillaries. Why is this important?

4   Within the islet of Langerhans can you distinguish between the **beta cells** which secrete insulin and the **alpha cells** which secrete glucagon? How do these cells differ in their appearance and position within the islet?

5   Use an eyepiece graticule and stage micrometer to compare the sizes of an acinus and an islet of Langerhans.

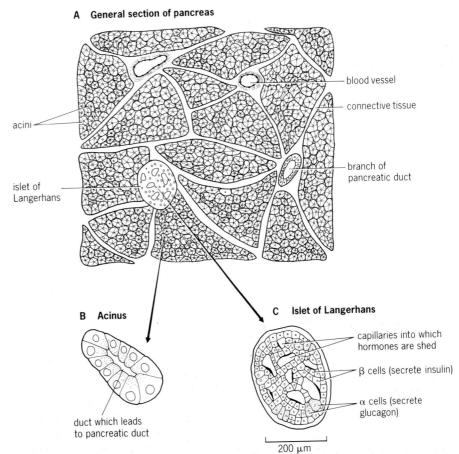

A   General section of pancreas

acini

islet of
Langerhans

blood vessel

connective tissue

branch of
pancreatic duct

B   Acinus

duct which leads
to pancreatic duct

C   Islet of Langerhans

capillaries into which
hormones are shed

β cells (secrete insulin)

α cells (secrete
glucagon)

200 μm

Figure 8.2 Microscopic structure of the pancreas.

REQUIREMENTS

Microscope
Eyepiece graticule and stage micrometer
Pancreas, TS

For consideration

1 Imagine you are a teacher and you wish to explain to your students how to find the islets of Langerhans in a section of the pancreas. Write precise instructions to guide the students.
2 How does the structure of the pancreas suit it for its functions?
3 If you were to examine a section through an islet of Langerhans in the transmission electron microscope, what special features might you expect to see?
4 What sort of experiments could have led scientists to conclude that insulin is secreted by the beta cells and glucagon by the alpha cells?

8.3 PRACTICAL EXERCISE

Microscopic structure of the liver

The liver has many functions. Here are two of the main ones:

- It secretes **bile** into the **bile duct** down which it flows, via a **gall bladder**, to the duodenum.
- It regulates the amounts of blood sugar, lipids and amino acids by removing them from the bloodstream or adding them to it, as appropriate.

Recall that the liver receives blood from two sources: oxygenated blood is taken to it via the **hepatic artery**, blood rich in food substances via the **hepatic portal vein** (see page 91). Blood is removed from the liver via the **hepatic vein**.

Knowing these facts about the liver, can you make any predictions about its microscopic structure?

Procedure

1 Examine a transverse section of mammalian liver under low power. It consists of numerous closely packed **lobules**, each approximately 1.0 mm in diameter. Locate the lobules and other structures shown in Figure 8.3A.

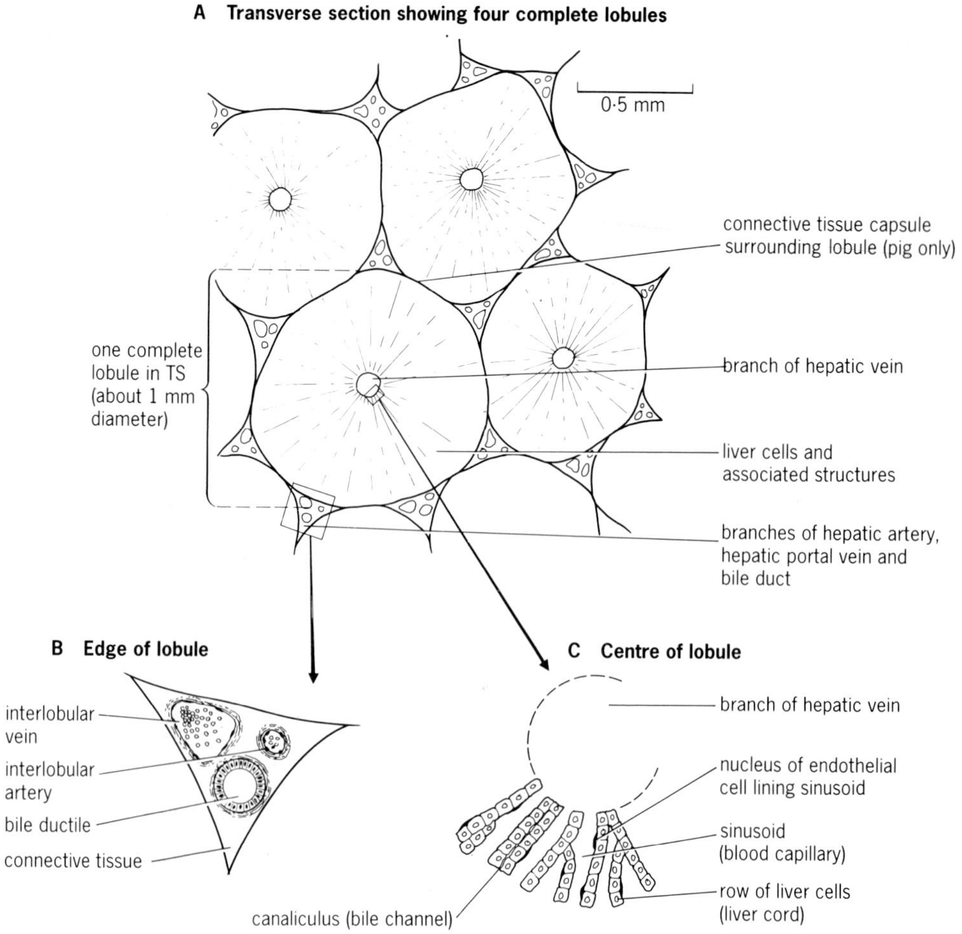

Figure 8.3 Microscopic structure of the liver.

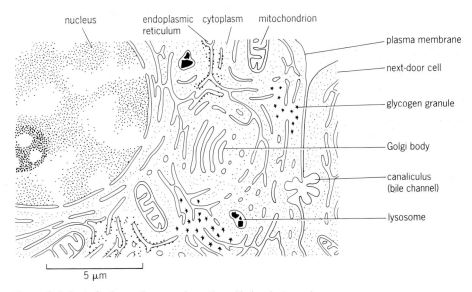

Figure 8.4 Part of a liver cell as seen in section with the electron microscope.

2   Look at the edges of the lobules and locate branches of the hepatic portal vein, hepatic artery and bile duct (Figure 8.3B). They can be distinguished by their relative sizes and the structure of their walls.

3   Now examine the centre of a lobule (Figure 8.3C). Observe the branch of the hepatic vein in the centre. **Sinusoids** (blood capillaries) radiate out from this vein. Between the sinusoids are rows of **liver cells (hepatocytes)** and very narrow bile channels (**canaliculi**).

4   Examine an electron micrograph of a section through a liver cell. Using Figure 8.4 to help you, identify the various structures in the cell, particularly the **glycogen granules**. If a canaliculus is visible, examine it carefully. What can you say about its lining? From the magnification of the micrograph, work out the widest diameter of the canaliculus.

For consideration

1   How does the microscopic structure of the liver, as seen under the light microscope, suit it for its functions?

2   Under what circumstances would you expect liver cells to contain fewer glycogen granules than usual?

3   Liver cells are unremarkable in structure but remarkable in function. Explain.

4   Recall the meaning of the term *acinus* as applied to the pancreas (see page 137). Now apply it to the liver. What comprises an acinus in the liver?

Instructions for dissecting the mammalian
urinary system are given on page 196.

Examination of the mammalian kidney

The kidney is the mammal's principal organ of **excretion** and **osmoregulation**: it extracts unwanted substances from the blood, adjusting the blood's composition so that it has the right osmotic and ionic concentration. The basic functional unit of the kidney is the **nephron**. In the human each kidney contains approximately 1.5 million nephrons.

The aim of this practical is to look first at the coarse anatomy of the kidney and then at its microscopic structure, concentrating particularly on the nephrons.

Procedure

Coarse anatomy of the kidney

1   You will be provided with a fresh sheep's or pig's kidney, still surrounded by fat. Remove the fat so as to expose the **ureter, renal artery** and **renal vein** (Figure 8.5). Be careful not to damage these structures.

2   Gently massage the kidney in warm saline (1% solution of sodium chloride) so as to empty the vessels of their contents.

Danger
Razor
blade

3 Using separate 5 cm³ syringes, inject
(a) the ureter with warm yellow latex, then tie a thread round it,
(b) the renal artery with warm red latex, then tie a thread round it,
(c) the renal vein with warm blue latex, then tie a thread round it.
Allow the latex to cool. As it does so it will harden like rubber.

4 Slice your injected kidney longitudinally with a sharp razor. Ensure that your cut passes as close as possible through the centre. Distinguish between the light-coloured cortex towards the outside and the darker **medulla** towards the inside. Which structures, if any, are shown up by the latex?

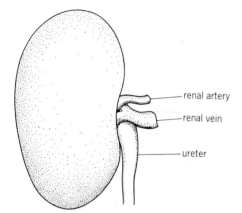

Figure 8.5 Mammalian kidney showing its attachment to the renal artery and vein, and the ureter.

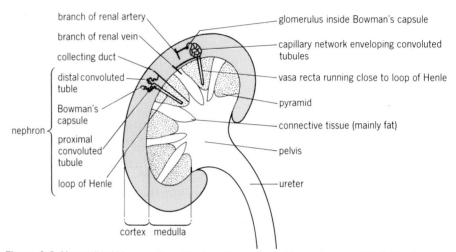

Figure 8.6 Mammalian kidney sectioned to show the position of the nephrons and their blood supply. For clarity the nephron and blood vessels are shown separately; in reality they are intimately associated. A Bowman's capsule and its associated glomerulus together constitute a Malpighian body. Note how the nephron and its blood supply are orientated relative to the kidney as a whole, and also which parts of the nephron are in the cortex and which ones in the medulla.

Microscopic structure of the kidney

Figure 8.6 shows how the nephrons and blood vessels are orientated in relation to the kidney as a whole. Use this diagram to predict what you should see in sections of the kidney cut in different planes (Figure 8.7).

1 Examine prepared longitudinal and vertical sections of a kidney under low power. Note the demarcation between the cortex and medulla.
2 Examine the cortex under low power. It contains **Malpighian bodies** which should be quite easy to see. Choose a good one and examine it in detail, using Figure 8.8 to help you.
3 The cortex also contains **proximal** and **distal convoluted tubules, collecting ducts** and **blood capillaries**. Try to distinguish between them, using Figure 8.9 to help you.

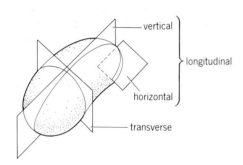

Figure 8.7 The different planes in which a kidney may be sectioned.

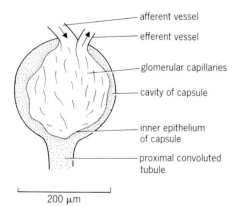

Figure 8.8 A Malpighian body as it may appear in a microscopic section of the kidney. This drawing is idealised; rarely would a section pass through the afferent *and* efferent vessels and the proximal tubule.

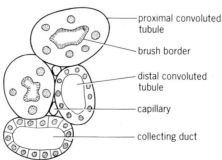

Figure 8.9 Tubules, collecting duct and capillaries as they appear in a microscopic section of the cortex of the kidney. Plasma membranes are not usually visible between adjacent cells in the walls of the tubules, hence their absence in this drawing. Red blood cells are sometimes present in the blood capillaries.

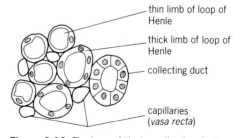

Figure 8.10 The loop of Henle, collecting duct and capillaries as they appear in a microscopic section of the medulla of the kidney. The thin limb is the top two-thirds of the descending limb of the loop of Henle; the thick limb is the rest of the descending limb plus the whole of the ascending limb. Plasma membranes are not usually visible between adjacent cells in the walls of the loop of Henle, hence their absence in this drawing.

4 Examine the medulla under low power. This contains **loops of Henle** (descending and ascending limbs), collecting ducts and capillaries (**vasa recta**). Try to distinguish between them, using Figure 8.10 to help you.

For consideration

1 The kidney adjusts the composition of the blood partly by a process of *ultrafiltration*. Whereabouts in Figure 8.8 does ultrafiltration occur, and what does this process achieve?

2 You will have noticed in the prepared sections of the kidney that the blood capillaries are very close to the tubules. How does this help the kidney to carry out its function of adjusting the composition of the blood?

3 The proximal and distal convoluted tubules are coiled whereas the loops of Henle are straight. What might be the *functional* significance of this?

8.5 INVESTIGATION

Action of a contractile vacuole

The **contractile vacuole**, found in freshwater unicellular organisms, is a comparatively simple osmoregulatory device. As quickly as water enters by osmosis, it is collected into the vacuole which expands and, when full, discharges its contents through a temporary pore in the plasma membrane.

If the function of the contractile vacuole is to eliminate excess water from the cell as fast as it enters, we may predict that increasing the solute concentration of the medium should decrease the activity of the contractile vacuole. In this investigation we shall test this prediction.

The organism

It is best to use a sessile organism, i.e. one that is attached to the substratum and therefore does not move around. A suitable organism is *Podophrya* (Figure 8.11). It has two contractile vacuoles which discharge relatively frequently while the organism, being sessile, will remain steady under the microscope. The organism has already been cultured for you and specimens will be provided attached to fine pieces of silk thread.

Guidance

Your task is to estimate the rate at which one of the contractile vacuoles discharges, first in pure water and then in a series of solutions of gradually increasing solute concentrations.

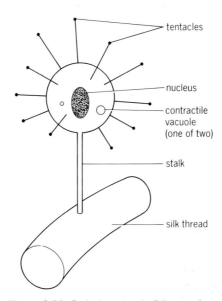

Figure 8.11 *Podophrya*, a unicellular sessile organism. The tentacles are used for catching and feeding on *Paramecium*. The two contractile vacuoles are easily seen from their glistening appearance.

Viewed from above

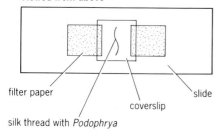

filter paper

silk thread with *Podophrya*

coverslip

slide

Viewed from side

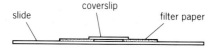

slide

coverslip

filter paper

Figure 8.12 A method of mounting *Podophrya* so that the mounting medium can be changed.

To see the contractile vacuole you should mount the organism on a slide and view it under the microscope. There's no problem with that. The problem is changing the medium without disturbing the organism.

Think of possible ways of doing this. One method, which has been tried and tested, is illustrated in Figure 8.12. The organism is mounted between two pieces of filter paper saturated with the mounting fluid. To change the mounting fluid you simply add the new fluid to one of the two pieces of filter paper with a pipette and withdraw the old fluid from the other piece of filter paper with dry filter paper. This must be done for sufficiently long to ensure that the mounting fluid is completely changed.

Make sure that, as far as possible, the only environmental factor which alters is the concentration of the medium. Other factors should be kept constant. Arrange the illumination in such a way that the temperature of the organism does not increase. Avoid using a microscope with a built-in lamp.

Feel free to improve this method, or use a different method if you prefer. Once you have decided what to do, proceed with the experiment.

When you have completed the experiment make an approximate estimate of the diameter of the whole organism and of a fully inflated contractile vacuole.

For consideration

1 How does the frequency of discharge of the contractile vacuole compare in the different media? Interpret your results.
2 Why is it important to ensure that all environmental factors apart from the concentration of the medium are kept constant?
3 Assuming that the organism and its contractile vacuole are both spherical, estimate the volume of fluid discharged per unit time in pure water. How long would it take for a contractile vacuole to discharge a volume of fluid equal to the volume of the organism's body?

8.6 INVESTIGATION

Comparison of water loss from arthropods in dry and humid air

Animal species differ markedly in their abilities to conserve water, and their distribution can often be related to this.

In this investigation the water-retaining ability of the woodlouse (*Armadillidium*), a terrestrial crustacean, is compared with that of an insect such as the flour beetle (*Tribolium*) or mealworm (*Tenebrio*). Water-loss will be estimated by measuring changes in mass.

Guidance

Devise a small receptacle which will hold the animals in a humane way and from which water can evaporate freely. You will need two such receptacles, one for the woodlice, the other for the insects. It must be possible to place the receptacles (with the animals in them) in a dry stmosphere, and to weigh them at frequent intervals. The animals themselves should be handled and/or disturbed as little as possible.

You need to decide how many animals to place in each receptacle, how often to carry out weighings and the length of time over which changes in mass should be measured. Avoid continuing the experiment for so long that the animals are caused distress.

You should also decide how best to express the results. For example, should you express them as absolute changes in mass or as percentage changes? Would it be helpful to draw graphs?

When you have decided exactly what to do and have assembled all the things you require, carry out the experiment.

For consideration

1 Which species appears to be better at controlling water loss? What structural and/or physiological features might explain its better water-conserving powers?
2 In this investigation we have assumed that the animals' loss in mass is equal to their *water* loss. Is this assumption justified? Can you think of a way of measuring an animal's water-conserving ability *without* making this assumption?
3 Can your results be related to the habitats of the two species? Speculate freely but beware of concluding more than is justified.

REQUIREMENTS

Materials for making animal receptacles, as requested by students
Balance
Anhydrous calcium chloride (drying agent)
Woodlice (*Armadillidium*)
Flour beetles (*Tribolium*)
Mealworms (*Tenebrio*)

Other items may be requested by individual students

Water conservation devices of plants

Water conservation is a problem that faces plants as well as animals. In plants the various adaptations that have evolved are relatively easy to detect in different species. The purpose of this investigation is to look at some of these adaptations in a range of plants.

Guidance

First make a list of as many *possible* adaptations as you can think of. Don't worry about whether or not the adaptation actually exists. Any suggestion is valid so long as it is sensible and theoretically possible. Include life cycle adaptations as well as structural and physiological ones.

The next step is to examine plants in one or more selected habitats to see if they possess any of the adaptations on your list. Be prepared to discover some adaptations that you have not thought of. Choose at least one habitat, e.g. a sand dune, where you suspect that obtaining water may be a problem. For comparison include one habitat, e.g. a water meadow, where water is normally readily available.

You may wish to examine the root systems of some of the species, in which case you will have to dig them up. In some cases you may need to bring the plants, or parts of them, back to the laboratory for closer examination, possibly under the microscope. If you wish to remove any specimens from the habitat, consult your teacher first.

Don't worry too much about the names of the plants. For identification purposes they can be given letters. However, if you wish to find out their names use a flora.

For consideration

1 How can you be sure that what you suspect is an adaptation for water-conservation really is? Give examples of where there could be some doubt.
2 To what extent are the water-conservation devices of plants comparable to those of animals?

REQUIREMENTS

Microscope
Polythene bags for collecting plant
   specimens
Scissors
Fork for digging up plants (if required)
Flora (Keble Martin, W. (1969) *The
   Concise British Flora in Colour* (2nd ed),
   George Rainbird; Stace, C. (1991) *New
   Flora of the British Isles*, Cambridge
   University Press)

Microscopic structure of mammalian skin

As the outermost part of the body, the mammalian skin is important in protection against, and adjustment to, changing external conditions. The purpose of this practical is to examine the microscopic structure of mammalian skin and relate it to this overall role.

Procedure

You will be provided with a prepared vertical section of mammalian skin. First, make a list of all the specific functions of the skin that you can think of. From your list *predict* what structures you would expect to see in a section of skin.

1 Examine your section under low power. Use Figure 8.13 to help you to distinguish between the **epidermis, dermis** and **subcutaneous tissue**.
2 Examine the epidermis in detail under high power. Use Figure 8.14 to help you identify the different layers. New cells are constantly formed by division of the cells in the **Malpighian layer**. Once formed, the cells get pushed upwards, flattening as they do so. Finally the cells die and become converted into scales of keratin which flake off. The cells of the Malpighian layer may contain the pigment **melanin** towards their outer surface. Function?
3 Now move to the dermis and examine it in detail. Note the structures shown in Figure 8.13 but bear in mind that your section is unlikely to be as complete as our drawing. The organisation of the dermis must therefore be pieced together bit by bit by searching the entire section for clues and, if necessary, looking at other sections.
4 Examine the subcutaneous layer in detail. It is composed mainly of **adipose (fatty) tissue**. What are its functions?
5 The skin contains numerous **receptors**. What kind of receptors would you expect to find in a section of human skin? Can you see anything in your section that might conceivably be a receptor? Most of the receptors require special staining techniques to show them up. If you can obtain a specially stained slide, see what you can discover about the skin receptors.

REQUIREMENTS

Microscope
Mammalian skin, VS
Mammalian skin, section stained to show
   receptors, if available

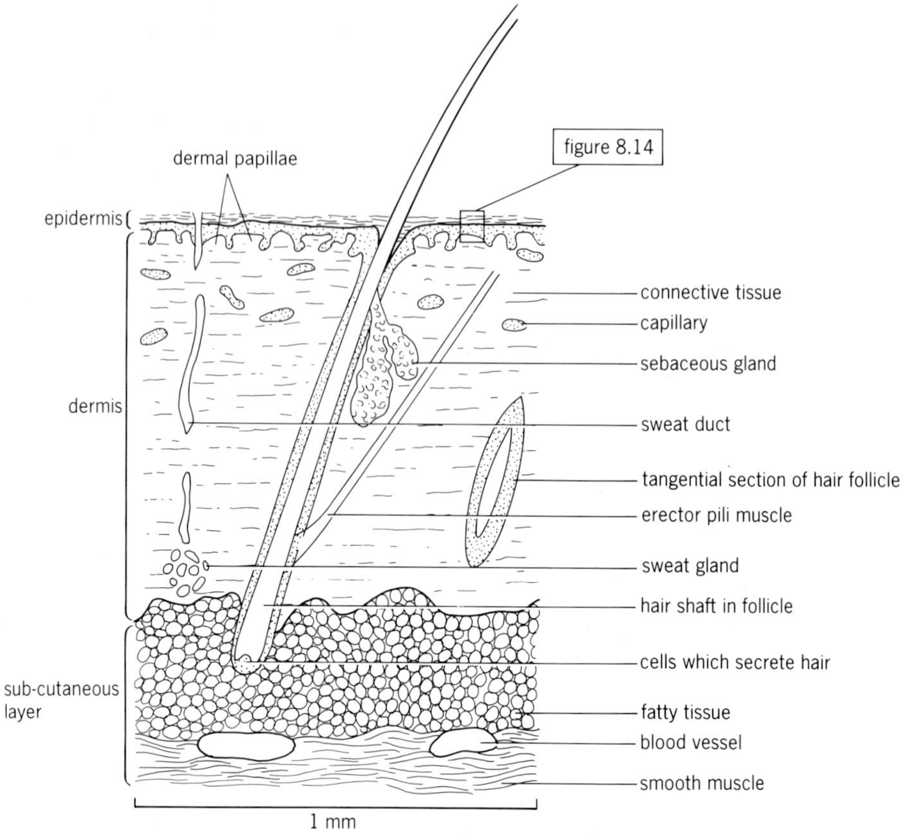

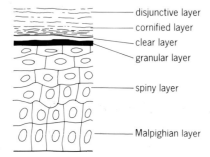

Figure 8.13 below:

dermal papillae
figure 8.14
epidermis
connective tissue
capillary
sebaceous gland
dermis
sweat duct
tangential section of hair follicle
erector pili muscle
sweat gland
hair shaft in follicle
cells which secrete hair
sub-cutaneous
layer
fatty tissue
blood vessel
smooth muscle
1 mm

Figure 8.13 Microscopic structure of human skin (scalp). Few sections will be as complete as this. Seldom will a hair follicle be cut throughout its length; usually it will be incomplete as shown on the right hand side of the drawing. The same applies to the sweat glands and their ducts.

Figure 8.14 labels:
disjunctive layer
cornified layer
clear layer
granular layer
spiny layer
Malpighian layer

Figure 8.14 The epidermis of human skin in detail. In the Malpighian layer new cells are constantly being formed by cell division. The spiny layer is composed of cells which may show a prickly (spiny) appearance; the cells of the granular layer have granules in their cytoplasm, those of the clear layer have a clear cytoplasm, and those of the cornified layer are keratinised and hard; and the cells of the disjunctive layer flake off.

For consideration

1 Which areas of human skin would you expect to have:
   (a) no hair follicles
   (b) particularly abundant subcutaneous fat
   (c) little or no subcutaneous fat
   (d) a particularly thick cornified layer
   (e) numerous receptors sensitive to touch?
2 Why is it a good thing for sunlight (in moderation) to fall on the skin? Why can excessive exposure to bright sunlight be dangerous?
3 A man may have a luxuriant beard but a bald head. Speculate as to the *biological* cause of this paradox.

8.9 INVESTIGATION

Heat energy loss from an insulated and a non-insulated hand

Birds and mammals maintain their body temperature by generating heat energy within their bodies, so insulation would appear to be of prime importance. But how effective is their insulation? In this investigation you will compare the heat energy loss from an insulated and a non-insulated human hand.

Procedure

Work in pairs, one of you acting as the subject, the other as experimenter.
1 Place two digital thermometers with probes in identical conditions and ensure that they both give the same reading.
2 With masking tape attach the thermometer probes to the subject's hands, one to each hand.

Caution

REQUIREMENTS

Digital thermometers with probes × 2
Clinical thermometer, in disinfectant
Duvet filling
Masking tape

3 Check that the **skin temperature** is the same for each hand. If the temperatures differ, check that the subject's clothing (shirt, sweater) comes to the same point on each arm.

4 Insulate one hand thoroughly with duvet filling, making sure that the insulation is of even thickness all round the hand. Tape the insulation to the hand, making sure that you can still read the thermometer.

5 Make sure that both hands and arms are in exactly the same conditions except for the presence of the duvet filling round the insulated hand. Allow time for equilibration.

6 Record the skin temperatures of both hands. Also record the subject's **core temperature** with a clinical thermometer placed under the tongue, and the **environmental temperature**.

7 Repeat step 6 at different environmental temperatures. Record your results in a table.

8 Graph your results in a way which best illustrates the effectiveness of the duvet material in insulating the hand. (You will have to decide what to plot against what.)

For consideration

1 What conclusions can you draw from your results about the effectiveness of human skin as an insulator?

2 Did you find that the skin temperatures of the two hands differed even when both were uninsulated and in the same conditions? If so, suggest an explanation.

3 Do the results of this experiment allow you to suggest a possible function for the thermoreceptors in the skin? How might your suggestion be tested?

4 How could you measure the rate at which heat energy is lost from the human body?

We are indebted to Dr J.M. Gregory of Winchester College for providing information on this experiment.

8.10 PRACTICAL EXERCISE

Effect of temperature on the heartbeat of *Daphnia*

Daphnia, the water flea, is a small freshwater crustacean which lacks physiological methods of maintaining a constant body temperature. This means that if the environmental temperature changes, its body temperature does so too and its metabolic rate will be expected to rise or fall accordingly.

In this investigation we shall test the hypothesis that as the environmental temperature rises the metabolic rate rises too. We shall use the rate at which the heart beats (**cardiac frequency**) as a measure of the metabolic rate. Fortunately *Daphnia* is relatively transparent and its heart can be seen quite easily under the low power of the microscope.

Procedure
Setting up the experiment

1 Select a large specimen and, with a pipette, transfer it to the centre of a small, dry Petri dish. With filter paper remove excess water from around the specimen so that it is completely stranded.

2 With a seeker place a small blob of silicone grease onto the floor of the Petri dish. Then wipe the needle clean and use it to gently push the posterior end of the animal into the grease so that it is firmly anchored. Now fill the Petri dish with water at room temperature.

3 Place the Petri dish on the stage of a microscope and observe the animal under low power. Figure 8.15 shows the position of the heart. Watch it beating. Don't confuse the beating of the heart with the flapping of the legs.

4 Surround the animal with a circular heating coil and fix it in position as shown in Figure 8.16. Also clamp a small mercury thermometer, or the temperature probe of a digital thermometer, into position.

Estimating the cardiac frequency

A convenient way of doing this is to time how long it takes for the heart to beat 50 times. If it is beating too frequently for every beat to be counted, make a mark on a

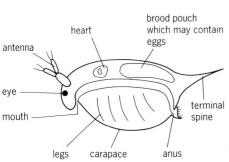

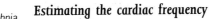

Figure 8.15 Diagrammatic side view of *Daphnia* as seen under low power to show the position of the heart.

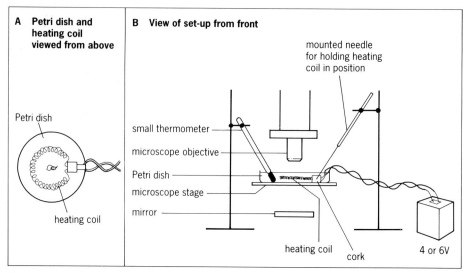

Figure 8.16 An experimental set-up for studying the effect of temperature on the heartbeat of *Daphnia*.

piece of paper every tenth beat. Do several practice runs to get used to the technique. When you feel ready, proceed as follows:

1   Replace the room temperature water in the Petri dish with water at 10 °C. Estimate the cardiac frequency and note the temperature .
2   Switch on the heater so that the water gradually warms up. Estimate the cardiac frequency at 5 °C intervals from 10 °C to 30 °C, noting the temperature each time. If the temperature of the water rises too rapidly, switch off the heater and, if necessary, add a few ice chippings.
3   Present your results in a table and, if you have sufficient readings, draw a graph of the cardiac frequency as a function of the temperature.

For consideration

1   What conclusions would you draw from your results? Do you think *Daphnia* has no means of controlling its body temperature? Explain your answer.
2   What criticisms can you make of the experimental technique? How might it be improved?
3   How could the same investigation be carried out on a human subject? In what respects would you expect the results to differ from those obtained with *Daphnia*?

8.11 PRACTICAL EXERCISE

Different types of white cells in human blood

Blood is the major fluid transport medium of many animal groups including annelids, arthropods, molluscs and chordates. In mammals blood consists of red blood cells, white blood cells and platelets suspended in a fluid medium, plasma. No staining is required to see the red blood cells (see page 105), but staining is necessary to distinguish the platelets and various types of white blood cells.

In this practical exercise, prepared slides of human blood are examined, and the various types of cells identified. Such slides are usually stained with either Leishman's stain or Wright's stain. Each of these contains eosin and methylene blue.

Procedure

1   Focus on a slide at medium power and notice the abundance of red blood cells, which lack nuclei. White blood cells possess nuclei, but can at first be difficult to find, both because they are rare, relative to red blood cells, and because they stand out less obviously.
2   Focus on your slide at high power and find a group of platelets.
3   Still at high power, find a white blood cell. Identify it by referring to Figure 8.17. **Lymphocytes** and **monocytes** are quite easy to identify, as are **basophils**. However, **neutrophils** and **eosinophils** can be difficult to distinguish.
4   Find at least twenty more white blood cells and identify them as far as you are able.

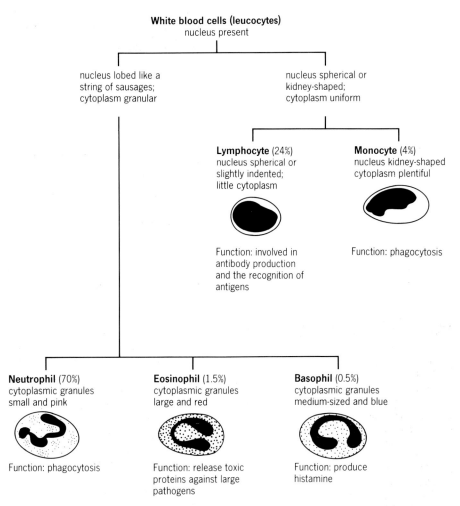

Figure 8.17 Key to the different types of white blood cell found in human blood as seen under the light microscope after staining. The figure in brackets after the name of each type indicates the typical percentage of white blood cells belonging to that type. Basophil nuclei are frequently indistinct.

For consideration

1 Which were the most numerous of the types of white blood cell you saw? Does this agree with the figures for frequency given in Figure 8.17?

2 Were there any types of white blood cell that you failed to see? If so, can you suggest why?

3 Leishman's stain and Wright's stain each contain acidic eosin (red) and alkaline methylene blue (blue). Can you suggest why eosinophils, neutrophils and basophils stain differently with these stains, and why they are given their respective names? (Hint: *philos* is the Greek for friend.)

4 Which types of white blood cell are capable of leaving capillaries by passing through the endothelial walls of the capillaries? Can you relate this to the structure of the cells?

5 Can you suggest circumstances which might cause one or more of these types of white blood cells to be produced by the body in greater numbers?

REQUIREMENTS

Microscope
Prepared slides of human blood stained
with Leishman's or Wright's stain

8.12 PRACTICAL EXERCISE

Presence and action of lysozyme

Lysozyme is an enzyme which kills bacteria and is present in certain body fluids. It was discovered by Alexander Fleming. The enzyme hydrolyses the main structural component of bacterial cell walls.

Some bacteria are more sensitive to lysozyme than others. **Gram positive bacteria** – which stain readily with a stain devised by C. Gram in 1884 – are particularly sensitive to the enzyme. The yellow bacterium *Micrococcus luteum* is especially sensitive to lysozyme, and so provides a convenient assay for it. The yellow culture rapidly becomes less turbid as the cells are broken open by the enzyme.

In this practical you can determine whether or not lysozyme is present in various sources, and its concentration in them.

Procedure

1 Collect the following fluids using the methods suggested. **Egg white**: break open a fresh egg and pour the white into a test-tube. **Sweat**: run up and down the stairs a few times, and collect some sweat from the surface of your skin with a pipette, taking especial care if the pipette is made of glass. **Tears**: expose one of your eyes to a polythene bag containing half a chopped onion, and allow your tears to drop into a test-tube. Do not put the tube too near your eye. **Saliva**: dribble into a test-tube.

2 Produce a **standard curve** for the action of lysozyme on *Micrococcus luteus* as follows:
  (a) Pipette 9 cm³ of phosphate buffer solution into a colorimeter tube, or a test-tube which fits into your colorimeter. Pipette 0.3 cm³ of *M. luteus* suspension into the buffer sample. Shake the mixture.
  (b) Place the tube in the colorimeter, and write the colorimeter reading on your recording sheet. You will be taking a reading every twenty seconds, so have a stopwatch ready.
  (c) Pipette 0.3 cm³ of the lysozyme solution (1 mg cm⁻³) into the colorimeter tube and start the stopwatch. Record a colorimeter reading every twenty seconds for three minutes, and then at one minute intervals for a further two minutes.
  (d) Plot a graph of the colorimeter readings against time.
  (e) Repeat in turn Steps 2(a) to 2(d), first with 0.3 cm³ of lysozyme solution diluted to half its original strength (0.5 mg cm⁻³), and then with 0.3 cm³ of lysozyme solution diluted to a quarter of the original strength (0.25 mg cm⁻³). The three curves, plotted on the *same* axes, constitute your standard curves.

3 Now test one of the fluids you obtained in Step 1. First dilute it to a fifth of its strength with distilled water, using a pipette. Follow the same procedures as outlined in Steps 2(a) to 2(c), and then plot a graph of the colorimeter readings against time.

4 Compare your graph with the standard curves you drew earlier (Step 2(e)). From the comparison, calculate the lysozyme concentration of the fluid you tested.

For consideration

1 A cup of egg white left on a kitchen shelf may take months to go bad. Hard-boiled eggs, on the other hand, go mouldy within days. Why?
2 Were the concentrations of lysozyme in tears and saliva different? If they were, can you account for the difference?
3 Do different people have different concentrations of lysozyme in their saliva? If so, can you suggest why?
4 Besides the ones you have tested, which other body fluids might you expect to contain lysozyme?

Danger

REQUIREMENTS

Access to colorimeter with filter allowing light at 600 μm to pass
Colorimeter tubes ×7
Stopwatch
Graph paper
Graduated pipettes (1 cm³ and 10 cm³, with rubber suckers)
Polythene bag
Test-tubes ×6
Lysozyme, 1 mg cm⁻³ in phosphate buffer solution (pH 8.0)
Phosphate buffer solution (pH 8.0) – see below
Egg white
Culture suspension of *Micrococcus luteus*, 10 mg cm⁻³ in sodium chloride solution (0.85%)
Onion

Note: *To prepare phosphate buffer solution (pH 8.0): mix 97.25 cm³ of 0.2 mol dm⁻³ sodium dihydro-genphosphate solution with 2.75 cm³ of 0.1 mol dm⁻³ citric acid solution.*

8.13 INVESTIGATION

Epidemiology of the common cold

Epidemiology is the study of the distribution and cause of disease. Epidemiologists are people who try to find out who becomes ill and why. Common colds are caused by a group of RNA viruses called rhinoviruses. In this investigation, it is suggested that you construct a **questionnaire** to determine who gets colds, and to begin to examine why some people get colds more often than others.

Guidance

First of all you need to think up a suitable hypothesis, or a series of hypotheses, to test. In addition to collecting such basic information as age and gender, the questions you include on your questionnaire will be determined by your hypotheses. Suppose you think that people who live in large families are more likely to catch colds. Then you will need to collect data on the frequency with which people catch colds (e.g. by asking people how many colds they have had in the last 12 months) and the number of people in their households. Alternatively, you may suspect that people are more likely to catch colds at times of stress. In this case you might see if there is any relationship between the incidence of colds and events such as examinations.

As well as requesting factual information, it is quite in order to ask your subjects such questions as 'What do you think leads to some people getting lots of colds?' or 'When do you tend to get colds?' You may need to produce a precise definition of the symptoms of a common cold, so that different individuals answer your questions consistently. For further guidance, see Box 10.1, page 180.

For consideration

1 What tentative conclusions can you draw from the analysis of your data?
2 List as many ways as you can in which the common cold virus is transmitted from one person to another. On the basis of the data you have collected, is it more likely that humans suffer from colds after picking up rhinoviruses from other people, or that the viruses exist permanently inside people and then suddenly multiply and cause colds in response to environmental triggers?
3 How could your questionnaire be improved?

BOX 8.1 Basic techniques of microbiology

Microorganisms can be grown in a variety of containers from Petri dishes and small bottles to industrial-sized **fermenters**. Over time a number of different culture media have been developed on which microorganisms can grow. A general-purpose medium, such as **nutrient agar**, allows a wide range of microorganisms to be cultivated. Such media can be purchased in dehydrated form.

Transferring microorganisms

When transferring microorganisms from one place to another, the two things to bear in mind are *safety* and *avoiding contamination*. These two aims can be achieved by using **sterile techniques** (**aseptic techniques**). Illustration 1 shows how bacteria (or fungi) may be transferred from a culture to a Petri dish containing solid agar. When transferring to liquid agar there is obviously no need to 'streak out'.

Preparing Petri dishes for the growth of microorganisms

In schools and colleges the following rules should be followed when using Petri dishes for the growth of microorganisms:

Biohazard

1 Use sterile techniques (see above) when transferring microorganisms to a Petri dish.
2 Ensure your name and any other relevant information (e.g. date, microorganisms used) are on the *underside* of the Petri dish.
3 *Never* attempt to culture microorganisms from food (whether cooked or uncooked), faeces, vomit, places that have been in contact with these (such as under the rim of a toilet) or any human body fluids.
4 Once microorganisms have been transferred to a Petri dish, always seal it with an adhesive tape as shown in Illustration 2 unless you have clearly been instructed otherwise by your teacher.
5 After use, deal with Petri dishes and their contents with care. The best procedure is to use **autoclavable plastic bags** obtained from laboratory suppliers. Glass Petri dishes (and any other non-disposable items such as McCartney bottles) are placed in *one* bag, and disposable materials (including plastic Petri dishes) into *another*. This is done without removing the contents or any adhesive tape. The two bags should each be lightly closed with a wire tie and then **autoclaved** (i.e. heated to 120 °C in a container filled with steam under pressure). After autoclaving, the plastic bag with disposable materials can be placed in a normal dustbin. The bag with non-disposable items can be opened and its contents cleaned in the normal way.
6 Wash your hands thoroughly with soap and water after all microbiology work.

(continued)

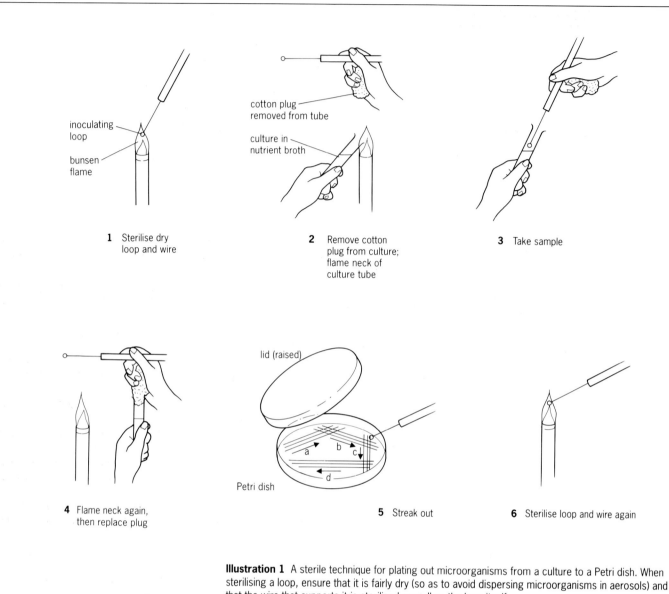

1 Sterilise dry loop and wire

2 Remove cotton plug from culture; flame neck of culture tube

3 Take sample

4 Flame neck again, then replace plug

5 Streak out

6 Sterilise loop and wire again

Illustration 1 A sterile technique for plating out microorganisms from a culture to a Petri dish. When sterilising a loop, ensure that it is fairly dry (so as to avoid dispersing microorganisms in aerosols) and that the wire that supports it is sterilised as well as the loop itself.

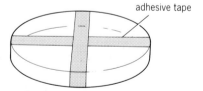

Illustration 2 Petri dishes should be sealed, but not completely (all the way round) as this might allow anaerobic microorganisms to grow, and some of these are harmful.

References

Department of Education and Science *Microbiology: An HMI guide for schools and non-advanced further education* (Her Majesty's Stationery Office, 1985).

Advice and information about all aspects of biotechnology and microbiology can be obtained from the National Centre for Biotechnology, Department of Microbiology, University of Reading, Whiteknights, Reading RG6 2AJ.

8.14 PRACTICAL EXERCISE

This exercise extends over more than one practical session.

Antibiotics and bacteria

Antibiotics are compounds, produced by certain microorganisms, which harm other microorganisms, including bacteria. Such substances, which include the well-known antibiotic penicillin, are of great medical and economic importance. This practical demonstrates the anti-bacterial action of certain antibiotics.

Procedure

1 Obtain a stoppered bottle or test-tube containing 15 cm³ of sterile nutrient agar. Melt the agar by placing the bottle in a water bath at 80–100 °C.

REQUIREMENTS

Hand lens or binocular microscope
Water bath at 80–100 °C
Incubator at 30 °C
Bunsen burner or spirit lamp
Petri dish
Inoculation loop
Small forceps
Sterile nutrient agar (15 cm³, in stoppered
    bottle)
Sterile cottonwool
Antibiotic discs (e.g. penicillin,
    streptomycin or aureomycin) or
    'mast ring'
Disinfectant for cleaning bench
Pure culture of non-pathogenic
    containment level 1 bacteria on agar
    slope in test-tube. (Suitable bacteria are
    listed in suppliers' catalogues.)
Sterile water

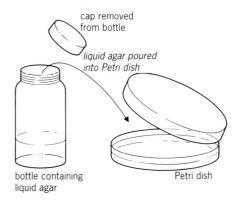

Figure 8.18 Procedure for transferring bacteria from a liquid culture to a Petri dish.

2 Remove the bottle and cool to about 45 °C. (At this temperature the agar will still be liquid, but will be cool enough to hold against your cheek. Most agars solidify at about 42 °C.)

3 Obtain a test-tube containing a culture of non-pathogenic bacteria on an agar slope (see list of requirements). The tube should be kept plugged with sterile cotton wool.

4 Transfer a sample of bacteria from the agar slope to the liquid agar in the bottle. (See Box 8.1 on page 149.)

5 Without delay pour the liquid agar containing the bacteria into a warm, sterilised Petri dish (Figure 8.18). (Warming the Petri dish prevents water condensing beneath the lid as you pour in the agar.)

6 After replacing the lid, ensure an even distribution of the agar by gently moving the Petri dish from side to side on a flat surface.

7 After the agar has solidified, use sterile forceps to place on the surface of the agar a small disc of filter paper impregnated with an antibiotic. As a control, place another disc of the same size (having previously soaked it in sterile water and then allowed it to dry) on a different part of the agar. Make sure you can distinguish these two discs.

8 As an alternative to Step 7, use a 'mast ring'. This consists of a central control disc – without antibiotic – surrounded by side-arms leading to small discs each impregnated with a different antibiotic.

9 Seal and label the Petri dish in the usual way (see the Section on 'Preparing Petri dishes for the growth of microorganisms' Box 8.1 on page 149).

10 Incubate at 30 °C and examine at daily intervals over the next week for signs of bacterial growth.

Biohazard

For consideration

1 Why is it necessary to ensure sterile conditions in this practical?

2 How do the areas where growth of bacteria has occurred relate to the positions of the antibiotic and control discs?

3 Antibiotics have been extracted from various species of fungi and other soil microorganisms. What functions might antibiotics have in such organisms?

PROJECTS

Before starting a project, discuss your intended procedure with your teacher.

1 Devise one or more homeostatic systems which demonstrate feedback. The system could be a modification of the aluminium block in Investigation 8.1 on page 136, or it could be some sort of machine which you construct yourself. Try out ways of minimising fluctuations. If your system involves temperature fluctuations, investigate the effect of e.g. insulating the system.

2 Investigate the ability of marine and estuarine invertebrates to osmoregulate when transferred into more dilute media. Failure to

osmoregulate would presumably result in water being retained in the body, which would cause an increase in mass. Increase in mass can therefore be used as an indication of whether or not osmoregulation has been taking place. If possible relate your findings to the ecological distribution of the animals. Suitable animals for investigation include molluscs and tubiculous polychaetes. Treat the animals with respect and do not subject them to undue stress.

3 Extend the investigation on the water-conserving powers of woodlice, beetles and mealworms (page 142) to other animal

species. Relate their different water-conserving powers to their anatomy, physiology, behaviour and/or habitats.

4 The water-conserving ability of insects is said to be due to the presence of a thin layer of wax on the surface of the cuticle. Test this hypothesis. The cockroach would be a suitable insect for this investigation. First you would have to find out if it really does have a layer of wax on its cuticle. Then you would need to devise a humane way of removing the wax. You could then compare loss of mass of normal and de-waxed specimens.

5 Select a species of moss growing in a moist situation, e.g. in or close to water, and a species growing in a dry place, e.g. on top of a wall. Compare the rates at which known masses of each species dry out when exposed to the same environmental conditions. Relate your results to the structure of the two species and their ability to trap and retain water.

6 Plan and create a small cactus garden. Suitable species are generally available from larger garden centres. Learn as much as you can about the requirements of the plants and how they are adapted to living in a dry situation.

7 Compare the effectiveness of different materials for insulating the human hand. Include natural materials such as hair and feathers as well as artificial materials.

8 Investigate the effect of size and/or shape on the rate at which a body loses or gains heat energy. Relate your results, as far as you can, to the structure of different animal species and their thermoregulatory abilities.

9 It is claimed that one function of transpiration is to cool plants. Test this hypothesis by recording the temperatures of a leaf (or leaves) transpiring at different rates. You will need to decide how many plants to use, and how to induce different rates of transpiration. Leaf temperatures can be measured with a temperature probe.

10 Investigate the effect on the heartbeat of *Daphnia* of other factors besides temperature. For example, you might investigate the effect of drugs such as alcohol, caffeine and nicotine, and of natural transmitter substances such as adrenaline and acetylcholine. The following article describes how you can keep *Daphnia*: C.D. Whittaker, Keeping *Daphnia* in the laboratory over a long time period, *School Science Review*, Vol. 70, No. 250, September 1988.

11 Investigate the factors that affect lysozyme activity (e.g. pH, length of time since sample was obtained, temperature).

12 Design and use a questionnaire to see whether people catch different diseases nowadays compared with fifty years ago.

13 ⚠ Investigate the effectiveness of different antibiotics against a non-pathogenic bacterium. Your teacher will provide you with a culture of a suitable bacterium and with a range of different antibiotics.

14 ⚠ Most toothpastes contain about 0.2% by mass of an anti-bacterial agent. Test the hypothesis that different toothpastes are equally effective against the growth of bacteria or other microorganisms.

15 ⚠ Compare the effect of different household disinfectants on the growth of microorganisms.

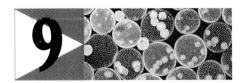

9 Nerves, receptors and hormones

Microscopic structure of the spinal cord and brain

The spinal cord and brain make up the **central nervous system** (**CNS**). Put simply, their job is to coordinate nervous information so that the right impulses are sent to the right place at the right time.

The purpose of this investigation is to examine sections of the spinal cord and brain and relate their microscopic structure to their overall function of coordination.

Procedure
Spinal cord

Before you look at the spinal cord under the microscope it is helpful to have the picture of a generalised **reflex arc** in your mind (see left hand side of Figure 9.1A). You will then know what to expect to find inside different regions of the cord.

1   Examine a prepared transverse section of spinal cord under low or medium power. Identify the structures shown on the right hand side of Figure 9.1A. Distinguish between the central **grey matter** and the more peripheral **white matter**. The grey matter contains the **cell bodies** of numerous neurones; the white matter contains slender **axons** which transmit impulses into and out of the spinal cord and axons which transmit impulses up and down the cord to and from the brain.

2   Note the **meninges** surrounding and protecting the spinal cord: the outer and inner layers are separated by a delicate vascular middle layer.

3   Locate the cell body of an **effector neurone** in the ventral part of the grey matter (Figure 9.1B). Examine it under high power. Note in particular its slender

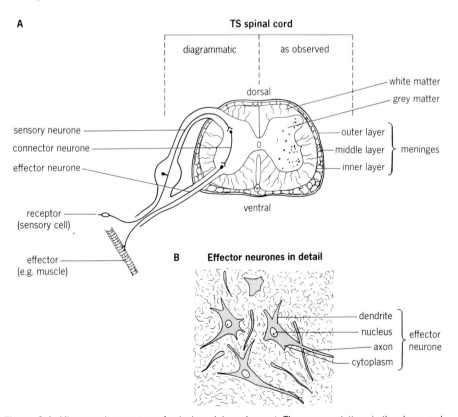

Figure 9.1 Microscopic structure of spinal cord, based on cat. There are variations in the shape and relative proportions of white matter and grey matter according to the part of the cord (neck, thorax etc.).

branches (**dendrites**). These connect with other neurones. Look for a particularly long branch which may be the **axon**.

4   Extend your study of the motor neurone by examining neurones in a prepared smear of spinal cord.

Brain

1   Examine a vertical section of the cerebral cortex and notice numerous **pyramidal cells**, so called because they are shaped like little pyramids (Figure 9.2). Examine one of them in detail under high power. Numerous dendrites connect with other neurones, and the axon transmits impulses to the spinal cord and thence, via reflex arcs, to the muscles.

2   Examine a vertical section of the cerebellum. Observe **Purkinje cells** (Figure 9.3). How do the Purkinje cells differ in appearance from the pyramidal cells in the cerebral cortex? The cerebellum controls fine movements by sending impulses down the axons of the Purkinje cells.

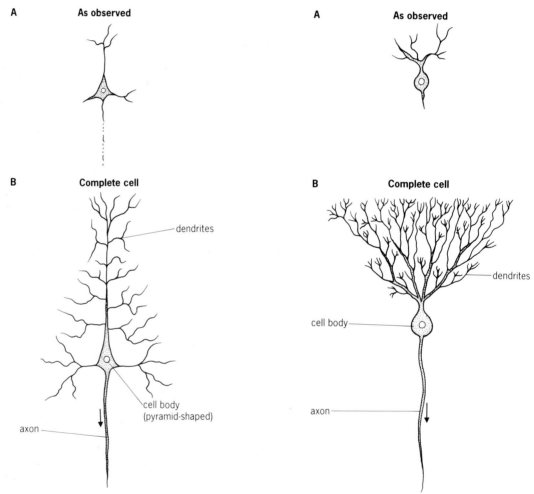

Figure 9.2 Pyramidal cell from the motor area of the cerebral cortex. The arrow shows the direction in which impulses are transmitted.

Figure 9.3 Purkinje cell from the cortex of the cerebellum. The arrow shows the direction in which impulses are transmitted.

REQUIREMENTS
Microscope
Spinal cord, TS
Spinal cord, smear
Cerebral cortex, VS
Cerebellum, VS

For consideration

1   Figures 9.2B and 9.3B show brain cells entire. However, when you look at sections of the brain under the microscope you can only see fragments of these cells. How, then, are we justified in making such complete drawings?

2   This investigation has been entirely about the microscopic *structure* of the CNS. To what extent can such structural studies help us to understand how the CNS carries out its function of coordination?

9.2 PRACTICAL EXERCISE

Microscopic structure of a nerve

Nerves transmit impulses from receptors to the CNS and from the CNS to effectors. In this investigation we shall examine the microscopic structure of a nerve and relate this to its function of transmitting impulses to and from the CNS.

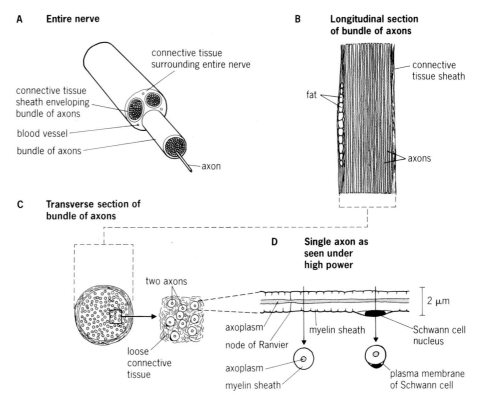

Figure 9.4 Microscopic structure of a myelinated nerve as seen under the light microscope.

Procedure

First appreciate that a whole nerve consists of numerous **axons** arranged in bundles as shown in Figure 9.4A. Try to *imagine* what a longitudinal section, and a transverse section, of a whole nerve might look like.

1 Examine a longitudinal section of a myelinated nerve, concentrating on the way the axons are arranged rather than on their detailed structure. Use Figure 9.4B to help you.

2 Examine a transverse section of a myelinated nerve, using Figure 9.4C to help you interpret it.

3 Now examine a longitudinal section of a myelinated nerve which has been specially stained to show the **myelin sheath** and associated structures. Use Figure 9.4D to help you identify the myelin sheath, **nodes of Ranvier** and nuclei of **Schwann cells**.

4 Examine an electron micrograph of a transverse section of an axon which passes through a Schwann cell (Figure 9.5). Look at the myelin sheath very closely and notice that it consists of an extension of the plasma membrane of the Schwann cell which is wrapped tightly round the axon. Since the plasma membrane contains a substantial amount of lipid, the myelin sheath too contains much lipid.

5 Now examine the inside of the axon (the **axoplasm**) in your electron micrograph. Can you see any **neurotubules**? These longitudinally orientated microtubules are thought to assist the transport of materials from the nerve cell body to the far end of the axon.

6 Certain axons innervate skeletal muscles. Examine a slide of skeletal muscle which shows **effector nerve endings** (Figure 9.6). Each ending makes synaptic contact with a muscle fibre at a **neuromuscular junction**.

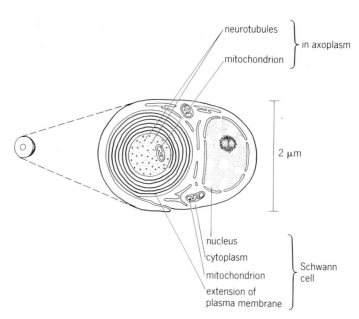

Figure 9.5 Diagram of a transverse section through an axon at the level of a Schwann cell. On the left is the section as it would appear under the light microscope. On the right is the section as it would appear in the electron microscope.

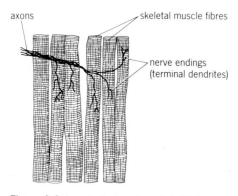

Figure 9.6 Longitudinal section of skeletal muscle fibres showing nerve endings. The nerve endings terminate at neuromuscular junctions.

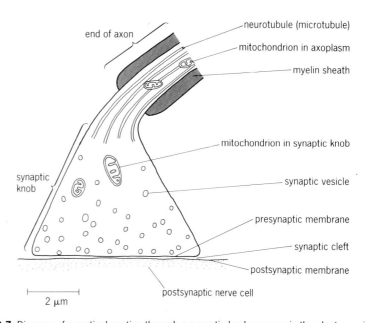

Figure 9.7 Diagram of a vertical section through a synaptic knob as seen in the electron microscope.

REQUIREMENTS

Microscope
Myelinated nerve, LS
Myelinated nerve, TS
Motor nerve endings in skeletal muscle
Electron micrograph of myelinated axon, TS
Electron micrograph of synapse, LS

Note: *The set of electron micrographs of tissues, available from Philip Harris Education, includes micrographs of nerve tissue.*

7 Examine an electron micrograph of a section through a **synapse**. What you will see depends on the plane in which the section has been cut. Use Figure 9.7 to help you interpret your particular section.

For consideration

1 Here are two well known observations about the human nervous system: (a) In a typical nerve, impulses can travel in two directions, i.e. towards the CNS and away from the CNS. (b) The muscles in the human leg are innervated by branches of a single nerve (the sciatic nerve), yet the muscles do not all contract at the same time. Which feature of a myelinated nerve, as observed by you in this practical, help to explain these two observations? Explain your answer.

2 The function of the myelin sheath is to *insulate* the axon. What exactly does this mean and why is it important?

Dissection of the mammalian brain

Brain tissue is very soft. The cranium which surrounds it, however, is made of bone and is very hard. In dissecting the brain, we are faced with the problem of having to remove the bony cranium without damaging the soft brain tissue underneath.

Procedure

Use the rat which you used previously for dissecting the abdomen and thorax.

1   Make a longitudinal slit in the skin on top of the head, then deflect the skin on either side. Note the hard cranium underneath. The parietal bone, which forms the central part of the roof of the cranium, is thin and the **cerebral hemispheres** can be seen beneath it (Figure 9.8A).

2   *Put on eye protection in case pieces of bone fly into your face.* Hold the head between your thumb and fingers. Insert the blade of a scalpel under the parietal bone, and carefully lift the bone away from the cerebral hemispheres underneath. Figure 9.8 shows you how to do this.

3   Deflect the neck muscles so as to expose more of the cranium. Then chip away the cranium, bit by bit, so as to expose the rest of the brain (Figure 9.9). Identify, in

A   From above

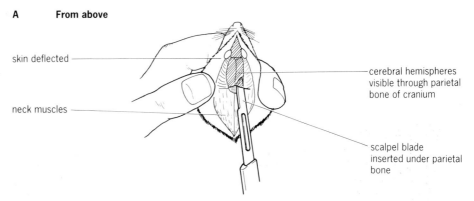

skin deflected

neck muscles

cerebral hemispheres visible through parietal bone of cranium

scalpel blade inserted under parietal bone

B   From the side

keep scalpel blade horizontal

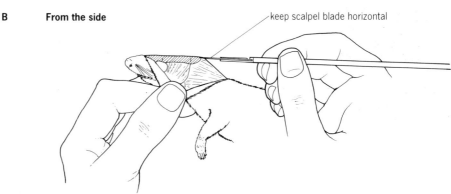

Figure 9.8 Dissecting the brain of a rat. The picture shows the parietal bone covering the cerebral hemispheres, and how to remove it. Keep the scalpel blade horizontal. If you point it downwards it will damage the brain. The parietal bone should break along the lines (called sutures) where it is joined to the other bones of the cranium.

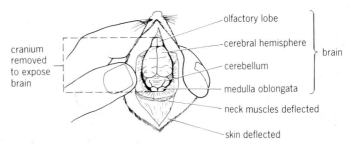

cranium removed to expose brain

olfactory lobe

cerebral hemisphere

cerebellum

medulla oblongata

brain

neck muscles deflected

skin deflected

Figure 9.9 The brain of the rat exposed by deflecting the skin and neck muscles and removing the top and sides of the cranium.

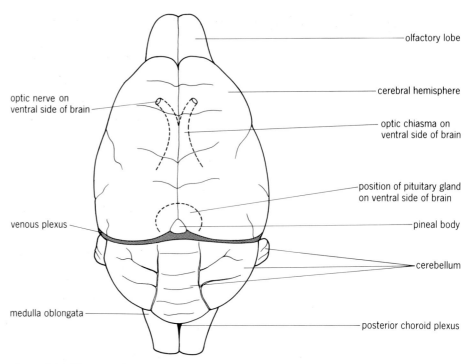

olfactory lobe

cerebral hemisphere

optic nerve on ventral side of brain

optic chiasma on ventral side of brain

position of pituitary gland on ventral side of brain

venous plexus

pineal body

cerebellum

medulla oblongata

posterior choroid plexus

Figure 9.10 The brain of the rat viewed from the dorsal side. The structures shown in broken lines are on the ventral side of the brain.

addition to the cerebral hemispheres, the **olfactory lobes**, **cerebellum** and **medulla oblongata**.

4 Observe the **cranial nerves** which arise from the ventral side of the brain and pass through holes (foramina) in the cranium to various receptors and effectors, mainly in the head.

5 Cut through the cranial nerves and remove the brain from the head. Place the brain in a Petri dish.

6 View the brain from the dorsal and ventral sides. Use Figure 9.10 to help you identify the main parts. On the dorsal side observe, in addition to the parts already mentioned, the **pineal body**. On the ventral side note the **pituitary gland** which projects downwards from the floor of the brain, and the **optic chiasma** where the optic nerves cross.

7 The optic nerves are one of twelve pairs of cranial nerves. Their stumps should be visible on the ventral side of the brain. If you are interested, details of the cranial nerves can be found in the dissection guide referred to below.

A further observation

Work out, as accurately as you can, the ratio between the volume of the cerebral hemispheres and the rest of the brain of the rat. Now do the same for the human, using either a preserved brain or a model of the brain. Compare the ratios for the two brains and discuss the possible significance of any difference found.

For consideration

1 Relative to the rest of the brain, the olfactory lobes of the rat are much larger than the equivalent structures (called olfactory bulbs) in the human. Suggest a reason for this.

2 Does it follow that the smaller an animal's brain, the less intelligent it is? (You will need to consider the meaning of the word *intelligence* before you answer this question.)

3 How would you define the word *brain*? Suggest why the brain is located in the head rather than in some other part of the body.

Reference

Rowett, H.G.Q. *Dissection Guides*, III The Rat, John Murray, 1951. This guide provides more detail of the dissection and includes the names of the twelve cranial nerves.

REQUIREMENTS

Dissecting instruments
Dissecting board
Dissecting pins
Petri dish
Safety goggles
Rat from previous dissections
Human brain, preserved or model

9.4 INVESTIGATION

Some human reflexes

A **reflex** is a brief, stereotyped response to a stimulus. Most reflexes involve the brain, but some use only the spinal cord. Either way, reflexes can give us important information about the functioning of the nervous system, and abnormalities in our reflex responses can help doctors to diagnose certain disorders of the nervous system.

The purpose of this practical is to look at some human reflexes and draw such conclusions as we can about the way the nervous system functions. Work in pairs, one of you acting as subject, the other as experimenter.

Procedure

Knee jerk

1   The subject should sit on a table with his or her legs hanging loosely over the edge. With a small **tendon hammer**, the experimenter should tap the tendon just below the knee cap. *There is no need to tap hard!* If the tap is applied correctly the extensor muscle in the front of the thigh contracts and the leg gives a little kick.

2   Practise eliciting the knee jerk until you get it right every time. Try varying the intensity and location of the stimulus. Note that a response is elicited only by applying a sudden tap in just the right place. This is one of the simplest reflexes in the human: tapping the tendon stretches the muscle which responds by giving a brief contraction.

3   Draw a diagram of the nervous pathways responsible for the knee jerk. Bear in mind that when an extensor muscle contracts its antagonist (the flexor) should relax, and that when the leg gives a kick more than one extensor muscle may be involved.

4   Compare your diagram with Figure 9.11. How many nervous pathways, if any, have you left out?

Ankle jerk

1   The subject should kneel on a chair with his or her feet hanging loosely over the edge. The experimenter should now tap the tendon at the back of the foot, just above the heel. Describe the response. Reconstruct the reflex arc involved, using your experience with the knee jerk to help you.

2   Repeat tapping the tendon at approximately two taps per second. Does the response decline, get larger or stay the same? Explain.

Danger

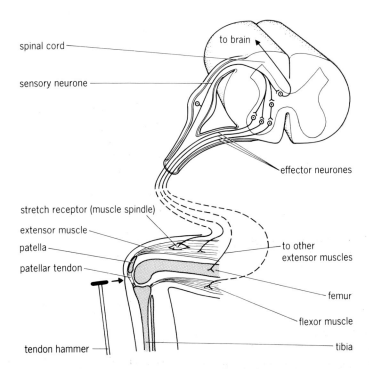

Figure 9.11 Nervous pathways involved in the knee jerk reflex.

Swallowing reflex

1   Swallow the saliva in your mouth cavity, and immediately afterwards try to swallow again – and again. You will probably find it difficult to swallow the second time, and even more difficult the third time. Why do you think this is?

2   Now drink a glass of water and note that you have no difficulty swallowing in rapid succession. Explain the difference.

Pupil reflex

This is the opening and closing of the pupil in response to light. Instructions for investigating it are given on page 167.

For consideration

1   What general conclusions about the working of the nervous system can be drawn from your observations of human reflexes?

2   The reflexes which you have looked at are simple, discrete responses. However, reflex actions may also form the basis of more complex activities such as locomotion. What part may reflex action play in locomotion?

3   In Figure 9.11 four of the synapses shown in the spinal cord are excitatory and one is inhibitory. Which one is likely to be inhibitory, and why?

REQUIREMENTS
Tendon hammer
Glass of drinking water

9.5 INVESTIGATION

Reaction times in humans

An organism's **reaction time** is the time interval between the moment the stimulus is applied and the moment when the response commences. Measuring reaction times can give us some indication of the speed at which impulses are transmitted in the nervous system. That is the main purpose of this investigation. Work in pairs, one of you acting as subject, the other as experimenter.

Method

Various devices can be used to measure reaction times but they all work on the same principle. There are two switches, one operated by the experimenter (switch E), the other by the subject (switch S). A recording device monitors the time interval between the operation of the two switches.

Procedure

It is important that the experimenter should avoid giving the subject any clue that he or she is about to press the E switch.

Reaction time to sight

1   With the subject watching, the experimenter presses switch E. As soon as the subject *sees* the experimenter pressing switch E, the subject presses switch S. The reaction time is then measured. Repeat at least ten times and calculate the average reaction time.

2   Test the hypothesis that the subject's visual reaction time decreases with practice.

Reaction time to touch

1   The subject should close his or her eyes, and the experimenter should rest his or her foot lightly on the subject's foot. The experimenter presses switch E and simultaneously treads on the subject's foot. Subject: as soon as you feel the pressure on your foot, press switch S. Measure the reaction time as before.

2   Assess whether the reaction time to touching the foot is slower than the visual reaction time. Identify possible sources of error and try to overcome them. (For example, errors may arise if the subject improves with practice.) If necessary use a statistical test to see if any difference is significant. Use the **t-test** (see page 251).

Reaction time to coloured lights

Switch E should be connected to two coloured lights, one red, the other green. Find out if a person reacts at the same speed to a red light as to a green light of the same intensity. Take precautions to avoid sources of error, as before. Use the **t-test** to see if any difference between the reaction times is significant. Do your results support the use of red as a warning colour?

Reaction time to sound

Switch E should be connected to a sound generator and headphones which should be worn by the subject. Test the hypothesis that a subject reacts more quickly to a loud sound than to a quiet sound. Take precautions to avoid sources of error, and apply the **t-test** as before.

Estimating transmission speed

With a ruler measure the length of the nervous pathway between the point where the stimulus is received (foot, eye, ear, as the case may be) and the part of the body which responds (the finger with which the subject presses the S switch). If available, use a text book of human anatomy to confirm the pathways. From your measurements calculate the speed in metres per second at which impulses are transmitted in the nervous system.

Variation in reaction times

What sort of variation is there in the reaction times of different people? Choose one of the reaction times you have measured (sight, touch, red light, green light or sound) and compare with other members of your class. Present the data as a histogram.

For consideration

1   What are the possible causes of delay between the application of a stimulus and the onset of the response?
2   Reaction times give only an approximate idea of how quickly nerve impulses are transmitted in the nervous system? Why only approximate? Suggest other, more accurate, ways of measuring transmission speeds in the human nervous system.

Suitable systems for recording reaction times include a pair of switches linked to a triggered cathode ray oscilloscope, microcomputer, chart recorder or stimulus marker writing on a kymograph. If none of these is available, reaction time may be measured by timing how long it takes for the subject to catch a falling ruler. The distance the ruler falls, d (in metres), can be converted to the time taken, t (in seconds), using the equation of motion $d = \frac{1}{2} at^2$ where a is the ruler's acceleration due to gravity, namely 9.8 m s^{-2}. Rearranging we have:

$$t = \sqrt{\frac{d}{4.9}}$$

Reference

Michael Buck, A non-invasive method for finding the speed of conduction of a nerve using a human subject. *Journal of Biological Education*, Vol. 21, No. 2, Summer 1987. This article describes a method for measuring the delay between the stimulus and response in the knee jerk by means of a simple electrical circuit and voltmeter, with optional use of an oscilloscope or microcomputer for recording.

Nerve physiology

Sheffield Bioscience Physiology Programs include a computer simulation of experiments performed on a frog sciatic nerve illustrating the properties of nerve action potentials.

REQUIREMENTS

Reaction time recorder
Lights, red and green
Sound generator with volume control
Headphones
Ruler
Textbook of human anatomy, if available

9.6 INVESTIGATION

Analysis of human skin as a receptor

The efficiency of the skin in monitoring changes at the surface of the body depends on:

• The range of stimuli to which the receptor cells respond
• The sensitivity of the receptor cells
• The ability of the receptor cells to distinguish between two identical stimuli applied simultaneously (two point touch discrimination)
• The rapidity with which the receptor cells adapt when stimulated repeatedly (sensory adaptation).

The purpose of this investigation is to explore these four aspects of the skin as a receptor.

Guidance

The range of stimuli to which the skin responds

Danger

With a fine ball-point pen, rule a grid of not less than 25 squares, each with an area of 4 mm², on the back of your partner's hand. Then explore each square in turn for its sensitivity to touch, heat, cold and pain. Devise your own method of applying each type of stimulus, ensuring that there is no confusion between one type and another. *Be sure that the skin is not damaged by any of the stimuli in this or any of the subsequent experiments.*

Sensitivity

Assess the sensitivity of different parts of the skin to touch. The difficulty in assessing sensitivity, if you apply the stimuli by hand, is quantifying the stimulus, i.e. knowing how strong it is. Try to overcome this difficulty as best you can.

Two point touch discrimination

The aim here is to find the minimum distance which must exist between two simultaneously applied identical stimuli for the stimuli to be detected as two separate stimuli rather than as a single stimulus. Use a pair of dividers to apply two simultaneous tactile stimuli to your partner's arm. Repeat, varying the distance between the two points of the dividers, until you find the minimum distance for discrimination. Repeat the experiment in different parts of the body, including the thigh and fingertips.

Adaptation

With a mounted needle wiggle one of the hairs on the back of your partner's hand until he or she ceases to feel it. In this way determine how long it takes for the receptors at the base of the hair to adapt to repeated stimulation.

For consideration

1   Make a list of all the difficulties you experienced in carrying out these experiments, and in drawing conclusions.
2   What are the roles of touch, temperature and pain receptors in the normal functioning of the human body?
3   Is the skin sensitive to any other types of stimulation besides the ones which you have investigated in this practical? What might be the function(s) of such sensitivity?
4   Which part of your skin is most efficient at two point touch discrimination? How would you explain this in terms of the receptors in the skin? What are its practical applications?

REQUIREMENTS
Fine ball point pen
Ruler
Dividers
Mounted needle
Items requested by individual students

9.7 PRACTICAL EXERCISE

Structure of the mammalian eye

You have probably seen a diagram of the mammalian eye like the one in Figure 9.12. But what is the inside of the eye really like? In this investigation you will dissect the eye of a large mammal such as a sheep or pig and examine prepared sections of the eye under the microscope. You will then appreciate how a combination of dissection and microscope work has enabled scientists to build up a picture of the eye.

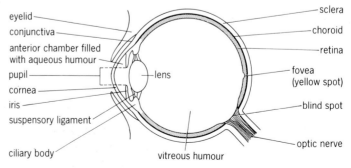

Figure 9.12 Structure of the mammalian eye as seen in a diagrammatic cross section through the centre of the eyeball.

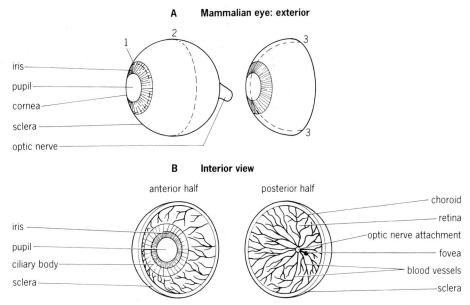

Figure 9.13 One way of opening up the eye. The dotted lines in diagram A show three different cuts that should be made in succession. Cut 1 is an *almost* complete circular cut, enabling the cornea to be deflected like opening a book. Cut 2 is a completely circular cut, dividing the eyeball into anterior and posterior halves; this enables you to see inside, as shown in diagram B. Cut 3 is a vertical cut through the anterior half of the eye; cut to one side of the lens so that it remains attached to the wall of the eye.

Guidance

Dissection of the eye

The posterior part of the eyeball will probably have fat clinging to it. Remove the fat so as to expose the **optic nerve** and **eye muscles**. Investigate the eye muscles and reflect upon their functions.

To see the inside of the eye necessitates cutting into the eyeball. The main objectives are to see how the **lens** is attached to the **ciliary body** and how the **optic nerve** is attached to the **retina**. Without looking at Figure 9.13, consider how best to cut into the eye so as to achieve these objectives with minimum destruction. You may find it helpful to examine a model of the eye first. This will help you to see where the various internal structures are in relation to each other, so you can decide where best to make your cuts.

Now look at Figure 9.13. This explains one way of cutting into the eye. However, it is not the only way; you may have thought of a better way.

After you have cut into the eye, you will need to remove the gelatinous **vitreous humour** from inside the eyeball. What is the function of the vitreous humour?

Which features of the eye shown in Figure 9.12 can you see in your dissected eye? Use a hand lens or binocular microscope as necessary.

Sections of the eye

Examine sections of the anterior and posterior portions of the eye. The anterior portion will give you details of the **conjunctiva**, **cornea**, **iris**, **ciliary body** and **lens**. The posterior portion will give you details of the **sclera**, **choroid** and **retina**. Use whatever magnification is necessary to see the parts of the eye shown in figure 9.12.

Further analysis of the eye

Find out, if you do not already know, the functions of the iris and ciliary body. Predict what structures should be present inside the iris and ciliary body to enable them to carry out these functions. Then examine the iris and ciliary body under high power to see if your predictions are correct.

For consideration

1   Which features of the eye shown in Figure 9.12 can be seen in your dissected eye, and which ones are only visible in the sections?
2   Assess the relative importance of dissection and microscopic studies in establishing the structure of a complex organ such as the eye.

9.8 PRACTICAL EXERCISE

Microscopic structure of the retina

The **retina** of the eye contains **photoreceptor cells** sensitive to light. Collectively the photoreceptor cells enable an accurate image of the environment to be registered and transmitted to the brain. In this practical we shall look in detail at the microscopic structure of the retina.

Procedure

1   Examine a vertical section of the retina which has been stained with a silver stain to show up the neurones and photoreceptor cells. Distinguish between the various layers, using Figure 9.14 to help you interpret them. Notice that the nerve fibres which lead to the optic nerve are on the inner side of the layer of photoreceptor cells. Light rays that have entered the eye have to pass through these fibres, and the layer of bipolar neurones, before they reach the photoreceptor cells. This **inverted retina** derives from the way the eye develops and is typical of all vertebrates.

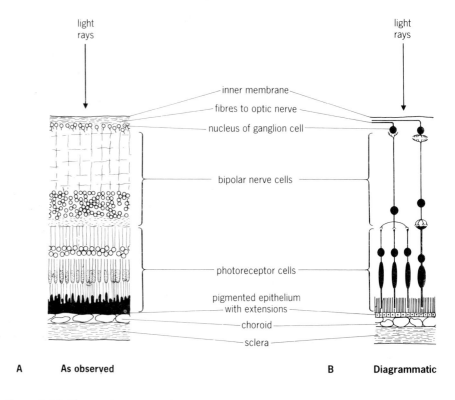

Figure 9.14 Microscopic structure of the mammalian retina and associated layers.

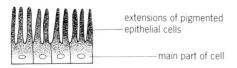

Figure 9.15 Detail of the pigmented epithelium on the inner side of the choroid.

2   Observe the **choroid** and **sclera** outside the retina. The choroid is vascular and its epithelial lining is pigmented (Figure 9.15). The sclera is composed of tough connective tissue: mainly collagen fibres with some elastic fibres. What are the functions of the choroid and sclera?

3   Examine the photoreceptor cells in detail under high power, preferably using oil immersion. Can you distinguish **rods** and **cones**? Whether or not you can will depend on which part of the retina your section passes through and how the section has been stained. Generally cones are fatter than rods (Figure 9.16). The centre of the **fovea** contains nothing but densely packed cones. Further out the cones are fatter and rods are present as well. As one moves further away from the fovea the number of cones decreases until, at the extreme edge of the retina, only rods are present.

4   If you have a well-stained section which passes through the fovea, use an eyepiece graticule and stage micrometer to estimate the relative frequencies of rods and cones at different distances from the fovea. Present your results as a graph.

5   Figure 9.17 is an electron micrograph of a vertical section through a single rod. Suggest two features which may tell us how rods work.

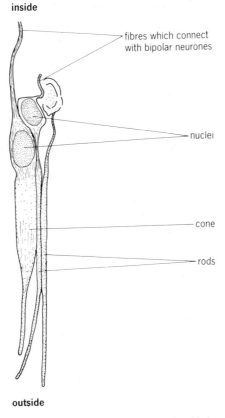

inside

fibres which connect
with bipolar neurones

nuclei

cone

rods

outside

Figure 9.16 A cone and two rods lying side by side as seen in a section of the retina under the light microscope.

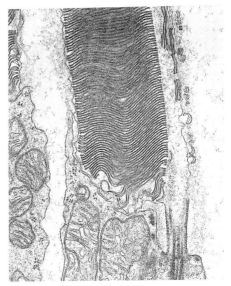

Figure 9.17 A single rod in detail, based on electron micrographs.

For consideration

1   What is the functional significance of the way rods and cones are distributed in the retina?
2   What are the possible functional consequences of having an inverted retina?
3   When a person gets a 'detached retina', part of the retina comes away from the choroid and sclera underneath. What effect would you expect this to have on vision, and why?

9.9 PRACTICAL EXERCISE

Visual acuity of the human eye

The efficiency of the eye at seeing objects clearly, that is its **visual acuity**, depends on the eye's **resolving power**. This is the ability of the eye to distinguish between two point stimuli, e.g. two dots on a piece of paper. In practice this depends on two factors: the distance between the two dots and their distance from the eye.

In this practical you will measure the resolving power and visual acuity of your own eyes.

Theoretical background

Figure 9.18 shows how light rays enter the eye from two dots, P and Q. The point X where the two light rays cross is called the **nodal point**. The angle PXQ is known as the **visual angle**. In Figure 9.18A the images of the two dots fall on two receptor cells separated by one in between. Because of this the person will see two separate dots.

Now consider what happens if the two dots are further away from the eye (Figure 9.18B). The visual angle is now smaller, and the images of the two dots fall on a single receptor cell. Under these circumstances the person sees only one dot. The same would apply if the images of the two dots fell on two next-door receptor cells. *The rule is that to be perceived separately the two images must fall on two receptor cells which are*

A

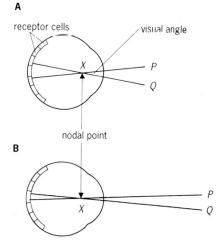

receptor cells   visual angle

X P

Q

nodal point

B

P

X Q

Figure 9.18 The theoretical basis of visual acuity.

separated by at least one receptor cell in between. (The same explanation applies to two point touch discrimination in the skin.)

Procedure
Estimating the visual angle

1 On a card draw two vertical lines, each 1 mm wide and separated by 1 mm. Hang the card on the wall. Stand 0.5 m from the card: at this distance you will have no difficulty distinguishing between the two lines. Now stand 5 m from the card: at this distance the lines will appear fused.
2 Starting at a distance of 5 m, gradually approach the card and note the maximum distance from the card at which you can see two separate lines. Measure this distance. We shall take this as the distance between the card and the nodal point in the eye.
3 Assuming that the distance between the nodal point and the retina is 15 mm, work out the distance between the two images on the retina. You can do this by calculation or by constructing a scale diagram similar to those in Figure 9.18.
4 From your calculation or diagram determine the visual angle. In this case, where the two dots can just be perceived separately, we call it the **minimum visual angle** or **angle of distinctiveness**.

Estimating visual acuity

1 Examine a **Snellen chart**. This is used by opticians to test people's eyes. On the chart you will see that each letter, or set of letters, has a number underneath: this is the maximum distance, in metres, at which a person with normal vision can see the letters distinctly.

   Visual acuity is given by the following equation:

$$V = \frac{d}{D}$$

   where V is the visual acuity, d is the maximum distance at which a given letter can be read by the subject, and D is the distance at which the same letter can be read by a 'normal' eye.
2 Hang the Snellen chart on the wall and determine the visual acuity of each of your eyes separately, and of both eyes together. If you wear glasses, determine your visual acuity with and without glasses. How does your eyesight compare with that of other members of your class?

For consideration

1 Explain your ability to see a given letter on the Snellen chart in terms of the visual angle and the size of the retinal image.
2 What is the relationship between visual acuity and the resolving power of the eye?
3 The width of a cone is approximately 5 μm. How does this relate to the distance between the two images on the retina which you calculated in this experiment? Account for any discrepancies.

REQUIREMENTS

White card
Felt pen
Ruler
Tape measure
Snellen chart

9.10 INVESTIGATION

Danger

Some functional properties of the human eye

Much can be learned about the way the eye works from simple experiments which you can do on yourself or your partner. In the investigations and tests suggested below, plan exactly what you are going to do beforehand. Make sure your plan has a sound theoretical basis and that unambiguous conclusions can be drawn from the results. *Do not try anything that may harm you or your partner:* check your plans with your teacher before you start.

Procedure
Investigations and tests

1 Investigate the effect of different light intensities on the diameter of the pupil.
2 Investigate the effect of viewing near and far objects on the diameter of the pupil.
3 Test the hypothesis that for judging distances two eyes are needed (**binocular vision**).
4 Under what circumstances do you see double images?

5   Test the hypothesis that the central part of your retina (i.e. the foveal region) can distinguish between different colours but the peripheral part cannot.

6   Test the hypothesis that the peripheral part of your retina is more sensitive than the central part in conditions of low illumination.

7   Investigate the ability of the eye to distinguish between colours in conditions of low illumination.

8   Investigate the effect of subjecting the eyes to a bright light on subsequent vision in dim conditions (**dark adaptation**).

Interpret the results of each of the above investigations and tests in the light of what you know about the structure and functioning of the eye.

Figure 9.19 Chart for demonstrating the blind spot.

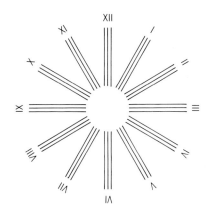

Figure 9.20 Chart for diagnosing astigmatism.

Other tests

1   Look at Figure 9.19 from a distance of at least 40 cm. Close your left eye and focus on A with your right eye. Now slowly move the book towards you. What happens to B as you do this? Repeat the process, but this time focus on B and see what happens to A. This is a way of demonstrating the **blind spot**. What is the blind spot caused by?

2   If you wear glasses or contact lenses, remove them. Look at Figure 9.20 through one eye from a distance of at least 30 cm. Do some of the radii appear darker and clearer than others? Repeat with the other eye. This is used as a test for **astigmatism**. Having carried out the test, explain what an astigmatism is.

3   Use colour vision test cards to find out if you, and/or others in your class, are **red-green colour blind**. Follow the instructions provided with the cards. Try to find out what red and green look like to a colour blind person. What causes this sort of colour blindness?

For consideration

Which of these investigations and tests
a   have a practical medical value,
b   tell us how the eye works,
c   provide information on the structure of the eye?

Explain your answers.

References

Ward, A. *Experimenting with Light and Illusions* (Batsford-Dryad, 1985); and 'Magic' in your eyes, *School Science Review*, Vol. 71, No. 256, March 1990. Some fascinating practical phenomena are described.

9.11 INVESTIGATION

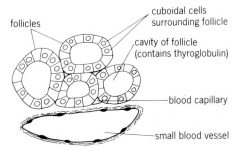

Figure 9.21 Part of a thyroid gland as seen in section under the microscope.

Microscopic structure of the thyroid gland

The **thyroid gland** is situated in the neck close to the larynx (see page 125). Its function is to secrete the hormone **thyroxine** into the bloodstream. A chemical which gives rise to the hormone is stored in special cavities within the gland.

The purpose of this investigation is to look at the thyroid gland under the microscope and relate its structure to its function.

Procedure

1   Examine a section of thyroid gland under medium power and use Figure 9.21 to help you interpret its structure. Notice in particular numerous **follicles**, each surrounded by a single layer of cuboidal epithelial cells (see page 76). The cavity (lumen) of each follicle contains a substance, **thyroglobulin**, which takes up stains and is usually visible in sections.

2   Consider the following information on how the thyroid works:

The follicle cells absorb iodide and other metabolites from the bloodstream. They synthesise thyroglobulin from these raw materials and secrete it into the lumen of the follicle for temporary storage. When required, they absorb thyroglobulin from the lumen and convert it into thyroxine which is then secreted into the bloodstream as instructed by thyroid-stimulating hormone from the pituitary gland.

What predictions can you make from this information about (a) the relationship between the follicle cells and the blood system, and (b) the fine structure of the follicle cells?

3   Examine your slide again, this time under high power. Also, if available, study an electron micrograph of thyroid tissue. To what extent are your predictions confirmed? What further information, if any, do you require?

For consideration

1   An essential requirement for the production of thyroxine is iodide. Where does this come from, and what sort of experiments would need to be carried out to confirm your suggestion?

2   Suggest a mechanism by which thyroid-stimulating hormone causes thyroxine to be secreted by the follicle cells.

9.12 INVESTIGATION

Examination of an adrenal gland

Often when we invite you to look at tissues and organs under the microscope we give you various clues as to what to expect to see, or we ask you to predict what you are likely to see from various theoretical considerations. However, no such help was given to the original research workers who looked at these things for the first time. Usually all they had to go on was the *appearance* of the material as they saw it under the microscope. The purpose of this investigation is to see how helpful predictions can be.

Procedure

1   Examine a section of an **adrenal gland**. If you already know a bit about this organ, forget it! Look at it without preconceived ideas. What do you make of it? Try to identify its various components (epithelia, blood vessels etc.). Is there *anything* about the microscopic appearance of this organ that gives you a clue, however slight, about its function?

2   Now read the following statements about the adrenal gland:

A The adrenal gland produces hormones which are secreted directly into the bloodstream.

B Two main hormones are secreted: **adrenaline** from the central part of the gland (medulla), **adrenal cortical hormones** (e.g. aldosterone) from the surrounding part (cortex).

C There are three types of adrenal cortical hormone, each with its own function.

D It has been suggested that the adrenal medulla may be a conglomeration of modified nerve endings.

3   From each statement make one or more predictions concerning the appearance of the adrenal gland under the microscope. Then look at your section and see if the predictions are correct.

4   Make a two-column table with predictions on the left and observed features of the gland on the right.

For consideration

1   How useful were your predictions in helping you to interpret the microscopic structure of the adrenal gland?

2   In what circumstances might predictions be unhelpful when trying to interpret objects under the microscope.

3   Was it sometimes difficult to see from your slide if a particular prediction was correct? Give an example, and suggest how a better, more informative slide might be prepared.

4   What has led scientists to suggest that the adrenal medulla might be a conglomeration of modified nerve endings?

Examination of the pituitary gland

The **pituitary gland** is the most complex of all the mammalian endocrine glands. It secretes numerous hormones many of which are responsible for controlling the activities of other endocrine glands. It is connected to the hypothalamus region of the brain with which it is closely associated functionally.

The aim of this investigation is to look at the general structure of the pituitary and gain some insight into how it works.

Guidance

The pituitary gland consists of two main parts, the **anterior lobe** and the **posterior lobe**. Examine a vertical longitudinal section of the pituitary gland under low power. Use Figure 9.22 to help you identify its parts.

This is how the anterior lobe secretes a hormone. Nerve cells in the hypothalamus secrete a chemical into a blood vessel. This chemical is carried in the blood vessel to the anterior lobe where it stimulates certain cells to release the appropriate hormone into the bloodstream.

The posterior lobe works differently. In this case nerve cells in the hypothalamus produce the hormone which flows down the axons to the posterior lobe where it is stored in expanded nerve terminals. The hormone is later released into the bloodstream in response to electrical impulses reaching the posterior lobe via the axons.

Examine the anterior and posterior lobes of the pituitary under high power. Can you find any features which support the description given above.

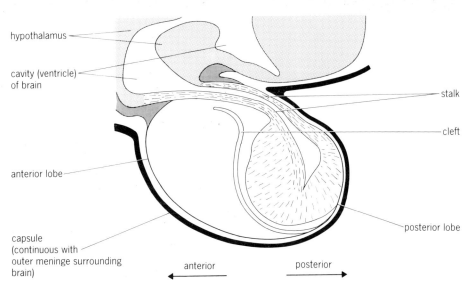

Figure 9.22 Vertical longitudinal section of a mammalian pituitary gland showing its main parts.

For consideration

1 During embryonic development the pituitary gland is formed by a downgrowth from the floor of the brain fusing with an upgrowth from the roof of the mouth cavity. Which lobe is formed in each of these two ways? Explain your reasoning.

2 What you saw in your section of the pituitary will have depended on how the section was stained. If you had stained the section yourself what sort of stain(s) would you have used, and why?

PROJECTS

Before starting a project, discuss your intended procedure with your teacher.

1 Devise a method for recording on a kymograph or chart recorder a person's knee jerk or ankle jerk. Then investigate factors that affect the size of the response, e.g. where precisely the stimulus is applied, the intensity of the stimulus, and which leg or foot (left or right) is tested. Can the subject consciously suppress the reflex? Is the size of the response larger if the subject is reading a book aloud while the test is carried out?

2 Construct your own reaction time recorder. Ideally this should be compact, easy to use and provide as many stimulus options as possible, e.g. touch, sight and sound. This provides a good opportunity to apply technology to biology.

3 Investigate the effect of different factors on a person's reaction time. Possible factors might include time of day (e.g. early morning and late at night) and drinking e.g. coffee or a measured amount of an energy drink such as lucozade.

4 Test the hypothesis that people who are good at fast ball games, e.g. tennis, squash and cricket, have quicker reaction times than other people. Be sure you obtain sufficient data from enough people, and evaluate it statistically.

5 Investigate the effect on a person's reaction time of combining different stimuli. For example, the subject might be asked to respond only when a certain type of light stimulus is combined with a certain type of sound stimulus. Is there any evidence that the subject improves with practice or that certain combinations of stimuli evoke quicker responses than others? Which properties of the nervous system are being demonstrated by such tests, and what use might be made of them in preparing people for different kinds of occupation?

6 Blind people can 'read' with their fingertips by using Braille. Investigate people's ability to recognise shapes and/or the positions of dots with their fingertips. You might use Braille itself and/or the alternative system Moon, both of which are available from the Royal National Institute for the Blind. Alternatively you might devise 'touch tests' of your own. This investigation will need careful planning. Decide exactly what you want to find out, and don't try to do too much.

7 Use a Snellen chart to estimate the visual acuity, without wearing glasses, of different people of approximately the same age. Does the variation between people show a normal distribution (see page 167)?

8 Test the hypothesis that the maximum distance from the eye at which letters of a certain size can be seen clearly decreases with age.

Figure 9.23 Computer representation of.....guess who?

9 Look at the face in Figure 9.23. Who is it? What features of this computerised image enable you to identify her? Use this as the jumping off point for investigating the minimum amount of visual information required by people to recognise an object. You might, for example, present volunteers with progressively more detailed pictures of a well known person and find out at what point they recognise him or her. Try to devise a way of quantifying the amount of information in the pictures. Assess which particular features (eyes, shape of mouth etc.) are most important in enabling recognition, and relate these to the drawings of well known people made by cartoonists.

10 Devise an optical illusion in which a picture or model can be seen as two different objects. Use it to test the hypothesis that, once a person 'sees' one of the two alternatives, it is difficult for him or her to see the other one.

11 Investigate the ability of different people to discriminate between sounds of slightly different pitch. Test the hypothesis that musicians are better at pitch-discrimination than non-musicians.

Muscles, movement and behaviour

Action of skeletal muscle

Some of the physiological properties of skeletal muscle can be investigated by recording the contractions of the flexor muscle of your index finger on a kymograph or chart recorder. That is what you will be trying to do in this practical. Work in pairs, one of you acting as the subject, the other as experimenter. The following instructions assume that a kymograph is being used.

Procedure

Tie one end of a length of thread to the subject's index finger as shown in Figure 10.1. Place the hand in a harness which immobilises the whole of the hand except the

A   The set-up

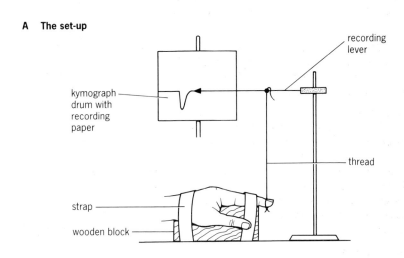

B   The lever in detail

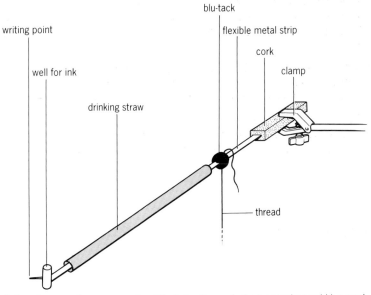

Figure 10.1 Set-up for recording movements of the index finger. A chart recorder could be used instead of a kymograph.

distal joint of the index finger. With a small piece of blu-tack attach the other end of the thread to a lever fitted with a writing point. Bring the writing point into contact with the recording paper so that it will record accurately the movements of the finger on the rotating drum of the kymograph. Run several trials in order to get used to recording the finger movements.

The maximum speed of contraction

With the kymograph set at about 10 mm per second, record a single very quick flexion of the finger, i.e. make the muscle contract as quickly as possible. Knowing the speed at which the kymograph drum is rotating, calculate the maximum speed of contraction of the flexor muscle. Think about how best to express the speed. Is the contraction produced by a single impulse in the nerve that supplies the muscle, or more than one impulse? Explain your answer.

The minimum speed of contraction

Repeat the previous experiment, but this time flex the finger as slowly as possible. Calculate the minimum speed of contraction of the flexor muscle.

The size of contraction

Record the smallest and largest flexions of the finger that you can produce, again as quickly as possible. What determines the size of the contraction undergone by the muscle?

A sustained contraction

With the kymograph set at a slower speed (about 1 mm per second), flex the finger slowly then keep it as still as possible in the flexed position for at least five seconds. Does the finger fluctuate? If so, suggest an explanation for the fluctuations. Relate your observations to the way posture is maintained.

Fatigue

With the kymograph still set at a slow speed, repeatedly flex your finger at maximum speed for as long as possible. Study the pattern of recordings as the muscle gradually fatigues. Suggest possible causes of muscle fatigue.

Presenting the results

Remove the paper from the kymograph drum. Cut out the recordings and stick them in your practical notebook. Write a full explanation alongside each recording, answering the questions asked above.

REQUIREMENTS

Kymograph or chart recorder with
   recording paper
Harness for hand
Recording lever
Thread
Ink for writing point of lever
Blu-tack

For consideration

1 Outline the sources of error and ambiguity in this investigation. Suggest a more accurate way of investigating the physiological properties of muscle.

2 One of the main observations to emerge from this investigation is how varied the speed, size and duration of a muscle's contractions can be. What part is played by the nervous system in producing such *graded* contractions, and why is this important in the normal functioning of the body?

Note: *Sheffield Bioscience Physiology Programs include a computer simulation of experiments on muscle contraction and neuromuscular transmission.*

10.2 PRACTICAL EXERCISE

Structure of skeletal muscle

Analysing the structure of skeletal muscle is a useful exercise for three reasons:
• It provides an excellent opportunity to relate structure to function
• It illustrates the limitations of the light microscope
• It shows how the electron microscope can be used to predict how a biological structure works.

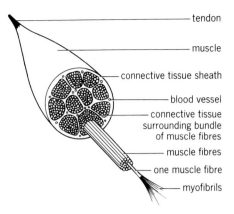

Figure 10.2 The structural components of a skeletal muscle.

- tendon
- muscle
- connective tissue sheath
- blood vessel
- connective tissue surrounding bundle of muscle fibres
- muscle fibres
- one muscle fibre
- myofibrils

Corrosive
Ethanoic acid

Procedure

1   Dissect out a whole muscle from the leg of the rat which you have dissected on previous occasions. Alternatively use shin meat from a butcher. Cut the **tendons** by which the muscle is attached to the bones.

2   The muscle is enclosed within a connective tissue **sheath**. Refer to Figure 10.2 to see how the **muscle fibres** are arranged within the sheath. With needles break through the sheath and tease out a few fibres on a slide. Crush some of them with a glass rod, add a drop of sodium chloride solution (0.75%) and put on a coverslip. Examine under the microscope. Can you see **striations** running across the fibres? Irrigate with ethanoic acid to see nuclei.

3   Examine a prepared longitudinal section of skeletal muscle under low power. You will now see the muscle fibres more clearly. Striations and nuclei should be plainly visible (Figure 10.3A).

4   Now turn over to high power and examine a single fibre in detail. In a good section, well stained and illuminated, you should be able to see very fine **myofibrils** inside the fibre, and some detail of the striations (Figure 10.3B).

5   Examine a low magnification electron micrograph of skeletal muscle. The myofibrils are now sufficiently magnified to enable you to see them in detail. Try to relate the pattern of striations in the electron micrograph to your section under the light microscope. Use Figure 10.3C to help you.

6   Now examine a high magnification electron micrograph of a single myofibril. Can you see that the myofibril is composed of **filaments**? Distinguish between the thick (myosin) and thin (actin) filaments. Can you see how they are arranged? Does their arrangement agree with the diagrammatic representation in Figure 10.3D?

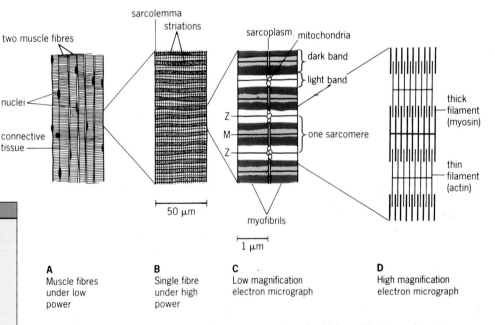

A
Muscle fibres under low power

B
Single fibre under high power

C
Low magnification electron micrograph

D
High magnification electron micrograph

Figure 10.3 The microscopic structure of skeletal muscle at, from left to right, increasing magnifications.

For consideration

1   Compare the information about the structure of skeletal muscle provided by the light microscope and electron microscope.

2   What contribution has the electron microscope made to our understanding of how skeletal muscle contracts?

3   What would you expect Figure 10.3D to look like if the muscle was fully contracted? Explain in as much detail as you can how the change from the relaxed to the contracted state comes about.

Comparison of smooth, cardiac and skeletal muscle

Vertebrate muscle is classified into **smooth muscle**, **cardiac muscle** (heart muscle) and **skeletal muscle** (striated muscle). We looked at skeletal muscle in detail in the last practical. The purpose of this investigation is to compare skeletal muscle with the other two types of muscle.

Guidance

Examine prepared slides of smooth, cardiac and skeletal muscle. Make drawings of all three types as they appear under the light microscope in the best possible conditions. Pay particular attention to the **muscle fibres**. Resist the temptation to include features which you think should be there but which you cannot actually see.

For each type of muscle try to answer these questions:
1 Are the muscle fibres separate or interconnected?
2 Is each muscle fibre composed of separate cells or are the cells combined into a **syncytium**? (Hint: locate the nuclei and see if they are separated from each other by 'partitions' running across the fibre)
3 Can **myofibrils** be seen inside the fibres?
4 Are **striations** visible inside the fibres?

Make a table comparing the three types of muscle. The table should provide answers to the above questions.

For consideration

1 Knowing where these three types of muscle occur in the body, predict the functional properties of each type.
2 For each type of muscle relate one structural feature, visible under the light microscope, to the functional properties of the muscle.
3 In the electron microscope, two of the three types of muscle appear very similar but the other one is quite different. Which two do you think look alike? How do you arrive at your answer?

REQUIREMENTS

Microscope
Skeletal (striated) muscle, LS
Smooth muscle, LS
Cardiac muscle, LS

The vertebrate skeleton

As the solid framework to which the muscles are attached, the skeleton is one of the most important parts of the body. The skeleton of all land-living vertebrates is essentially the same, but the detailed structure of the component parts varies according to the method of locomotion.

In this practical exercise you will compare the skeletons of different vertebrates, relating the differences to their respective methods of locomotion.

Procedure

1 Start by examining the skeleton of a **rabbit** or **rat**. Of the animals whose skeletons you will study, this has the most conventional method of locomotion, i.e. walking on all fours. Identify the parts of the skeleton, using Figure 10.4 to help you. Observe the **articulating surfaces** where one bone moves against another, and various **processes** (projections) for the attachment of ligaments and tendons. Such processes are sometimes flattened to allow the attachment of particularly large muscles.
2 Examine the skeleton of a **frog**. Compare it with the rabbit or rat skeleton, particularly with respect to the sacral vertebrae, pelvic girdle and hindlimbs. How is the structure of the frog's skeleton related to its method of locomotion?
3 Examine the skeleton of a bird, e.g. **pigeon**. Compare it with the rabbit or rat skeleton, particularly with respect to the pectoral girdle and forelimbs. Notice that the sternum is drawn out into a deep **keel**. This is for the attachment of the flight muscles. There are two flight muscles on each side of the body. One of them pulls the wing down, and the other one pulls it up. How do you think the flight muscles are arranged in order to achieve these actions?
4 Examine a **human skeleton**, or a model of one. Compare it with the rabbit or rat skeleton, particularly with respect to the structure of the pelvis and vertebral column. To what extent is the structure of the human skeleton related to the fact that the human is bipedal?

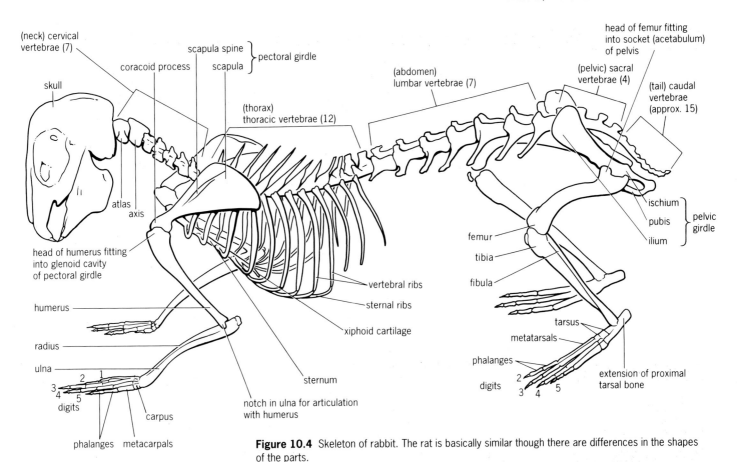

Figure 10.4 Skeleton of rabbit. The rat is basically similar though there are differences in the shapes of the parts.

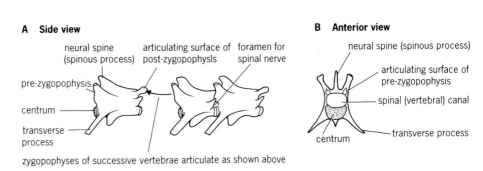

Figure 10.5 Lumbar vertebrae of rabbit.

Other things you can do

1 Compare an individual lumbar vertebra of the rabbit or rat with that of the human. Identify the parts of the rabbit or rat vertebra, using Figure 10.5 to help you. Find the equivalent parts in the human vertebra. Try to explain the differences in functional terms.

2 Study individual vertebrae from different regions of the vertebral column of the rabbit or rat and human. Relate any regional differences to the functions of the vertebrae in different parts of the body.

3 Examine the skeletons of other vertebrates, as available. If possible include a **bony fish (teleost)**, **lizard** and **snake**. Try to relate the structure of their skeletons to their different methods of locomotion.

For consideration

1 The skeleton of a mammal that walks on all fours has been likened to a bridge. In what sense is the skeleton a bridge, and what sort of bridge do you think it is?

2 To what extent does the human skeleton depart from a bridge construction? Can you think of a more appropriate analogy for the human skeleton?

REQUIREMENTS

Mounted skeletons of rabbit or rat, frog, bird (e.g. pigeon) and human (or model)
Vertebrae of rabbit or rat
Vertebrae of human

10.5 PRACTICAL EXERCISE

Microscopic structure of bone

First think about the stresses and strains to which a bone such as the femur is subjected. What sort of properties will it need to possess? How can a bone be formed, during a mammal's growth, so that it finishes up with these properties? Bear these questions in mind as you look at the microscopic structure of **bone tissue**.

Bone tissue varies in its microscopic structure according to where it occurs. Here we shall look at **compact bone**, a very dense and hard kind of bone tissue which occurs in the shaft of limb bones such as the femur.

Procedure

Bone tissue consists of a non-living **matrix** (an organic material impregnated with mineral salts) and the cells which give rise to it (**osteoblasts**). In compact bone tissue these two components are arranged in a characteristic pattern.

1   Examine a transverse section of compact bone. It consists of numerous **Haversian canals** each surrounded by a series of concentric rings of bone matrix (Figure 10.6A).

2   Examine an individual Haversian system in detail (Figure 10.6B). Notice that the central Haversian canal contains blood vessels. The concentric layers of bone matrix are called **lamellae**. Observe **lacunae** and **canaliculi** which house the bone-forming osteoblasts and their fine processes.

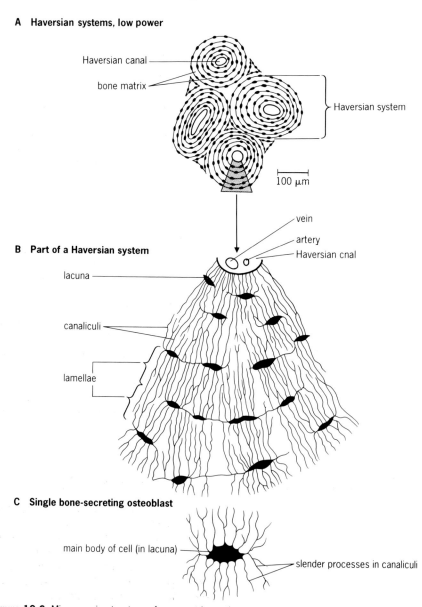

A   Haversian systems, low power

Haversian canal

bone matrix

Haversian system

100 μm

B   Part of a Haversian system

vein

artery

Haversian cnal

lacuna

canaliculi

lamellae

C   Single bone-secreting osteoblast

main body of cell (in lacuna)

slender processes in canaliculi

Figure 10.6 Microscopic structure of compact bone tissue as seen in a transverse section.

3 Focus on an individual lacuna and the canaliculi extending from it. Reconstruct the shape of a single osteoblast (Figure 10.6C).

4 To gain a three-dimensional picture of compact bone, examine a longitudinal section as well as a transverse section. Make a three-dimensional model of a sample of compact bone tissue, based on your observations.

For consideration

1 Suggest as many functions as you can think of for the blood vessels in the Haversian canals.

2 The canaliculi are important during the development of bone tissue. Explain.

3 Suppose you were employed by a construction firm as a consultant to suggest a building technique based on compact bone tissue. What might you suggest, and what would be the scientific basis for your suggestion?

REQUIREMENTS

Microscope
Plasticine
Compact bone, TS and LS

10.6 INVESTIGATION

Analysis of the muscles in the leg of a mammal

The purpose of this is to study the muscles in the hind leg of a mammal. There are two ways of carrying out such an analysis. One way is to adopt an anatomical approach, each muscle being carefully dissected away from the skeleton and named according to its position. This is what medical and veterinary students do in their anatomy courses. We shall adopt a functional approach, the muscles being described in terms of the actions they produce.

Guidance

The analysis can be carried out on the leg of the rat that you have been using for dissection, or on a pig's trotter obtained from the butcher.

Systematically dissect all the muscles of the leg, starting with the superficial ones and then proceeding to the ones underneath. Free each muscle from its neighbours by cutting away the connective tissue in between. Follow the muscle upwards to its **origin** and downwards to its **insertion**. The origin and insertion are usually on bones, but in some cases they may be on the connective tissue sheath surrounding other muscles.

When you have freed a muscle from its neighbours, pull it so as to determine its action. Then, and only then, cut it at its origin and/or insertion and either deflect it or remove it. This will enable you to see, and dissect, the deeper muscles beneath.

At appropriate stages of your investigation, make diagrams of the leg showing the various muscles. Name the muscles according to their action on the leg (protractor, retractor, abductor, adductor, flexor, extensor, rotator). Make clear which joints the muscles act on, and which muscles are antagonistic to each other.

For consideration

1 How many muscles have you accounted for in the leg? Are there any which you expected to find but have not?

2 How many muscles belong to each of the groups mentioned above?

3 Which muscles do you consider to be the most important in propelling the body forward during normal locomotion?

4 Numerous muscles are responsible for operating the leg, yet only one nerve leads to the leg (the sciatic nerve). How can one nerve coordinate the actions of so many muscles?

REQUIREMENTS

Rat's leg or pig's trotter for dissection
Dissecting instruments
Dissecting board and pins

10.7 INVESTIGATION

Types of musculo-skeletal system

Skeletons can be classified according to their position in relation to the muscles which act on them. Thus the mammal, which you have already studied, has an **endoskeleton** where the skeleton is internal to the muscles. In contrast, arthropods have an **exoskeleton** where the skeleton is external to the muscles.

In both these types of skeleton the skeleton itself is hard, being composed of **cartilage** or **bone**. Certain soft-bodied invertebrates, however, have a **hydrostatic skeleton** where the muscles surround, and act against, a fluid under pressure.

The purpose of this investigation is to compare these three types of skeleton.

Guidance

Endoskeleton

All vertebrates have this type of skeleton. To demonstrate that an animal has an endoskeleton you must show that the skeleton is internal to the muscles which move it. (If you have carried out Investigation 10.6, you have already done this.)

Exoskeleton

To demonstrate that an animal has an exoskeleton you must show that the muscles are inside the skeleton. Observe a live cockroach or locust, noting the action of the legs. The exoskeleton is the hard cuticle. Cut a window in the cuticle of the leg of a dead crab, lobster or crayfish and observe the muscles within. Investigate the action of the muscles by pulling on the **apodemes**, tendon-like strands by which they are attached to the inner side of the cuticle.

Hydrostatic skeleton

The best animal in which to investigate this type of skeleton is the earthworm. Watch a live earthworm crawling on damp blotting paper, and burrowing into the soil. Predict how the inside of the worm must be organised so as to permit this kind of movement. You may wish to dissect an earthworm to see if your predictions are correct. The muscles responsible for locomotion are in the body wall. How do you think the muscle tissue is arranged? Examine transverse and longitudinal sections of the earthworm under the microscope and see if your suggestion is right.

For consideration

1 The hydrostatic skeleton of the earthworm is its fluid-filled body cavity. Is it valid to regard this as a *skeleton*?
2 Assess the advantages and disadvantages of an exoskeleton. How do its disadvantages appear to have been overcome in arthropods?

REQUIREMENTS

Microscope
Dissecting instruments
Dissecting board and pins
Damp blotting paper
Cockroach or locust, live
Earthworm (*Lumbricus*), live
For dissection: crab, lobster or crayfish leg; earthworm
Earthworm, TS and LS

10.8 INVESTIGATION

Orientation response of blowfly larvae to light

Blowflies (also known as bluebottles and greenbottles) lay their eggs in a variety of habitats. In some species the larvae feed on decaying meat; in others they live in dung. A few species are parasites. *Lucilia*, for example, often lays its eggs in sores or cuts on sheep. The eggs hatch and the larvae bury into the sheep's flesh. In this investigation you can study the response of blowfly larvae to light and relate this to their way of life.

Guidance

You will need to devise a way of observing the response of blowfly larvae to light. It will probably be necessary to work in a darkened room and to use one or two laboratory lamps which can be switched on or off. You can vary the intensity of the light and its direction. Look carefully at how the larvae move and see what happens if a light is switched on and off at different frequencies. After making preliminary observations, suggest some hypotheses and test them rigorously. Can you separate the larvae's response to light and their response to gravity?

For consideration

1 Relate your findings to the life style of blowfly larvae in their natural habitat.
2 Find out as much as you can about the larva's sense organs and nervous system. Put forward a hypothesis to explain the *mechanism* by which the larva detects and responds to light.

REQUIREMENTS

Lamps ×2
Sheet of white paper (at least 25 cm square)
Pencil
Stopwatch
Beaker of damp sawdust or bran
Blowfly larvae (ideally 8–10)

10.9 PRACTICAL EXERCISE

Learning in rats and gerbils

A number of animals, from several phyla, can learn to find their way through mazes of varying degrees of complexity, particularly if encouraged by a reward. This practical involves training rats or gerbils to master a comparatively simple maze.

Procedure

1 Use a maze of the type shown in Figure 10.7. Such a maze can be constructed from a cardboard or wooden box fitted with hardboard or polystyrene partitions.

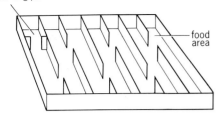

Figure 10.7 Plan of maze suitable for use with rats and gerbils. The maze should be at least 10 cm in height and have sides approximately 50 cm long.

REQUIREMENTS

Maze of the type shown in Figure 10.7 (or the means of making one)
Stopwatch
Camcorder (not essential)
Non-odorous rat or gerbil food (e.g. solid food pellet)
Rat or gerbil, not overfed and with no experience of mazes

At one end there is a 'starting point'. At the other end there is a 'food area'. The whole maze should have a transparent cover.

2   Place a gerbil or rat at the starting point *without* there being any food in the food area. For obvious reasons the animal should not have had any previous experience of mazes nor should it have eaten large amounts immediately before the exercise. However, the animal must not be unduly deprived of food for the purposes of the exercise.

3   Now run a trial. This consists of letting the animal find its way to the food area. Time how long this takes *and* score the number of errors it makes in doing so. You must decide what constitutes an error; for example, does the animal have to insert all of its body, or only part of it, to make an error? A camcorder would be valuable, if you have access to one. If not, ensure you have decided what constitutes an error *before* you carry out the first run.

4   When the animal reaches the food area, reward it with a small item of food. Once it has eaten it, transfer the animal to the starting point and run another trial. As before, record the time taken to complete the maze and the number of errors made *en route*.

5   Repeat the procedure, ideally until the animal can complete the maze several times in a row without making any errors.

6   Plot two graphs: (a) the time taken to complete the maze (vertical axis) against the number of trials; (b) the number of errors made in each trial (vertical axis) against the number of trials (**trial and error** graph).

For consideration

1   What conclusions can you draw regarding the ability of rats or gerbils to learn?
2   What bearing do your results have on the behaviour of these animals in their natural habitats?
3   Can you suggest any factors that might speed up the rate at which these animals learn to master the maze?

10.10 PRACTICAL EXERCISE

Learning in humans

Memory is one of the most important human attributes and is the basis of much of our behaviour. In this practical you will construct a trial and error graph illustrating your ability to recall a list of words, and then consider some of its implications.

Procedure

1   A list of 20 words will be read to you (e.g. by a teacher). Listen carefully, and then, once the entire list has been read out, write down as many of them as you can. They need not be in the right order. Head your list *Trial 1* and fold the paper so that you cannot see what you have written.

2   The list will then be read out again. As before, wait until the entire list has been read out and then write down as many of them as you can. Head the list *Trial 2* and fold the paper as before.

3   Repeat the above procedure until you can remember all 20 words. Head your lists *Trial 3, Trial 4,* etc.

4   You will now be given a copy of the list of words. Score the result of each trial as the number of *errors*. An 'error is a word left out or a wrong one included. (Don't count simple misspellings as errors.)

5   Make a trial and error graph of your results. Plot the number of errors (vertical axis) against the number of the trial (horizontal axis).

6   Now look again at the master list of the 20 words. Divide them up into five groups as follows: *Group A* consists of the first four words, *Group B* the second four, *Group C* the third four, *Group D* the fourth four, and *Group E* the fifth and last four.

7   Look at your *Trial 1* list and score how many words in each of the five groups you included in your list. It doesn't matter whereabouts in your list the words occur as long as they occur somewhere. Write the five scores at the end of your list.

8   Plot the results of Step 7 as a bar chart, putting the number of correct words in each group on the vertical axis and the letters designating the groups on the horizontal axis (Figure 10.8).

9   Repeat Steps 7 and 8 for the rest of your trials.

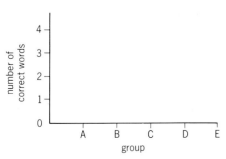

Figure 10.8 Axes of the graph for analysing the results of your trial and error experiment.

For consideration

1   Which features of *your* trial and error graph (Step 5) are also seen in the graphs of any others who have carried out this practical with you? Are there any features peculiar to you?

2   What factors might cause you to learn the list of words more slowly? How could you investigate such factors?

3   It has been suggested that when you try to learn a list of words, you tend to remember the ones at the *beginning* and *end* of the list more quickly that the ones in the middle. These phenomena are known to psychologists as **primacy** and **recency**. Do your results support this suggestion? Of what value might primacy and recency be in everyday life?

4   It could be argued that the test carried out in this investigation is a measure of concentration and intelligence as well as of memory. How might the test be modified to eliminate the influence of these alternative factors?

10.11 INVESTIGATION

Foraging in honeybees

Honey is produced as a food store by the honeybee *Apis mellifera*. Bees have fascinated people for thousands of years and honey is treasured in many cultures as a rich and delicious food source. In order to make honey, honeybees need both nectar and pollen. In this investigation it is suggested that you investigate some features of their **foraging** (movement for the purpose of obtaining food).

Guidance

Honeybee foraging provides countless possibilities for investigations. Here are some suggestions to get you started. Take care that you don't get stung. Many of these investigations would make the basis for a longer and more detailed project. Before starting any such project, discuss your intended procedure with your teacher.

Biohazard
Being
stung

a   What is the relationship between the weather and the number of honeybees out foraging? (You will need to measure such parameters as temperature, cloud cover, wind speed and rainfall, and attempt to correlate such measures with some index of honeybee abundance.)

b   How do honeybees obtain pollen and nectar? (Seat yourself comfortably near a plant with lots of flowers that are being visited by honeybees and make careful observations.)

c   Follow some honeybees and record the plants visited. Do the bees visit the flowers of some species in preference to others? If so, why?

d   When visiting a plant for nectar, does a honeybee move randomly from one flower to another or does it follow some sort of rule to ensure that no flower is visited more than once in a given visit?

e   Can you test the theory that honeybees can communicate to tell one another about the position of rich, new food sources?

For consideration

1   How might the results of your investigation have differed if you had been studying a more solitary species (such as one of the bumble bees), rather than the highly colonial honeybee?

2   Do you think honeybee foraging behaviour is instinctive or learned? Explain your answer.

BOX 10.1 Designing a questionnaire

1 A questionnaire must be designed as a tool to help you investigate a particular problem. For example, suppose your questionnaire is meant to help you study the extent to which people of different ages enjoy different leisure activities. Clearly, your questionnaire will need to ask questions about age and preferred leisure activities.

2 Before starting your questionnaire, think carefully about the following points:

a   What sort of people will be completing it?

b   Will they complete the questionnaire on their own or will you interview them and record their answers?

(continued)

c   Should the questionnaire be anonymous?
d   How will you distribute and collect your questionnaires so that as many as possible are completed and returned?
3   Consider your sampling strategy. Are you going to give your questionnaire to everyone in a few classes, or to, say, every tenth person in your school or college?
4   Think carefully about how precise you want the answers to be. If you are asking questions about age, do you want the answers to be in ten year units (i.e. 0–9 years, 10–19 years, 20–29 years, etc.) or to the nearest year, or to the nearest month? There is no single right answer to this question. It will depend on the range of ages of people answering the question, and on the reason you have for asking the question. For example, if all your sample lies within the range 17 to 18 years, you may need to know each person's age to the nearest month.
5   Ensure your questions are unambiguous and easy to understand.
6   Decide approximately how long you want the questionnaire to be. Too short and you may end up wishing you had asked more questions; too long and people may be put off completing it and you will also waste time analysing answers to unimportant questions.
7   Think carefully about how you are going to analyse the results you obtain *before* you finalise your questions (see pages 247–256). Appropriate statistical analysis will probably mean that you need a minimum of fifty returned questionnaires.
8   Take care with the design and layout of your questionnaire. If it looks boring or is poorly designed, fewer people will complete it.
9   Produce a first draft of your questionnaire and try it out on a few friends to identify any problems.
10   Finally, before you run off copies of your questionnaire, show it to your teacher and discuss it with him or her.

10.12 INVESTIGATION

Parent–offspring interactions

In many animal species, parents provide little or no parental care once the eggs are laid or young born. In others, at least one of the parents looks after the offspring for some time before they become independent. During this time, the parent(s) and offspring interact with each other. In this investigation it is suggested you explore some aspects of such **parent–offspring interactions**. Many species can be studied. Examples include sheep, cats, dogs, ducks, certain aquarium fish (e.g. guppies) and some birds (e.g. blackbirds). Whichever species you investigate, take great care not to disturb the parent(s) and offspring.

Guidance

The interactions between parents and offspring provide many possibilities for investigations. Here are some suggestions to get you started. Many of these investigations would make the basis for a longer and more detailed project. Before starting any such project, discuss your intended procedure with your teacher.
a   How do the behaviours of the parent(s) and the offspring change over time as the offspring grow? (You will need to record the age of the offspring and look consistently at certain behaviours – such as the time spent asleep or the distance between the parent(s) and the offspring – as the offspring grow older.)
b   How much food do parents provide? (Try timing suckling bouts in sheep or counting the number of feeding visits made by parent birds.)
c   How do parents react if their offspring appear to be in danger? (You should not startle offspring or parents, but wait for natural disturbances.)

For consideration

1   Can you suggest how the behaviours you have observed may have evolved as a result of natural selection?
2   Why do you think species vary so greatly in the amount of help parents give their offspring?

10.13 INVESTIGATION

Do parents treat daughters and sons the same?

In humans it is relatively easy to distinguish males from females by their external appearance, even when young. This gives you the opportunity to investigate whether parents treat daughters differently from sons.

Guidance

Before carrying out any of these investigations on human behaviour, you must show your proposal to your teacher. This is because it is important that you don't upset any parents, or their children, by carrying out observations of which they might not approve. Here are some suggested investigations on children of different ages. For some of them, you may find it helpful to consult Box 10.1, page 180.

a   Watch parents and their young children (18 months to five years) in public parks or supermarkets (Figure 10.9). Confine your observations to cases where you are certain of the sex of the child, without asking the parent. Don't let parents realise you are watching their children. Are girls and boys spoken to equally often by the parent? Is one sex allowed to go further from the parent before being recalled? Does it make a difference if the parent is the mother or the father?

b   Ask children of compulsory school age (5–16 years) such questions as: 'How much pocket money do you get'? and 'What did you get for your last birthday'? Do girls and boys give different answers?

c   Ask 16–19 year-olds such questions as: 'What time do your parents (or guardians) expect you to be in at night'?, 'Have you been abroad without your parents (or guardians)'? and 'What would your parents (or guardians) like you to be doing in five years time'? Do male and female students give different answers?

Figure 10.9 A biology student observing parent–offspring interactions.

For consideration

1   Did you find that parents treated daughters the same as sons?
2   If there were differences, were these differences more apparent among younger or older children?
3   Why do you think some parents treat daughters and sons differently?
4   Do you think daughters and sons should be treated the same or differently?

PROJECTS

Before starting a project, discuss your intended procedure with your teacher.

1   The violinist in Figure 10.10 is moving the bow backwards and forwards with the right hand while simultaneously performing a vibrato wrist action with the left hand and pressing the appropriate strings (in the correct places) with the fingers. This may look easy but in fact it is remarkably difficult if you're not a string player (try it yourself). Devise a test which assesses a person's ability to perform different actions with his or her right and left hands simultaneously. Test the hypothesis that, although most people can learn to do this with practice, some are innately better at it than others.

Figure 10.10 The violinist Nigel Kennedy in action. The left and right hands perform different actions simultaneously.

2 Compare the maximum load which can be carried by various muscles (arm and/or leg) of human subjects. See if you can correlate the results with the different sports and recreational activities engaged in by the subjects (tennis, gymnastics, weight-lifting etc.). Obtain volunteers from a wide range of sports, and include some subjects who do no sports at all.

3 Investigate how stick insects walk. Insects have six legs and the way these are coordinated makes a fascinating study. Stick insects have the advantage that they move slowly and are easy to observe. They can be kept in the laboratory without difficulty and they readily shed their legs by a natural spontaneous process called autotomy. In any colony of stick insects there will always be some specimens that lack one or more legs. The effect of this on locomotion can therefore be studied without deliberately harming the animals. Observe the order in which the legs are raised in different conditions and consider how balance is maintained.
Reference: P. Bragg, The use of stick insects in schools, *School Science Review*, Vol. 73, No. 264, March 1992.

4 Test the hypothesis that for an insect to fly, the tarsi (i.e. the terminal part of the legs) must *not* be in contact with a solid object. Possible insects to use include housefly, bluebottle and dragonfly. The insect can be suspended in mid-air by attaching its dorsal side to the end of a matchstick with wax or glue. Don't do anything that is likely to hurt the animal. For how long will an insect beat its wings when suspended? Do the wings stop beating when contact of the tarsi with a solid object is restored?

5 Devise a method of estimating the frequency of an insect's wing-beat. If available, use a stroboscope or high-speed cinematography. Alternatively suspend the insect in mid-air as in the previous project and allow one of its wings to beat against a rapidly revolving kymograph drum fitted with sooted paper. From the positions of the marks and the known speed of the drum, the wing frequency can be estimated. Once you have perfected a method, find the effect of various external factors, e.g. temperature, on the wing frequency.

6 Study the method of locomotion of the garden snail *Helix*. It appears to glide along the surface of the ground. What is happening on the underside of its foot that allows this to happen? Are cilia involved or is propulsion achieved only by muscular contractions? And if muscular contractions take place, what sort are they and how do they propel the body forward? Snails leave a trail of slime (mucus)

behind them. Where does the mucus come from and does it play a part in locomotion?

7 The earthworm, *Lumbricus*, is an ideal animal on which to carry out simple experiments on response and coordination. Take its escape response, for example. This consists of a rapid shortening of the body in response to a stimulus at one end. What sort of stimuli evoke the escape response? What part do the chaetae (bristles) play in the response? Try to think of simple, clear-cut hypotheses which you can test. What is the role of the escape response in the normal life of the animal? Go out into a garden on a warm wet night and observe earthworms lying on the surface of the ground. Assess the effectiveness of their escape response in these natural conditions.

8 Observe the walk, trot, canter and gallop of horses. Take still photographs and/or make slow-motion films. How do the gaits differ? In what order are the legs raised? How many legs are in contact with the ground at any one moment? At what speed does the horse change from one gait to another? Similar studies can be carried out on many other animals, e.g. dogs and cats.

9 Investigate the effect of partial and complete decalcification on the mechanical properties of a limb bone. Progressive decalcification can be achieved by immersing bones in a 3% solution of hydrochloric acid for different lengths of time. Consider how you might assess the amount of decalcification that has taken place. The mechanical properties may be investigated by measuring the bending when masses are hung on the bone placed horizontally.

10 Study the movement of snails in a pond or aquarium. Is their movement random or related to stimuli? Is an individual's movement affected by the presence of other individuals? Is movement more usual at certain times of the day?

11 Devise and carry out experiments to compare the maze-learning abilities of two different species (e.g. gerbil versus laboratory rat *or* cockroach versus locust).

12 Investigate the responses of earthworms to different stimuli (e.g. light, sound, vibrations). What sorts of learning do earthworms show (e.g. habituation, trial and error learning, conditioned reflexes)?

13 Study the foraging behaviour of garden snails. Combine observations in the field with experiments in the laboratory designed to test hypotheses you have generated.

14 Carry out a project on the courtship behaviour of aquarium fish (e.g. guppies) or garden birds (e.g. blackbirds or house sparrows).

15 Investigate territorial behaviour in humans by studying seating arrangements in a library. After initial observations, try placing piles of books on tables or jackets over the backs of chairs to manipulate conditions.

16 Identify the factors that affect the length of time that kestrels spend hovering and the success rate of their dives (e.g. weather, time of year, sex of bird).

17 Examine web building in spiders. How do spiders construct a web? What happens when an insect lands on a web? An excellent guide to finding, collecting and identifying spiders is provided by Jones-Walters, L.M. *Keys to the Families of British Spiders* (AIDGAP Field Studies Council, 1989). This book also has drawings of the different kinds of webs made by spiders. Details of the British Arachnological Society may be obtained from S.H. Hexter, 71 Havant Road, Walthamstow, London E17 3JE.

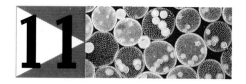

Cell division and reproduction

Observation of stages of mitosis in a growing root

In most tissues, new cells are formed as a result of **mitosis**. If the chromosomes of such cells are selectively stained with a dye such as acetic orcein, stages in mitosis can be observed. An example of a tissue where mitosis occurs is the meristematic tissue located in the **zone of cell division** in the apical meristem near the tip of a growing root. In this practical you can try to prepare your own microscope slides. Skill and good fortune are required to obtain good results.

Procedure

1 Carefully cut the apical 5 mm from the tip of a growing *lateral* root of, e.g., broad bean.
2 Place the root tip in a watch glass containing acetic orcein stain and 1.0 mol dm^{-3} hydrochloric acid in the approximate proportions of ten parts of stain to one part of acid.
3 Warm, but do *not* boil, for five minutes on a hotplate or by passing repeatedly through a low Bunsen flame.
4 Place the fixed root tip on a microscope slide and add two drops of acetic orcein.
5 Without interfering too much with the arrangement of the cells, break the root tip up with a mounted needle so as to spread it out as thinly as possible.
6 Put a coverslip over it, cover it with filter paper and squash gently by pressing down on the coverslip. Take care to avoid any lateral movement and don't break the coverslip.
7 Warm the slide on a hotplate for about ten seconds, or quickly pass it through a Bunsen burner a few times. (This helps to intensify the staining. The slide should be hot, but not too hot to touch.)
8 Carefully examine the slide and identify any stages of mitosis. It may help to make annotated sketches showing the arrangement of the chromosomes.
9 Supplement the information obtained from your own slide by observing a prepared slide showing mitosis in a plant root tip (e.g. *Allium*) or an animal (e.g. *Ascaris*).
10 If possible, watch a film or video recording of mitosis. Notice in particular that it is a dynamic and continuous process. Dividing it up into a series of discrete stages is a helpful but arbitrary convention.

For consideration

1 The acid added in Step 2 helps to soften the tissue. Why is this desirable?
2 How many chromosomes do there seem to be in each cell? Is this the haploid or diploid number?
3 Sometimes, search as one may, no dividing cells are visible in a root squash. Suggest possible reasons for this. (The authors hope that you have not been so unlucky!)

⚠️
Corrosive
Acetic orcein
Hydrochloric acid

REQUIREMENTS

Microscope
Slide and coverslip
Hotplate or Bunsen burner
Filter paper
Mounted needle
Razor blade or fine scissors
Watch glass
Acetic orcein
Hydrochloric acid (1.0 mol dm^{-3})
Lateral root of, e.g., broad bean
Slide of a LS through a plant root tip (e.g. *Allium*)
Slide of an animal (e.g. *Ascaris*) showing mitosis

Note: *Broad bean seeds should be germinated in blotting paper 10 days before the laboratory session. When the radicle is approximately 12 mm long, cut off its tip to stimulate growth of lateral roots. Suitable alternatives to broad bean include sunflower, hyacinth and garlic. Roots growing out from bulbs often give good results.*

The cell cycle in the tip of a growing root

In a cell dividing by mitosis, the **cell cycle** is the series of events from a particular stage in a mother cell (e.g. interphase) to the same stage in the two daughter cells. In this practical you will be able to work out the relative amounts of time spent in interphase and the various stages of mitosis by examining a prepared slide.

Procedure

1 Place a prepared slide of a longitudinal section through a root tip under a light microscope and focus at medium power.
2 Find the zone of cell division – just behind the root cap. (Too near to the tip and you will focus on the protective root cap where little cell division occurs; too far from the root tip and you will be in the zone of cell differentiation.)
3 Ensure that you can identify the various stages of mitosis – **prophase**, **metaphase**, **anaphase** and **telophase**, as well as **interphase** (the stage between mitotic divisions). If necessary, refer to photographs or annotated diagrams in a textbook.
4 Count a representative number of cells (50–100) and classify each of them into its stage.
5 Pool your results with others and work out the percentage of time spent in each of the five stages.
6 On the assumption that the cell cycle lasts approximately eight hours in the cells in the zone of cell division, work out the duration of each of the five stages.

For consideration

1 Which stage lasts the longest and which the shortest?
2 Can you account for the differences in the lengths of the stages?
3 Explain how looking at a prepared slide enabled you to work out the relative lengths of the stages of mitosis.
4 Suggest how your results might have differed if you had been looking at a tissue in which the cells divide much more slowly.

REQUIREMENTS

Microscope
Photographs or diagrams of stages of
  mitosis
Slide of a LS through a plant root tip (e.g.
  Allium)

11.3 INVESTIGATION

The stages of meiosis

The stages of meiosis can most easily be seen in immature anthers that are still enclosed inside the flower bud. Within such anthers diploid **pollen mother cells** may be found dividing meiotically to form haploid pollen grains. In this investigation it is suggested that you examine prepared slides showing the stages of meiosis in a lily or other flowering plant and relate what you see to your knowledge of the movement of the chromosomes during these stages.

Guidance

1 Focus on your slide at high power.
2 Identify the various stages of meiosis – **prophase I**, **metaphase I**, **anaphase I**, **telophase I**, **prophase II**, **metaphase II**, **anaphase II** and **telophase II**, as well as **interphase I** and **interphase II**. If necessary, refer to photographs or annotated diagrams in a textbook.
3 Concentrate on cells in prophase I. Can you observe **chiasmata**? If possible, use oil immersion.

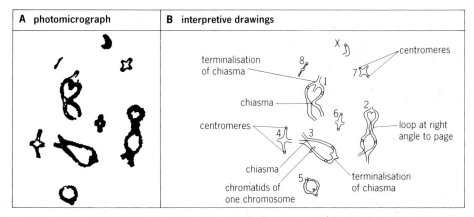

Figure 11.1 Chromosomes at late prophase I in a meiotically dividing cell from the testis of a grasshopper. **A** Photomicrograph. **B** Interpretative drawing. Note the pairing of homologous chromosomes, though the X chromosome has no partner in the males of this species while individual chromatids cannot really be detected in bivalents 5 and 8. Terminalisation is a phenomenon in which the chiasmata appear to move towards the end of the chromatids at the end of prophase I.

4 If chiasmata are visible, distinguish between **bivalents** with one chiasma, bivalents with two chiasmata, and, if present, bivalents with three chiasmata. Use Figure 11.1 to help you.
5 Try to determine the diploid number of the species you are observing.
6 Compare your results with those obtained by observing a prepared slide of an animal testis.

For consideration

1 Why can meiosis more easily be observed in immature than mature anthers?
2 Were there any stages of meiosis you failed to see? If so, why do think this was?
3 Why does the number of chiasmata in a bivalent in prophase I affect the appearance of the chromosomes?
4 What differences are there between meiosis in an anther and meiosis in a animal testis?

11.4 PRACTICAL EXERCISE

Fertilisation in a marine worm

The aim of this practical exercise is to see fertilisation in an animal. We shall use the marine annelid *Pomatoceros*, an animal found on rocks and pebbles on almost every rocky shore round the British coast (Figure 11.2). It is easily identified by its curved, white case which is triangular in cross section. Within this protective case lives the worm itself. The useful thing about *Pomatoceros* from our point of view is that males and females can be distinguished and fertilisation observed at any time of year.

Procedure
Observing the production of gametes

1 Find a pebble or piece of rock with one or more *Pomatoceros* worms attached. Using a pair of forceps, break off the posterior (narrow) end of the tube of one of the worms, taking care not to damage the animal.
2 Insert a blunt seeker into the anterior (front) end of the tube and gently push the worm out of the broken end of its tube into a dish of sea water at approximately 10 °C.
3 Identify whether the worm is male or female. Adult males are yellow at their rear ends, adult females almost violet.
4 Repeat steps 1–3, using separate dishes of sea water, until you have one adult male and one adult female. Put to one side any worms of uncertain sex.
5 Observe the dishes at frequent intervals. Gametes will probably be shed almost immediately, and almost certainly within 40 minutes.
6 Remove a few eggs with a pipette and examine them on a cavity slide under low power and high power.
7 Estimate approximately how many eggs were released by the female.
8 Make an annotated sketch of a single egg, showing the position of the pigmented area and the nucleus.
9 Remove some sperm with a pipette and examine them on a cavity slide under high power and low power. Do the sperm stick together? How do they move?
10 Estimate approximately how many sperm were released by the male.
11 Make a sketch of a single sperm as best you can.

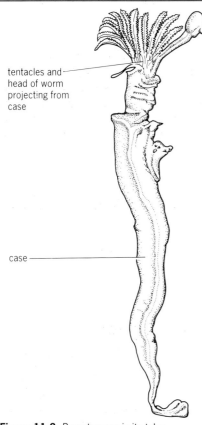

tentacles and head of worm projecting from case

case

Figure 11.2 *Pomatoceros* in its tube.

Observing fertilisation

Fertilisation usually occurs rapidly, so you will need to have everything ready in position before adding the sperm in step 2 below.

1 By means of a fine pipette put some sea water containing one or two unfertilised eggs on a cavity slide.
2 Add some water containing sperm. Put on a cover slip and examine under high power and low power. It may help to try dark ground illumination (see Box on page 71) as well as transmitted light.
3 Make annotated sketches at intervals after fertilisation. Note particularly the behaviour of the pigmented region of the egg and any changes that can be seen in the nuclei.
4 Compare fertilised eggs with others shed at the same time which remain unfertilised. Interpret your findings as far as you are able.

For consideration

1 Why do you think *Pomatoceros* adults release their gametes almost immediately after being forced from their cases?
2 Why is it easier to observe fertilisation in *Pomatoceros* than in a mammal?
3 List and comment on the differences between eggs and sperm.

11.5 INVESTIGATION

Incidence of smoking

Disruption of the cell cycle can result in **cancer**. A cancerous cell is one in which the normal controls that *prevent* excessive cell division have failed. As a result, the cancerous cell divides repeatedly. After a while, a mass of cancerous cells, known as a **tumour** may result. In many countries lung cancer is one of the most common of cancers. Well over 90% of all cases of lung cancer are a direct consequence of smoking cigarettes. Cigarette smoking also causes death through heart disease and breathing disorders. In this investigation it is suggested that you carry out a study using a questionnaire to determine the incidence of smoking among fellow students, and to investigate why some people smoke and others do not.

Guidance

You will probably find it helpful to consult the Box 10.1, page 180. You will need to think of factors that might affect why some people smoke and others don't. Such factors might include age, gender and whether or not their parents smoke. You may have your own hypotheses that you want to test. For example, are people who study biology at advanced level less likely to smoke than people studying other subjects? You might try asking people who smoke how old they were when they first started to smoke and why they started.

For consideration

1 What conclusions can you draw from your investigation?
2 What other methods, aside from using a questionnaire, could be used to tackle the same questions?
3 How could your questionnaire be improved?
4 From your results, can you build up a profile of a typical smoker?

11.6 INVESTIGATION

Vegetative reproduction and perennation

Many herbaceous plants survive the winter by means of a **perennating organ** which lies dormant in soil over the winter and develops into one or more new plants the following year.

The perennating organ may be a modified stem, root, bud or leaves, depending on the species in question. But from whatever structure the perennating organ develops, the fundamental cycle of events is the same: food materials are translocated from the leaves of the plant to the developing organ; and the following year these food reserves are mobilised and moved to the growing regions of the new plant.

Perennation is often associated with **vegetative reproduction** (a form of asexual reproduction). In this investigation we shall look at some of the methods by which perennation and vegetative reproduction take place.

Guidance
Swollen taproot

As the name implies, in many plants the perennating organ is formed from the **taproot**, i.e. the main root (Figure 11.3). At the end of the growing season the above-ground parts of the plant die except for **axillary buds** at the base of the stem. From these buds new shoots develop the following year.

Examine a swollen taproot of a radish or carrot. How could you ascertain that this is a modified root and not some other part of the plant? Carry out tests to find out in what form the food is stored.

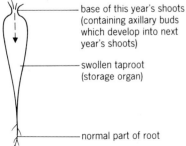

swollen taproot

— base of this year's shoots (containing axillary buds which develop into next year's shoots)

— swollen taproot (storage organ)

— normal part of root

Figure 11.3 A perennating organ formed from a taproot. Broken arrow indicates movement of food materials from the foliage leaves of this year's plant into the swollen taproot.

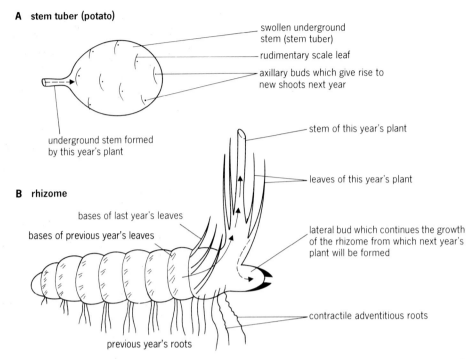

A stem tuber (potato)

- swollen underground stem (stem tuber)
- rudimentary scale leaf
- axillary buds which give rise to new shoots next year
- underground stem formed by this year's plant

B rhizome

- stem of this year's plant
- leaves of this year's plant
- bases of last year's leaves
- bases of previous year's leaves
- lateral bud which continues the growth of the rhizome from which next year's plant will be formed
- contractile adventitious roots
- previous year's roots

Figure 11.4 Two types of perennating organs formed from stems. Solid arrows indicate movement of food materials from the perennating organ to the new plant or new perennating organ. Broken arrows indicate movement of food materials from the foliage leaves into the perennating organ.

Stem tuber

A **stem tuber** is a swollen underground stem which stores food, survives the winter, and gives rise to new plants from axillary buds the following year (Figure 11.4A).

Examine a potato plant showing new tubers and, if possible, the remains of the old tuber. Now look at a single tuber. Being a stem, albeit a modified one, it possesses axillary buds and leaves in much the usual way. These are the so-called 'eyes' of a potato. Can you distinguish the leaves and the buds? You will probably know that the bulk of a potato tuber contains starch, but try testing different parts of a tuber for protein.

Rhizome

A **rhizome** is a horizontally growing underground stem which continues to live for many years (Figure 11.4B). Each year the **terminal bud** at the end of the stem turns up and produces leaves and flowers above the ground. At the same time contractile adventitious roots are formed below ground. The lateral bud closest to the terminal bud continues the growth of the rhizome, food materials for this being supplied by the aerial shoot. In some species the rhizome is short and thick and grows slowly. In others it is long and thin and grows quickly. Which type do you think is shown in Figure 11.4B?

Examples of the short, thick type include iris (*Iris*), water-lily (*Nymphaea*) and Solomon's-seal (*Polygonatum*). Examples of the long, thin type include bracken (*Pteridium aquilinum*), couch grass (*Elymus repens*), marram grass (*Ammophila arenaria*) and groundelder (*Aegopodium podagraria*).

Examine both types and test for food reserves. Cut transverse sections. Wear eye protection and stain in acidified phloroglucinol. What do you conclude?

Bulb

A **bulb** consists of a short vertical stem bearing adventitious roots, thick fleshy leaves (or leaf bases) and a variable number of axillary buds (Figure 11.5): In the centre is the terminal bud which develops into a new plant after the winter is over. The axillary buds develop into new bulbs.

Examine a bulb (e.g. an onion or a daffodil). Cut it vertically in half. Identify the various features, particularly the terminal bud and the fleshy leaves. Is each fleshy structure a complete leaf or just a leaf base? How do the outermost leaves differ from those further in, and what is their function? Test a leaf for food reserves.

Eye protection must be worn

Harmful
Phloroglucinol

Corrosive
Phloroglucinol
Hydrochloric
acid

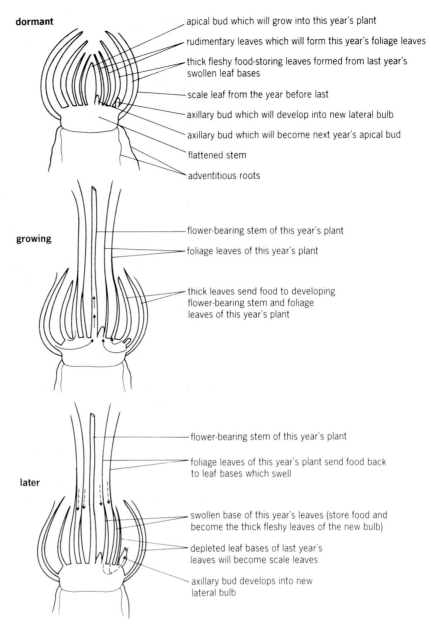

dormant

apical bud which will grow into this year's plant

rudimentary leaves which will form this year's foliage leaves

thick fleshy food-storing leaves formed from last year's swollen leaf bases

scale leaf from the year before last

axillary bud which will develop into new lateral bulb

axillary bud which will become next year's apical bud

flattened stem

adventitious roots

growing

flower-bearing stem of this year's plant

foliage leaves of this year's plant

thick leaves send food to developing flower-bearing stem and foliage leaves of this year's plant

later

flower-bearing stem of this year's plant

foliage leaves of this year's plant send food back to leaf bases which swell

swollen base of this year's leaves (store food and become the thick fleshy leaves of the new bulb)

depleted leaf bases of last year's leaves will become scale leaves

axillary bud develops into new lateral bulb

Figure 11.5 Diagram of a bulb. Solid arrows indicate movement of food materials from the perennating organ to the new plant or new perennating organ. Broken arrows indicate movement of food materials from the foliage leaves into the perennating organ.

Runner

Vegetative reproduction does not necessarily involve the formation of a perennating organ. Some plants reproduce vegetatively by sending out side-branches which develop into new plants. Such is the case with **runners** (Figure 11.6, page 190).

A runner is a horizontally growing, above-ground stem which grows from one of the lower axillary buds on the main stem. At intervals along the length of the runner are small axillary buds which give rise to new plants. Once the new plants are self-supporting, the internodal sections of the runner may wither away.

In the field find some creeping buttercups (*Ranunculus repens*) with several runners and note the above features. Do the runners appear to be sent out randomly, or are they concentrated in one direction?

Cuttings

Danger
Razor blade

Though not a natural method of vegetative reproduction, propagation by means of **cuttings** is widely used by gardeners. A stem is cut and pushed into the soil or some other suitable medium. Adventitious roots grow out from the underground part of the stem, particularly if the cut end is treated with a growth substance.

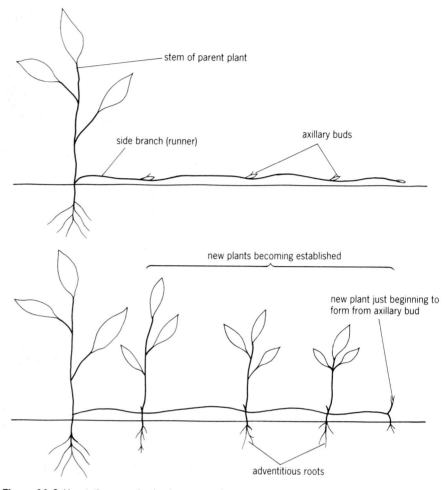

stem of parent plant

side branch (runner)

axillary buds

new plants becoming established

new plant just beginning to
form from axillary bud

adventitious roots

Figure 11.6 Vegetative reproduction by means of a runner.

Try taking cuttings of, e.g., a geranium or Busy Lizzie. Cut off the end of a branch just below a node. Place the cut end in a boiling tube of water (*not* a tube of boiling water!) so that you can watch any adventitious roots that develop. Take several cuttings and dip the cut ends of some of them in 'rooting powder'. Leave the others untreated and compare the speed and manner in which the two groups develop adventitious roots.

For consideration

1 Which structure or structures mentioned in this investigation involve:
   a perennation *and* reproduction;
   b perennation *without* reproduction;
   c reproduction *without* perennation?
2 The products of asexual propagation of an individual are genetically identical. Why might it be useful for gardeners or farmers to grow genetically identical plants? What problems might be encountered as a result of this practice?
3 How could you test the hypothesis that creeping buttercups send out more runners in poorer soil?

11.7 PRACTICAL EXERCISE

Life cycle of a moss

Mosses show alternation of generations between a small leafy haploid **gametophyte** and a diploid spore-producing **sporophyte** which grows out of, and is dependent upon, the gametophyte.

Gametophyte

1 Examine a whole gametophyte of a moss such as Mnium, noting the simple stem, leaves and rhizoids (Figure 11.7A). Mount a leaf in water and examine at low

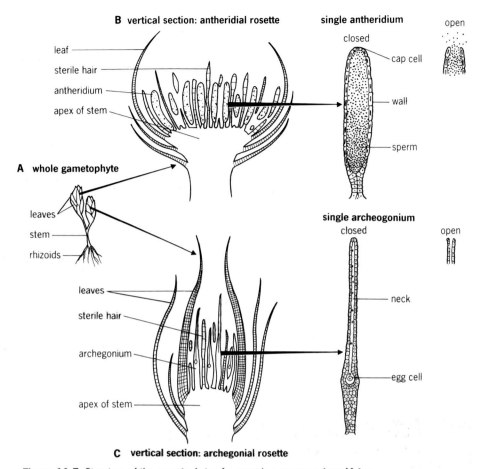

B vertical section: antheridial rosette

leaf
sterile hair
antheridium
apex of stem

single antheridium

closed
cap cell
wall
sperm

open

A whole gametophyte

leaves
stem
rhizoids

single archeogonium

closed
neck
egg cell

open

C vertical section: archegonial rosette

Figure 11.7 Structure of the gametophyte of a moss in a genus such as *Mnium*.

power under the microscope. What can you say about its structure? Observe a rhizoid under the microscope. How does it compare with a true root?

2 Examine prepared transverse sections of the leaf and stem under high power. In the leaf note the lamina and, if present, midrib. In the stem note the epidermis, cortex and conducting tissue (if present). Note that there is no vascular tissue and that the leaves are only one cell thick. Can you see any adaptations for water conservation?

3 Examine gametophytes under a hand lens or binocular microscope and look for male and female rosettes. The male rosette consists of a group of **antheridia** enveloped by a 'cup' of leaves; the female rosette consists of a group of **archegonia** enveloped by a separate 'cup' of leaves. In some mosses male and female rosettes are on separate plants. In other mosses, they are found on the same plant with male rosettes at the top of certain branches, and female rosettes lower down.

Harmful
Noland's
solution
Iodine

4 Tease out the contents of a male rosette in a drop of water on a slide and examine under high power. Observe antheridia, sterile hairs and, if possible, sperm cells. If sperm are present irrigate the slide with iodine or Noland's solution to help see their flagella.

5 Tease out the contents of a female rosette in a drop of water and observe under high power. Note archegonia, each with an egg cell.

6 Examine a prepared vertical section of a male rosette under low power. Note enveloping leaves, sterile hairs, antheridia and sperm cells (Figure 11.7B).

7 Examine a prepared vertical section of a female rosette under low power. Note enveloping leaves, sterile hairs and archegonia with egg cells (Figure 11.7C). How is fertilisation brought about?

Sporophyte

1 After fertilisation the zygote develops into the young sporophyte. This grows out of the female rosette carrying with it the upper part of the archegonium which eventually falls off. Examine sporophytes in various stages of development. Note

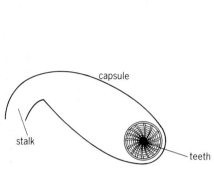

Figure 11.8 Diagram of the spore capsule of a moss in a genus such as *Mnium* after removal of the operculum.

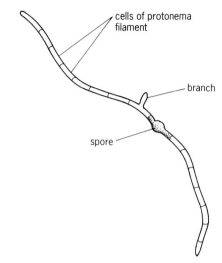

Figure 11.9 Young protonema of a moss.

how the **spore capsule** is located at the upper end of a stalk whose foot is embedded in a female rosette. The stalk contains vascular strands continuous with those in the gametophyte.

2 Remove a capsule and a short length of its stalk. With a needle take off the operculum (lid). Insert the stalk into a piece of plasticine on a slide in such a way that you can look down a microscope at the teeth (Figure 11.8). Now breathe on the capsule and observe down the microscope. What happens? Can you explain why this is? How do you think in nature the spores are released and dispersed?

3 The spores give rise to a filamentous alga-like **protonema** (Figure 11.9). This produces buds which give rise to mature gametophytes. Examine a protonema under high power. Note the spore, the branching of the filament and the presence of chloroplasts. Buds with rhizoids may also be seen.

For consideration

1 The sterile hairs in the male and female rosettes absorb water. Why might this be of value?

2 Mosses have been described as the amphibians of the plant kingdom. Do you think this is justified? Explain your answer.

3 Is the protonema part of the gametophyte or the sporophyte generation?

4 Where in the life cycle, and in the plant itself, does meiosis occur?

11.8 PRACTICAL EXERCISE

Life cycle of a fern

In ferns the diploid sporophyte is the dominant generation and the haploid gametophyte is greatly reduced.

Sporophyte

1 Examine an entire plant of a large fern such as *Dryopteris* (Figure 11.10). Note the horizontal rhizome (see page 193) with adventitious roots and old leaf bases. Note too the **fronds** (leaves) subdivided into pinnae and pinnules.

2 Examine a prepared section of a leaf or leaf stalk, noting the vascular tissues. The vascular tissues have xylem and phloem. How does a fern sporophyte compare with that of a moss?

3 Certain pinnules produce spores. These are formed in **sori** on the undersides of the spore-producing pinnules (Figure 11.11A). In some species each sorus is protected by an umbrella-like cover, the indusium (Figure 11.11B). With a needle remove one of these protective covers so as to reveal spore capsules beneath. Mount a mature spore capsule (sporangium) in water and notice the annulus cells and other features shown in Figure 11.11C.

4 Place a few mature spore capsules on a dry slide and either mount them in glycerol or leave them under a hot lamp to dry out. Examine under low power.

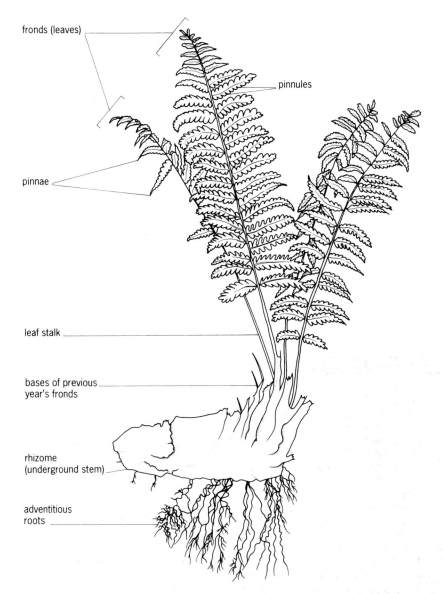

fronds (leaves)

pinnules

pinnae

leaf stalk

bases of previous
year's fronds

rhizome
(underground stem)

adventitious
roots

Figure 11.10 The sporophyte of the fern *Dryopteris* with a creeping underground stem, fronds and
adventitious roots.

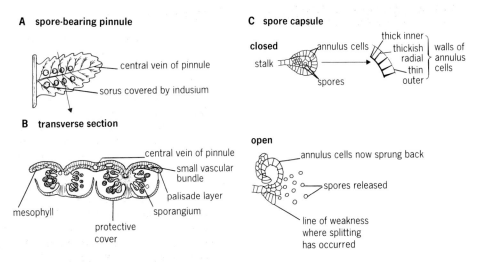

A   spore-bearing pinnule

central vein of pinnule

sorus covered by indusium

B   transverse section

central vein of pinnule

small vascular
bundle

palisade layer

sporangium

mesophyll

protective
cover

C   spore capsule

closed

annulus cells

stalk

spores

thick inner
thickish
radial
thin
outer

walls of
annulus
cells

open

annulus cells now sprung back

spores released

line of weakness
where splitting
has occurred

Figure 11.11 Structure of the spore-producing apparatus of the sporophyte of a fern such as
Dryopteris.

Can you see the capsule dehiscing? Whereabouts in the wall of the capsule does splitting occur? Compare with Figure 11.11C. Can you explain the mechanism of dehiscence?

5 Examine a transverse section of a spore-bearing pinnule, noting the structures shown in Figure 11.11B.

Gametophyte (Prothallus)

1 Each spore is potentially capable of developing into a small, reduced gametophyte known as a **prothallus**. A prothallus lives on the surface of damp soil. Examine a mature prothallus, noting its simple structure and its shape. Mount it in water, lower surface uppermost, and examine it under low and high powers. In what ways is it adapted to lead an independent existence? Note that there is no vascular tissue. In its structure the prothallus is on about the same level as a simple multicellular alga.

2 Examine a prepared whole mount and/or horizontal section of a prothallus. Observe antheridia and archegonia in surface view. Both are located on the underside of the prothallus, as are the rhizoids. Archegonia are closer to the apical notch than the antheridia (Figure 11.12A). In some preparations coiled sperm may be visible in the antheridia, and an egg cell in some of the archegonia (Figure 11.12B).

3 Examine a vertical section of a prothallus to see archegonia and antheridia in side view (Figure 11.12C, D). How do you think the sperms are released from the antheridia and how do they enter the archegonia? How do the antheridia and archegonia of ferns compare with those of mosses?

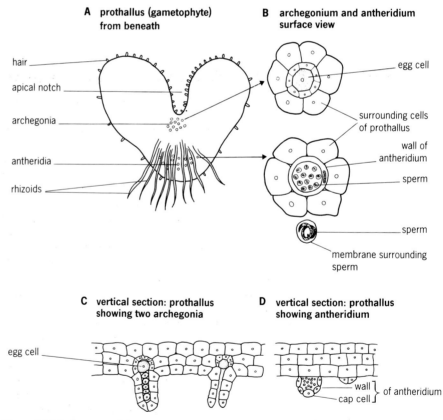

Figure 11.12 Structure of the gametophyte of a fern such as *Dryopteris*.

4 After fertilisation the zygote develops into the sporophyte. At first this is a small structure, with its foot embedded in the *lower* side of the prothallus. (Why the lower side?) Later, when the sporophyte's roots and leaves develop, the prothallus – no longer required – withers and dies. Examine a prothallus with a young sporophyte attached (Figure 11.13). Note the young leaves and roots and the foot embedded in the prothallus.

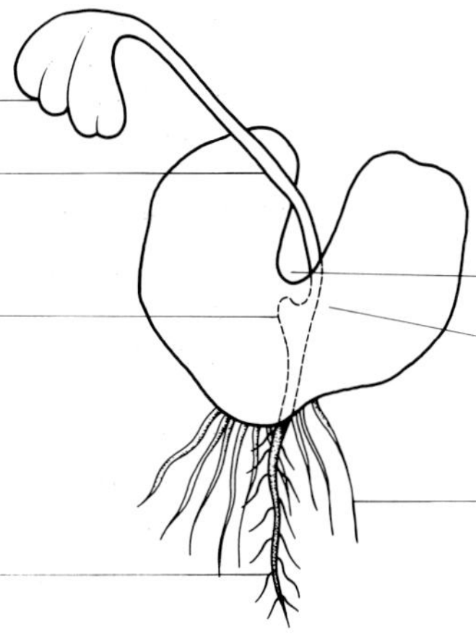
young sporophyte
prothallus
first leaves
stalk
foot embedded in underside of prothallus
apical notch
archegonial region
rhizoids
root

Figure 11.13 Young sporophyte of a fern growing out of a prothallus.

REQUIREMENTS

- Microscope
- Hand lens or binocular microscope
- Slides and coverslips
- Mounted needle
- Lamp
- Glycerol
- Fern sporophytes (entire)
- Fronds with sori
- Fern gametophytes (prothalli) with archegonia and antheridia
- TS frond *or* leaf stalk
- TS spore-bearing pinnule showing spore capsules
- WM and HS gametophyte
- VS gametophyte showing archegonia and antheridia
- WM fern gametophyte with young sporophyte attached

For consideration

1 To what extent are ferns adapted to life on land?
2 To what extent is the sporophyte dependent on the gametophyte?
3 Where in the life cycle, and in the plant itself, does meiosis occur?
4 Make a table to list the major differences between mosses and ferns with respect to their structures and life cycles.

11.9 INVESTIGATION

Sexual reproduction in frogs or toads

Frogs and toads are amphibians and need to return to water to breed. Fertilisation is **external**. This means that the male must be present when the female lays her eggs. In this investigation it is suggested you study aspects of amphibian reproduction.

Guidance

Frogs and toads reproduce in spring. Males can be difficult to tell from females. They arrive at ponds before females, croak repeatedly and are on top of the female when they mate. Frogs and toads use the same ponds year after year, so before the start of the reproductive season you should identify a suitable place for your observations. Because most of the action takes place at night take particular care that the pond you are studying is in a safe place. A garden pond that belongs to someone you can really trust might be ideal. Work in pairs and let your teacher and parents/guardians know where you are.

Danger

Here are some suggestions for possible investigations. Many of these investigations would make the basis for a longer and more detailed project. Before starting any such project, discuss your intended procedure with your teacher.

a Produce maps showing where individuals are in relation to the pond. Do individuals move around or occupy the same place? You may be able to distinguish individuals by natural differences in size and patterning.
b Do males or females spend longer at the pond?
c Do males and females differ in size?
d Is there any relationship between the size of a male and the pitch of his croak or the frequency with which he croaks?
e What is the function of a male's croak? Try tape recording some croaks and playing them back at other males or at females.
f Does the size of a male affect his reproductive success?
g Do females lay their eggs randomly within the pond or are there preferred sites?

REQUIREMENTS

- Access to a safe pond with frogs or toads present
- Torch
- Small outdoor chair
- Ruler
- Tape recorder

For consideration

1 Why do males arrive at ponds before females?
2 Can you think of any disadvantages to a male of croaking?

Dissection of the reproductive system of the rat

Despite its apparent complexity, the mammalian reproductive system is essentially quite simple. In each sex there are two **gonads** (**ovaries** in the female, **testes** in the male). Tubes lead from these gonads to the midline where they join a single tube to the exterior. In the male this latter tube is shared by the urinary system.

Note: This dissection can be carried out on a rat which has been deep frozen or preserved in some other way following a dissection of some other system(s).

Caution

Although your laboratory rat is unlikely to carry any infections that can be transmitted to you, you are advised to wear thin surgical gloves while dissecting. You *must* wash your hands thoroughly after each dissection with soap and hot water.

Procedure

1 Before starting the dissection, identify the urinary and genital openings on the ventral side (Figure 6.1, page 88). Note that in the female there are separate urinary and genital openings – the former being located just anterior to the latter – whereas in the male there is just one urinogenital opening – at the end of the **penis**.
2 In a female, identify the **nipples**. In a male, notice the **scrotal sacs**.
3 Open up the abdominal cavity as instructed on page 90, cutting round the urinary and genital openings (dotted line in Figure 6.2). Pin back the skin and cut back the body wall in the usual way (see page 90). In the female notice the **mammary glands** adhering to the inside of the skin.
4 Ligature the hepatic portal vein and remove the gut as instructed on page 92.
5 Notice that in both sexes the tubes leading to the urinogenital openings are covered by a layer of muscle beneath which lies the pubis, part of the pelvic girdle (Figure 11.14A for female; 11.14B for male).

How you should proceed from here depends on whether you are dissecting a female or a male rat. If possible, work next to someone who has a rat of the opposite sex, so that you can compare findings.

Female

1 Remove the muscle overlying the pelvic girdle (dotted lines in Figure 11.14A). With large scissors cut through the pelvic girdle on either side of the midline and remove the pubis. Take care to keep the ends of the scissors as horizontal as possible. This will expose the narrow urethra beneath which is the larger **vagina** (Figure 11.15A).
2 Identify the small ovaries and – with the aid of a hand lens – the short, coiled **oviducts** (Figure 11.15B).
3 The oviducts on each side lead to a long V-shaped **uterus**, the two horns of which unite in the midline to form the vagina (Figure 11.15A).
4 The bladder receives the ureters from the kidney, and opens into the anterior end of the urethra. Confirm this in your dissection. A pair of **preputial glands** can be seen at the posterior end of the urethra.
5 Note that (in the female) the urethra (urinary duct) and vagina (genital duct) are separate.
6 Identify the ovarian and uterine arteries and veins. With which major blood vessels do these connect? The uterine blood vessels are especially large and prominent during pregnancy.
7 If the rat is pregnant the much expanded uterus will be seen to contain a variable number of **fetuses** each with an **umbilical cord** and **placenta**.

Male

1 With scissors cut open one of the scrotal sacs (dotted line on left-hand side of Figure 11.16A).
2 With forceps grasp hold of the testis, or the fat attached to it, and draw it forwards.
3 Identify the structures seen in Figure 11.16B, if necessary using a hand lens.
4 Remove the muscle overlying the pelvic girdle (dotted lines in Figure 11.14B). With large scissors cut through the pelvic girdle on either side of the midline and

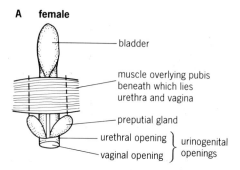

A   female

- bladder
- muscle overlying pubis beneath which lies urethra and vagina
- preputial gland
- urethral opening ⎫
- vaginal opening ⎬ urinogenital openings

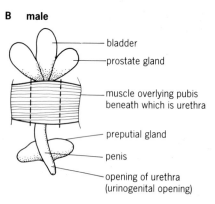

B   male

- bladder
- prostate gland
- muscle overlying pubis beneath which is urethra
- preputial gland
- penis
- opening of urethra (urinogenital opening)

Figure 11.14 The urinogenital openings and associated structures in the rat.

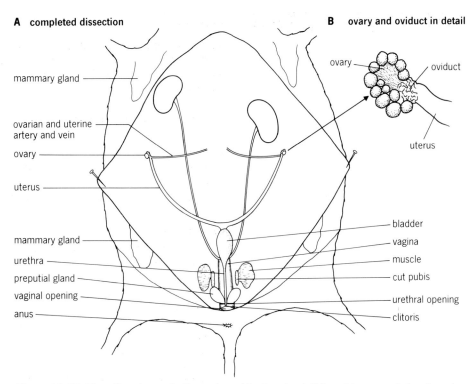

A completed dissection

mammary gland

ovarian and uterine
artery and vein

ovary

uterus

mammary gland

urethra

preputial gland

vaginal opening

anus

B ovary and oviduct in detail

ovary

oviduct

uterus

bladder

vagina

muscle

cut pubis

urethral opening

clitoris

Figure 11.15 Dissection of reproductive system of the female rat. If the rat is pregnant, the uterus is larger and the uterine artery and vein more extensive.

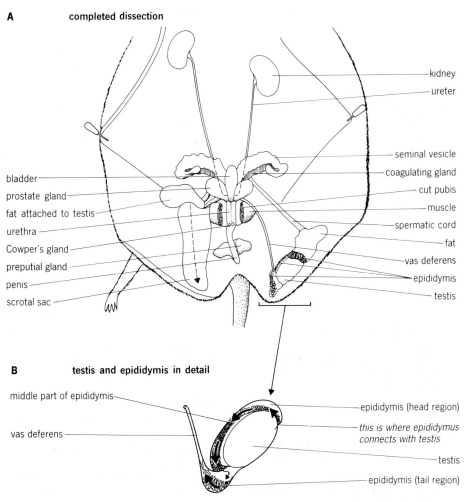

A   completed dissection

kidney

ureter

seminal vesicle

coagulating gland

cut pubis

muscle

spermatic cord

fat

vas deferens

epididymis

testis

bladder

prostate gland

fat attached to testis

urethra

Cowper's gland

preputial gland

penis

scrotal sac

B   testis and epididymis in detail

middle part of epididymis

vas deferens

epididymis (head region)

this is where epididymus connects with testis

testis

epididymis (tail region)

Figure 11.16 Dissection of reproductive system of the male rat.

remove the pubis. Take care to keep the ends of the scissors as horizontal as possible. This will expose the urethra which leads into the penis.

5 Identify the **epididymis** and **vas deferens** leading from the testis. Follow the vas deferens to the midline and ascertain that it, along with its fellow from the other side, opens into the anterior end of the urethra.

6 Also opening into the urethra at this point is the duct of the bladder, which receives the ureters from the kidney. Check that these structures and their connections are visible in your dissection.

7 Now identify the glands associated with the reproductive tract: a large **seminal vesicle** and **coagulating gland** at the inner (penis) end of each vas deferens; **prostate glands** lying next to the bladder; a pair of **Cowper's glands** at the base of the penis, and a pair of **preputial glands** towards the tip of the penis.

8 Note that (in the male) the urethra serves as a common urinogenital duct.

9 Finally, investigate the blood vessels serving the reproductive organs, particularly the spermatic artery and vein, derived (usually) from the dorsal aorta and posterior vena cava respectively. Together the spermatic artery and vein constitute the spermatic cord.

For consideration

1 What are the principal similarities and differences between the male and female reproductive systems?

2 List those structures in the urinogenital system of a female rat that function solely in reproduction, those that function solely in excretion and those that serve both functions. Now repeat the exercise for the male.

3 You will have noticed that in the male the urethra serves as a common urinogenital duct conveying both urine and sperm to the exterior (though not at the same time!), whereas in the female the urinary and genital systems have separate openings to the exterior. Can you explain the reason for this difference between the two sexes? What are its physiological consequences?

4 What do you think might be the functions of the glands associated with the male reproductive tract?

REQUIREMENTS

Hand lens
Dissecting instruments
Male and female rats for dissection

11.11 PRACTICAL EXERCISE

Microscopic structure of mammalian ovary and testis

The ovary and testis contain developing eggs and sperm respectively. In each case diploid primordial **germ cells**, associated with **germinal epithelium**, divide mitotically to form **oogonia** and **spermatogonia**. These grow and then undergo meiosis to form, ultimately, **ova** and **spermatozoa** respectively.

Ovary

1 Look at a section of mammalian ovary under low power and identify the structures shown in Figure 11.17A.

2 Now turn to high power and examine as many stages in the development of a **Graafian follicle** as you can find. Use Figure 11.17B to help you.

3 How does **ovulation** take place? If available, examine a slide which shows this.

4 After ovulation the hollow Graafian follicle develops into a solid **corpus luteum**. Examine a section of an ovary containing a corpus luteum (Figure 11.17C).

Testis

1 Examine a prepared section of mammalian testis under low power (Figure 11.18A). Observe numerous seminiferous tubules cut in various planes.

2 Examine the wall of a seminiferous tubule under high power. Can you identify the structures shown in Figure 11.18B? Trace the sequence of developmental stages: spermatogonia $\longrightarrow$ spermatocytes $\longrightarrow$ spermatids $\longrightarrow$ spermatozoa. Can you see any stages of meiosis?

3 Observe that the tails of the spermatozoa hang into the lumen of the seminiferous tubule while their heads are buried in large Sertoli cells.

4 Examine the tissue between adjacent seminiferous tubules under high power (Figure 11.18C), noting interstitial cells and capillaries embedded in connective tissue.

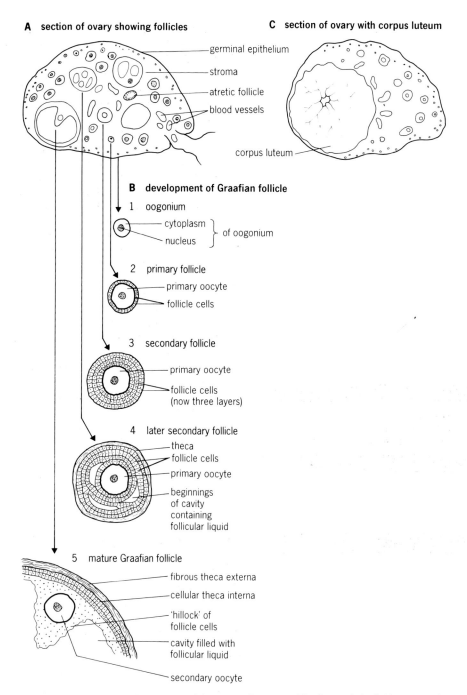

A   section of ovary showing follicles

- germinal epithelium
- stroma
- atretic follicle
- blood vessels

C   section of ovary with corpus luteum

- corpus luteum

B   development of Graafian follicle

1   oogonium

- cytoplasm ⎱ of oogonium
- nucleus ⎰

2   primary follicle

- primary oocyte
- follicle cells

3   secondary follicle

- primary oocyte
- follicle cells (now three layers)

4   later secondary follicle

- theca
- follicle cells
- primary oocyte
- beginnings of cavity containing follicular liquid

5   mature Graafian follicle

- fibrous theca externa
- cellular theca interna
- 'hillock' of follicle cells
- cavity filled with follicular liquid
- secondary oocyte

Figure 11.17 Microscopic structure of the mammalian ovary. (The first meiotic division occurs just before ovulation, the second meiotic division just after fertilisation).

REQUIREMENTS

Microscope
Section of mammalian testis
Section of mammalian ovary showing developing Graafian follicles
Section of mammalian ovary showing corpus luteum

For consideration

1   What are the essential similarities and differences between the development of sperm and eggs in a mammal?

2   In humans as many as 400 000 primary follicles may be present at birth, but normally fewer than 400 develop into mature Graafian follicles. The rest degenerate into atretic follicles. How often and under what circumstances are Graafian follicles formed?

3   Can you think of a reason why the interstitial cells in the testes are located close to capillaries?

A seminiferous tubules of testis

C interstitial cells of testis

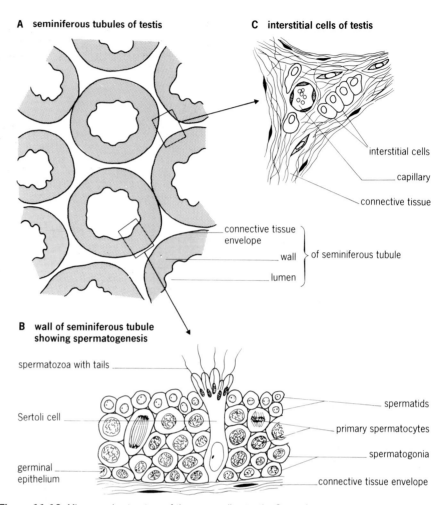

interstitial cells

capillary

connective tissue

connective tissue envelope

wall

lumen

of seminiferous tubule

B wall of seminiferous tubule showing spermatogenesis

spermatozoa with tails

spermatids

Sertoli cell

primary spermatocytes

spermatogonia

germinal epithelium

connective tissue envelope

Figure 11.18 Microscopic structure of the mammalian testis. Secondary spermatocytes are short-lived and are rarely seen in microscopic preparations.

11.12 INVESTIGATION

The life cycle of fast plants

'Fast plants' or 'rapid cycling brassicas' (*Brassica campestris*, Figure 11.19) are closely related to the turnip and the Chinese cabbage. They were selected in Wisconsin, USA from cultivated ancestors for small size, short life cycle, uniform flower maturation, high fertility and absence of seed dormancy; they flower after two weeks and the life

Figure 11.19A 'Fast plants' growing beneath a bank of high-intensity lights.

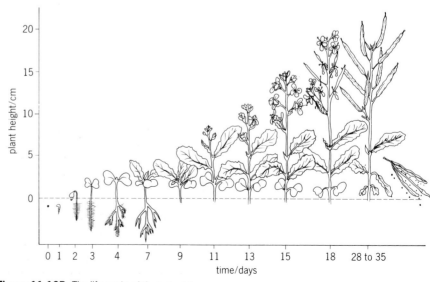

Figure 11.19B The life cycle of 'fast plants'.

cycle lasts only 35 days. In order to grow and develop so rapidly they must be reared in peat/vermiculite in small containers under high-intensity lights. The aim of this practical is to demonstrate all the stages in the life cycle of a flowering plant in a very brief period of time.

Guidance

Sow three seeds of fast *Brassica* about 5 mm below the surface of a 1:1 mixture of sieved peat and vermiculite and place the pot on the capillary mat in the light cabinet provided.

Examine and water the plants every three days, taking notes and drawing sketches to show the development of the organs. Many of the practicals and investigations over the next few pages can be performed on fast plants.

For consideration

1   Fast plants only retain their short life cycles if individuals which appear to have longer life cycles are persistently eliminated. A population of fast plants, left alone to reproduce, gradually reverts to a longer and longer average life cycle. Explain in detail why this happens.

References

Tomkins, S.P. & Williams, P.H. Fast plants for finer science – an introduction to the biology of rapid-cycling *Brassica campestris (rapa)* L. *Journal of Biological Education* **24** (4), 239–250, 1990. Price. R. Perfect plants for projects. *Biological Sciences Review* **4** (1), 32–36, 1991.

REQUIREMENTS

Equipment for growing fast plants, including light bank, capillary mat, small polystyrene containers such as test tube caps, nutrient pellets, water with 30 ppm copper (II) sulphate and mixture of 1:1 sieved peat and vermiculite. Details from Science and Plants for Schools (SAPS), Homerton College, Hills Road, Cambridge, CB2 2PH.

Note: *'Fast plants' and kits for growing rapid-cycling B. campestris are available from MacIntyre Mottingham, Mottingham Lane, London SW12 9AW.*

11.13 PRACTICAL EXERCISE

Microscopic structure of anthers and ovules

The internal structure of stamens and carpels can be seen most clearly in cross-sections of unopened flower buds. The stamens produce **pollen grains**, the male spores, in **pollen sacs** in the **anthers**. The carpels ultimately contain **egg cells**, the female gametes, produced inside the **ovules** within the **ovaries**.

Procedure

1   Examine, under low power, a cross-section of a flower bud of lily (Figure 11.20A) and identify the **anthers**.
2   Examine an anther under high power (Figure 11.20B). Notice the four pollen sacs and examine their contents.
3   The contents depend on the state of maturity of the anther:
    (i) If immature, the pollen sacs will be full of closely packed pollen mother cells.
    (ii) If more mature, they will contain pairs or tetrads of cells (pollen tetrads) which result from meiotic division of the pollen mother cells. Chromosomes may be visible within the cells, revealing the stage of meiosis at which the cells were fixed.
    (iii) If completely mature, the anthers will contain separate pollen grains, each with a sculptured wall and one or two haploid nuclei (Figure 11.20C).
4   Notice the tapetum, the layer of closely-packed columnar cells which immediately surrounds each pollen sac and nourishes the developing pollen grains.
5   Look at the wall of the pollen sac and identify the middle and fibrous layers. When cells in the fibrous layer dry out, the tension causes the anther to split open at the stomium, a line of weakness which runs from the top to bottom of each side of the anther, and the pollen grains are released.
6   Return to low power and identify the ovary in the centre of the flower bud (Figure 11.20A). Then make sure that you can find the six **ovules** within it.
7   Examine an ovule under high power, and observe the structures labelled in Figure 11.20D.

8 Focus on the embryo sac in the centre of the ovule. How many nuclei can you see inside it? This depends on its state of maturity and on the level of the section:

The embryo sac starts by having a single haploid nucleus which is formed by meiosis from an embryo sac (megaspore) mother cell. The haploid nucleus of the megaspore then undergoes successive mitotic divisions to give a total of eight haploid nuclei, three at each end of the embryo sac and two in the centre (the polar nuclei). The nuclei at the ends of the embryo sac become surrounded by membranes to give the cells shown in Figure 11.20E. One of them is the female gamete (egg cell).

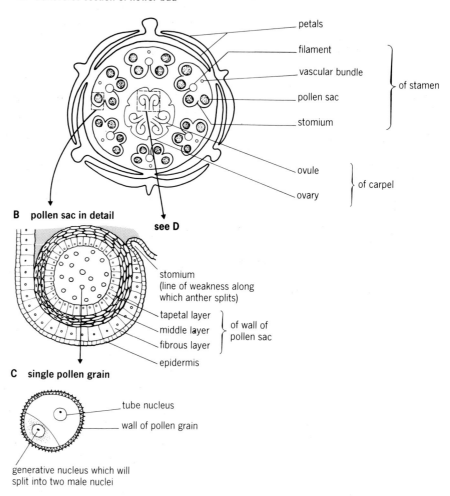

A   transverse section of flower bud

petals
filament
vascular bundle
pollen sac
stomium
} of stamen

ovule
ovary
} of carpel

B   pollen sac in detail

see D

stomium
(line of weakness along
which anther splits)
tapetal layer
middle layer
fibrous layer
} of wall of
pollen sac
epidermis

C   single pollen grain

tube nucleus
wall of pollen grain

generative nucleus which will
split into two male nuclei

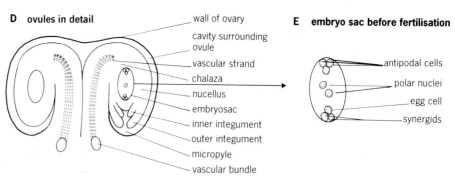

D   ovules in detail

wall of ovary
cavity surrounding
ovule
vascular strand
chalaza
nucellus
embryosac
inner integument
outer integument
micropyle
vascular bundle

E   embryo sac before fertilisation

antipodal cells
polar nuclei
egg cell
synergids

Figure 11.20 The microscopic structure of the flower bud of a lily (*Lilium* sp.)
A Transverse section of flower bud
B Detail of one pollen sac from an anther
C Single pollen grain
D One pair of ovules
E Embryo sac.

In the act of fertilisation the female gamete fuses with one male nucleus (from a pollen tube) to give the zygote, which ultimately produces the embryo and the next generation. The two polar nuclei fuse with the other male nucleus to form a triploid nucleus which gives rise to the endosperm tissue. The latter envelops and nourishes the embryo.

After fertilisation an ovule develops into a seed and the ovary wall becomes the fruit wall or pericarp.

For consideration

1 When and where does meiosis take place in a flowering plant?
2 In terms of the 'alternation of generations', the pollen grains represent the *male spores* and the germinated pollen grains represent the *male gametophytes*. What structures on the female side represent the equivalent *female spores* and *female gametophytes* in the life cycle of a flowering plant?
3 Compare the gametes, and the way in which they develop, in a flowering plant and a mammal.

REQUIREMENTS

Microscope
TS Flower bud of lily (*Lilium* sp.)

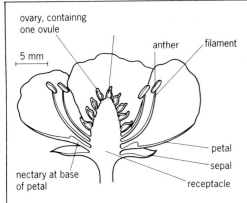

Illustration 1 Vertical section through the flower of buttercup (*Ranunculus* sp.).

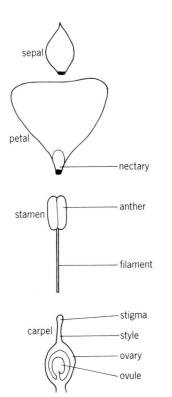

Illustration 2 Detail of the component parts of a buttercup flower.

BOX 11.1 ## Recording floral structure

A flower consists of whorls (rings) of modified leaves which collectively produce, protect and ensure the union of the gametes. The whorls are attached to a receptacle, the expanded end of the flower stalk.

There is a wide variation in flower structure. Flowers of different species may differ in the numbers, arrangement and degree of fusion of the component parts. This box provides convenient and standardised ways of recording their structure.

Flower parts

In a flower which possesses all four whorls which sit on a (usually) expanded end of the flower stalk, called a **receptacle**, the parts are, from the outside inwards (Illustrations 1, 2):

• **Calyx (sepals):** usually small, green and leaf-like, protecting the flower in bud.
• **Corolla (petals):** often coloured and scented, sometimes fused into a tube or shaped to provide a landing platform, sometimes with **nectaries** (sacs which secrete a sugary solution) towards the base.
• **Androecium (stamens):** produce pollen grains. Each stamen consists of an **anther** and a **filament**. Anthers usually contain four pollen sacs in which the pollen grains develop.
• **Gynoecium (carpels):** each gynoecium consists of **stigma**, **style** and **ovary**, composed of one or more carpels, compartments each representing in evolution a single modified leaf. The ovary contains one or more ovules, potential seeds, in each of which there is an egg cell.

It is sometimes difficult to see how many carpels there are in the gynoecium. The number of carpels usually equals:
  (i) the number of stigmas
  (ii) the number of chambers in the ovary
  (iii) the number of lines down which the fruit wall splits to release the seeds.

Symmetry

Actinomorphic flowers, such as buttercup, lily and tulip, are radially symmetrical. They may be cut in more than one plane to give two equal and opposite halves (Illustration 3a).
Zygomorphic flowers, such as sweet pea, deadnettle, snapdragon and orchids, are bilaterally symmetrical. They can be cut in only one plane to yield two equal and opposite halves (Illustration 3b).

Half flower

This is a way of showing the internal stucture of a flower. First slice the flower vertically. It is usually best to cut from the base upwards, since if you slice from above you may miss the centre of the ovary. You should cut the flower

Danger
Razor blade

along the median plane, i.e. the plane in line with the main stem (Illustration 4). In bilaterally symmetrical (zygomorphic) flowers cutting along this plane will give two equal and opposite halves.

Then draw an inside view of one half of the flower (Illustration 5A).

Floral diagram

This provides a plan of the flower as viewed from above. It looks like a diagrammatic cross-section (Illustration 5B).

Look at the flower from above. If a bract, a leaf-like structure immediately beneath the flower, is present it should be facing you, the flower stalk should be furthest away and the main stem of the plant should be at the top of the flower. You will probably have to cut a cross-section of the ovary so that you can show the position of the ovules on your diagram.

If the petals, sepals or stamens are joined, link them with simple brackets; if the stamens arise from the petals, link them with radial lines.

Floral formula

This is the simplest and quickest way of representing flower structure (e.g. Illustration 5C).

Each whorl, from the outside of a flower to the inside, is represented by a capital letter followed by a number denoting the number of units in the whorl. The letters are **K** for calyx, **C** for corolla, **A** for androecium and **G** for gynoecium. If the number is over twenty and variable it is expressed as infinity (∞). Actinomorphy is designated by writing + at the beginning of the formula. Zygomorphy is designated by writing ↑ at the beginning of the formula.

A **superior** ovary, one at the same level, or above, the insertion point of the stamens and petals, is represented by putting a line below the gynoecium number, e.g. G$\underline{5}$. An **inferior** ovary, one below the insertion point of the stamens and petals is designated by putting a line above the gynoecium number, e.g. G$\overline{5}$.

If units are joined, put their number in brackets e.g. K(5). If some units are joined but the others are free, the former only are put in brackets e.g. A(4)+2.

If one whorl is united with another, their symbols should be tied, e.g. $\overset{\frown}{C5A5}$. If the sepals and petals cannot be distinguished, the symbol used instead is **P** (for **perianth**).

a actinomorphic flower (radially symmetrical)

b zygomorphic flower (bilaterally symmetrical)

Illustration 3 The two types of symmetry found in flowers. The dotted lines indicate the planes through which the flowers can be cut so as to give two equal and opposite halves.

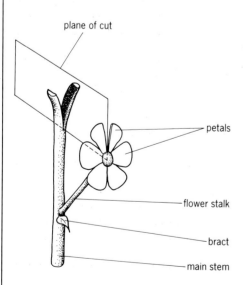

plane of cut

petals

flower stalk

bract

main stem

Illustration 4 To prepare a half flower, cut the floral structures along the median plane as shown on this diagram. If possible, however, start the cut at the base of the flower and work upwards.

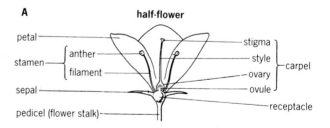

A   **half-flower**

petal — anther — stigma
stamen { anther — style } carpel
         { filament — ovary }
sepal — ovule
pedicel (flower stalk) — receptacle

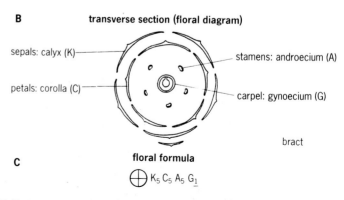

B   **transverse section (floral diagram)**

sepals: calyx (K) — stamens: androecium (A)

petals: corolla (C) — carpel: gynoecium (G)

bract

C   **floral formula**

$\oplus$ K₅ C₅ A₅ G$_1$

Illustration 5 Three representations of the structure of the same flower.

Structure and dispersal of fruits and seeds

A **fruit**, in the strict sense of the word, is formed from the ovary. The ovary expands, once the ovules in it have been fertilised and begin to develop into seeds. The wall of the fruit, known as the **pericarp**, is derived from the ovary wall. It encloses and protects the seeds and frequently promotes their dispersal.

In practice a number of other floral structures besides the ovary may contribute to the formation and distribution of the fruits. These include the style, receptacle, sepals and bracts (Figure 11.21). Constantly refer to this diagram as you investigate various fruits.

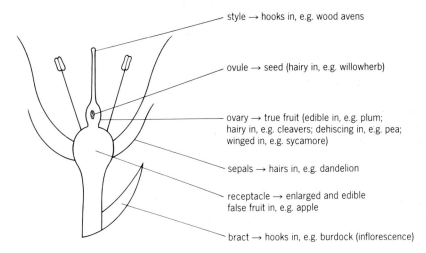

style → hooks in, e.g. wood avens

ovule → seed (hairy in, e.g. willowherb)

ovary → true fruit (edible in, e.g. plum; hairy in, e.g. cleavers; dehiscing in, e.g. pea; winged in, e.g. sycamore)

sepals → hairs in, e.g. dandelion

receptacle → enlarged and edible false fruit in, e.g. apple

bract → hooks in, e.g. burdock (inflorescence)

Figure 11.21 Schematic diagram summarising the contribution made to fruit formation and dispersal by floral structures other than the ovary. In most cases the ovary is situated above the receptacle as shown here (superior ovary); in other cases the ovary is sunk down into the receptacle (inferior ovary). There may, of course, be more than one carpel present, and in some cases the whole inflorescence may enter into the formation of the fruit.

Procedure

1 To set the scene, examine a pod of pea or bean. The pod is a fruit formed from a single carpel, whose leathery pericarp splits along one or both sides. It used to be the ovary of a flower. The peas or beans inside it are seeds which began life as unfertilised ovules. The wild ancestors of our domesticated species probably released the seeds explosively, flinging them some distance, as in gorse (*Ulex* spp.) or broom (*Cytisus scoparius*) today.

2 Examine a fruit of buttercup, or one of its close relatives, such as *Clematis* or *Anemone*. Notice that the fruit is little more than an expanded carpel containing a single seed (Figure 11.22A). Such fruits are known as **achenes**. How might they be dispersed?

3 Look at a fruit of wood avens. This is an achene too, but in this case the style becomes woody and its tip is hooked. It may cling to the fur of animals. Test its ability to cling to your clothes.

4 Examine a fruit of goosegrass. Notice the hooked hairs on the pericarp. It is another animal-dispersed species.

5 Members of the daisy family (Asteraceae, formerly known as compositae) have flowers aggregated into heads known as **capitula**. A group of florets is situated on a platform and surrounded by modified leaves (bracts). Each floret produces a single fruit. In some species the whole capitulum is dispersed as a unit after fertilisation, and the seeds fall out one by one.

Look at a bur of burdock, test its ability to cling to your clothes and look for the single-seeded fruits inside.

6 Cut open a plum or cherry and examine its contents. This fleshy, succulent fruit, called a **drupe,** develops from a single carpel containing a single seed (Figure 11.22B). The pericarp is three-layered. A thin outer **epicarp** surrounds a fleshy and tasty **mesocarp**. Inside this the **endocarp** (the 'stone') protects the seed (against what?). How are these seeds dispersed?

Danger
Razor blade

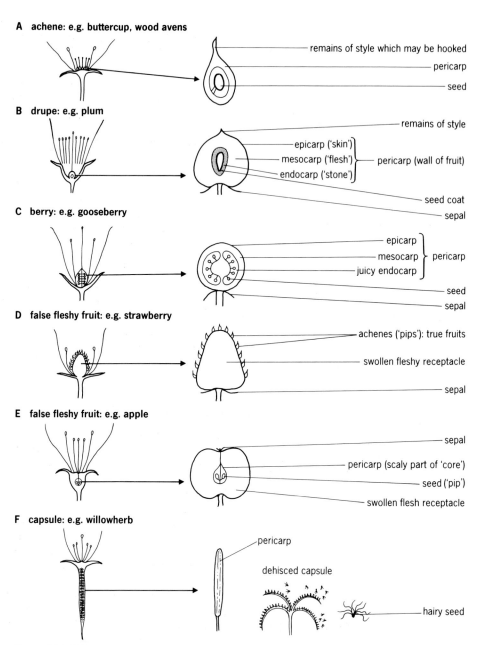

Figure 11.22 Diagrams of a selection of fruits showing how, in all cases, the fruit is formed from the ovary and the seeds from the ovules.

Danger
Razor blade

Danger
Razor blade

Danger
Razor blade

7 Cut a tomato in half vertically, and another one horizontally. This kind of fruit (a **berry**) consists of several multi-seeded carpels fused together (Figure 11.22C). Suggest other examples of this kind of fruit. Count the number of carpels in your cross-section.

In a tomato the epicarp is thin and red, and the mesocarp and endocarp are soft, fleshy and juicy. The seeds have hard protective seed coats. How are they dispersed?

8 Examine the external features of a strawberry. In this case the red, edible part of the 'fruit' is formed from a swollen receptacle to form a **false fleshy fruit** (Figure 11.22D). Embedded in its surface are the numerous small dry fruits (achenes), each containing a single seed. Cut the strawberry vertically and notice the relationship between these achenes and the receptacle.

9 The apple is another example of a false fleshy fruit (Figure 11.22E). The sweet-tasting swollen receptacle surrounds the 'core', which represents the true fruit. In the centre, the pericarp surrounds the seeds ('pips'). The pear is similar.

Cut an apple or pear vertically and horizontally through the centre. How many carpels are there, and how many seeds in each carpel?

11.15 INVESTIGATION

Corrosive   Iodine
Phenol   solution
Methyl green in
ethanoic acid
Acetocarmine

Toxic
Chloral hydrate
Phenol

10 Examine the fruit of rosebay willowherb. It is a **capsule**, formed from several carpels fused together. Investigate the number of carpels by cutting the capsule transversely, which should also allow you to examine the hairy seeds (Figure 11.22F).

Investigate the mechanism by which the seeds of rosebay willowherb are released. Place the unopened capsule on a hotplate and observe the dispersal mechanism in action. What happens if you breathe onto the open capsule, or place it in a drop of water?

11 Examine the fruit of a sycamore tree. The wall of the carpel is expanded to form two (or in some species three) wings. Notice the twirling parachute effect when thrown into the air.

12 Relatively few fruits are habitually dispersed by water. The coconut is an exception. Examine a half-coconut. It is a drupe, a fleshy fruit containing one or more seeds each surrounded by a fibrous layer. In coconut, however, the epicarp has usually been lost and the mesocarp, instead of being fleshy, is fibrous and contains air spaces to aid floating.

For consideration

1 Some seeds are dispersed on animals' coats and others are dispersed in animals' guts. Discuss the advantages and disadvantages of these methods.
2 Lines of hawthorn seedlings are sometimes seen to sprout up along fences or beneath telephone wires, and seedlings of many exotic plant species (e.g. tomatoes) are found on sewage sludge. Suggest explanations.
3 What type of fruit is a raspberry or blackberry and what sort of flower gives rise to it?

Structure and germination of pollen

By using evidence from a variety of sources – scanning electron micrographs, microscopic examination and pollen germination – we can gain a comprehensive understanding of the role of pollen in the life cycle of a flowering plant.

Guidance

Collect pollen grains from the anthers of the plants provided, mount them in water and examine under medium power. Can you deduce from the structure of its pollen grains whether a species is insect- or wind-pollinated?

Look at pollen grains under high power. Clear some in chloral hydrate, and mount in iodine solution, or methyl green in ethanoic acid. Can you see the two-layered wall (functions?) and the two nuclei?

Next try to germinate some pollen grains. Transfer the grains of a mixture of species with a paint brush into a drop of sucrose solution (0.4 mol dm⁻³) in the depression of a cavity slide. Put your slide in a dark place at 20–30 °C and examine at intervals for 1–2 hours. Once you can see pollen tubes add a coverslip, irrigate with acetocarmine or neutral red, and look for nuclei. What normally happens at germination to the two male nuclei in a pollen grain?

Examine prepared longitudinal sections of pollinated gynoecia. Make sketches to illustrate the growth of the pollen tube into the stigma and down the style into the ovary.

Alternatively, squash the ripe stigmas of 'fast plants' (see page 200), or a member of the daisy family, beneath a coverslip on a microscope slide. Irrigate with methylene blue and examine under medium power. You should be able to see germinated pollen grains with pollen tubes protruding from them.

Examine scanning electron micrographs of the pollen grains of different species. What can you infer from your observations?

For consideration

1 How could your germination experiment be extended to investigate the effect of temperature?
2 It is said that when a pollen grain lands on a suitable stigma, the latter produces a 2–4% sugar solution, which holds the pollen grains and facilitates their germination. How would you test the claim that the sugary secretion facilitates pollen germination? How would you determine the optimum concentration of the solution?

Value of appendages in fruit dispersal

Many fruits and seeds have various appendages, such as the hairy 'pappuses' on dandelion fruits or the 'rotor blades' of sycamore, which are frequently interpreted as aiding wind dispersal. How much do they help? In this investigation you will assess the distances to which seeds fall with and without the dispersal structures (wings, pappuses) normally attached to them, in both windy and still conditions.

Guidance

Look at the wild species with wind-dispersed fruits accessible to you, and the range of fruits available to you in the laboratory. Concentrate upon two or three species. Collect fruits if necessary.

If you have selected a tree you can assess the efficiency of its fruit dispersal by (i) making careful observations and notes about the distances to which fruits fall around fruiting trees, and (ii) laying quadrats at measured distances from the trunk and counting the numbers of fruits per unit area.

In the laboratory, evaluate the roles of the appendages by dropping a sample of fruits from the same position onto large sheets of paper and recording the places where they land or come to rest. Measure and record the distances from the origin. Try this also in air blown from a hair dryer. Then cut off the appendages and repeat the experiments. Use a t-test (see Statistical Appendix) to test the hypothesis that there is no difference in the distance travelled by the fruits as a result of each treatment.

You could also find the dry mass of an appendage.

For consideration

1 Is the only role of the appendages you have investigated to help wind dispersal? Might they (i) reduce the numbers of seeds eaten by animals, (ii) aid water uptake for germination (iii) facilitate burial when the seed reaches the ground or (iv) place the embryo the right way up when the seed germinates? Evaluate each alternative.

2 Calculate the total annual investment by a parent plant in the appendages on its seeds or fruits, in terms of either mass or energy (appendages contain about 22 kJg^{-1} dry mass). Is this investment by the parent plant worthwhile?

⚠️

Razor blade

REQUIREMENTS

Quadrats
Measuring tape
Clip-board and recording paper
Large sheets of paper
Pencils
Metre rule
Hair dryer
Safety razor blade
Balance

Fruits or seeds of species which appear to be wind-dispersed

Propagation of clones of cauliflower, carrot or potato by tissue culture

It was discovered in the 1950s that whole plants could be grown from single cells. Unspecialised plant cells are **totipotent**, that is, they retain the potential to generate the whole range of specialised tissues which occur in an adult plant. The production of new plants from tissue fragments ('explants') or individual cells in sterile solution culture or on nutrient agar has become routine in agriculture and horticulture. It enables hundreds of individuals to be produced from a single plant. This is very useful if the parent plant is of a rare species, or has a unique genotype, or is a virus-free individual.

The investigation has a considerable success rate with the 3 mm tip of an eye of a potato, the mini-florets from the florets of a cauliflower head, or a segment of a carrot tap root treated with the plant growth regulator 2,4-D. In all such cases, it is essential to use sterile apparatus and technique. It is also just about possible to isolate single plant cells, and (we hope!) watch them grow into new plants on sterile nutrient agar or nutrient solution, but this technique is much more 'hit or miss'.

Guidance

Throughout the setting up of this experiment, take care to avoid contamination. Close windows and doors, swab your bench with 70% ethanol, wash your hands in 70% ethanol, and use sterilised instruments and glassware.

After carefully cutting off several fragments of the appropriate tissue, sterilise them in bleach solution for ten minutes. Then, using sterile forceps, transfer the fragments through four separate washes of sterilised distilled water before placing them, widely spaced and gently pressed into the agar, in sterilised Petri dishes. As each culture is

REQUIREMENTS

Beakers
Microscope
Sterilised forceps
Sterilised Petri dishes
Illuminated growth cabinet at 25 °C
Insulating tape
Cling film

Sterilised distilled water (500 cm^3)
Ethanol, 70%
Bleach solution (250 cm^3 10% sodium chlorate (I) solution with 2 cm^3 teepol)
Nutrient agar containing mineral salts, sucrose, vitamins, 0.1 mg dm^{-3} of 2,4-D (2,4-Dichlorophenoxyacetic acid) and 2.5 mg dm^{-3} of kinetin, a cytokinin growth regulator.

Floral meristems of cauliflower, tap root of carrot or tuber of potato prepared, seal it with insulating tape and loosely surround it with cling film. Transfer it to the growth cabinet at 20–28 °C in the light.

Clumps of cells, resulting from the cell division, known as **calluses**, will develop over the next few weeks, and new plantlets will then develop from buds on their surfaces. Examine from time to time under a microscope, write detailed notes and keep a photographic record if possible.

For consideration

1   Similar procedures have been used for a long time in industry and horticulture. What has been their commercial value?

2   Individual plants can now be grown from pollen grains. What is unusual about such plants?

11.18 INVESTIGATION

Relating the structure of flowers to their method of pollination

Most of the differences between flowers can be attributed to their modes of pollination. In this investigation examine carefully the wind-pollinated flower of a grass, and then compare two insect-pollinated flowers.

Guidance

First, examine the inflorescence of Species A, a grass (Figure 11.23). The individual flowers are known as **florets**. They are aggregated into groups known as **spikelets**. Different groups of grasses differ in the number of florets per spikelet; the species illustrated in Figure 11.23B has one floret per spikelet.

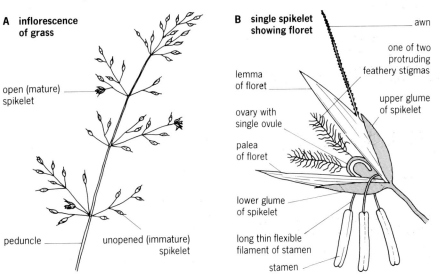

Figure 11.23 The inflorescence and flower of a typical grass.

Examine a spikelet, and notice that at its base there is a pair of modified leaves (**glumes**). Now examine an individual floret under a binocular microscope. The floret consists of two leaves, the **lemma** (larger) and the **palea**, surrounding one ovary and three stamens. The ovary contains one ovule and supports two feathery stigmas.

Examine the spikelet again with the following contention in mind. Wind-pollinated flowers tend to lack showy petals, nectar guides, nectar, nectaries and scent. They usually have stamens which hang outside the flower and which produce large quantities of smooth, light pollen grains. The stigmas are exposed to the wind and have a large surface area.

Now predict the features which insect-pollinated flowers might have in common. Then examine flowers of species B and C, both insect-pollinated, and write a careful comparison of their flowers, perhaps in the form of a table. You might like to start by writing the floral formulae for both flowers (see Box 11.1, page 203). Are your predictions about the structures of the flowers of insect-pollinated species borne out in practice?

For consideration

1 Speculate on the types of insect which might pollinate flowers B and C. Which is more likely to be pollinated by large insects? List the adaptations of flower C to attract and reward its pollinating insects, and to protect its pollen and nectar from thieving.
2 In what ways are the fertilised ovules of grasses economically important?

PROJECTS

Before starting a project, discuss your intended procedure with your teacher.

1 Try using the technique suggested on page 184 (for staining cells dividing by mitosis) to stain ones dividing by *meiosis*. Such cells can be obtained from immature anthers in the dormant inflorescence of a hyacinth bulb. Vary your approach (e.g. maturity of anther, length of time acetic orcein applied) to get the best results.

2 From your knowledge of cell size, the size of different organisms and the length of time its takes them to reach maturity, calculate the average length of the cell cycle in different species. Do your results suggest that the average length of the cell cycle is relatively constant for different species, or varies greatly? Attempt to explain your findings.

3 A **corm** is a short, swollen vertically growing underground stem (Figure 11.24). It stores food and survives the winter, giving rise the following year to the above-ground parts of the plant and to new corms. Examine corms (e.g. of a crocus) in conjunction with Figure 11.24. Cut one corm vertically in half. Note the central vascular strand. Stain with acidified phloroglucinol. What is the function of the adventitious roots? Distinguish between the functions of the apical and axillary buds. Grow corms and examine at various stages of development.

4 Grow onions or daffodils and examine the bulbs at various stages of development.

5 Compare the success of different commercial rooting powders at getting cuttings to root.

6 Set up a laboratory colony of reproducing mosses and study the life cycle in detail.

7 Mosses and ferns require water for reproduction. It is often stated in text books that they therefore depend on water to a greater extent than flowering plants. Test this assertion by examining the distribution patterns of mosses, ferns and flowering plants in habitats near where you live or study.

8 Try to determine the potential number of offspring that different species of mosses, ferns and flowering plants can have. You will need to calculate the number of spores or seeds that various species can produce.

9 Compare the reproduction and growth of two different species of mammal, for example rabbit and cat. You will need to make accurate observations of such things as number of offspring in a litter, their weight gain and their development. Supplement your findings with information from secondary sources (e.g. on age at first reproduction and gestation length).

10 Compare the structure of the urinogenital system of a rat with that of a mouse or rabbit. Dissect the urinogenital system of a mouse or rabbit and compare your findings with those obtained in Practical Exercise 11.10.

11 Compare the different methods of human contraception in terms of how they work and their advantages and disadvantages. Your school or college may have a pack with different types of contraceptives. Alternatively, these can be obtained from the Family Planning Association, the Health Education Authority or hospital health education units.

12 Interview adults about their knowledge of, and views on, contraception.

13 Sample different newspapers and see how often they refer to sexually transmitted diseases and from what standpoint. Interpret your findings.

14 The 'pollen count' is the number of pollen grains caught on a sticky microscope slide, exposed to the air for 24 hours. Record the daily pollen count. Devise a brief questionnaire which can be rapidly completed each day by classmates who suffer from hay fever to record their degree of suffering. Then correlate your pollen counts with a 'suffering index'. Do some types of pollen grain contribute more to suffering than others?

15 Investigate the pollinators and pollination mechanism of any species which interests you, for example Lords and Ladies (*Arum maculatum*) – see Jones D.H.T. *Journal of Biological Education* **11**, 253–60 (1977), who gives fascinating suggestions for project work.

16 Capture and etherise a small sample of bees from one specific area (care! stings). Relate the average tongue length of each bee species to the flowers it has visited (as shown by the range of species amongst the pollen grains it has collected), and the average corolla tube lengths of each flower species.

17 Investigate the structure and movement of the awns attached to the fruits of grasses such as wild oats, *Avena fatua*. These awns are said to be hygroscopic, altering in shape as the relative humidity of the atmosphere changes. It has been suggested that they facilitate burial of the fruit in soil or, by twisting and turning, enable the fruit to travel over a surface (see, for example Hou, J.Q. & Simpson, G.M. The adaptive significance of awns and hairs on grasses. *Journal of Biological Education* **26** (1), 10–11, 1992).

18 Investigate the effect of plant growth substances on the growth of calluses in tissue culture.

19 Evaluate the hypotheses that the dispersal appendages of wind-dispersed seeds or fruits (a) reduce the numbers of seeds eaten by animals, (b) aid water uptake for germination, (c) place the embryo the right way up when the seed germinates.

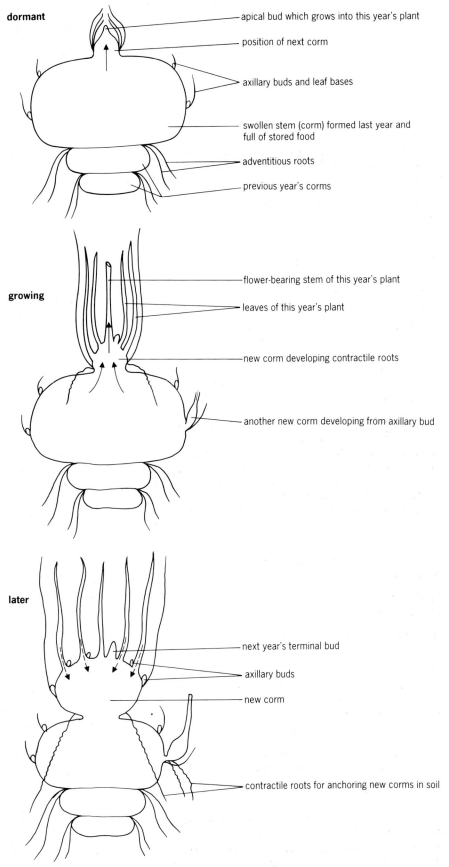

dormant

apical bud which grows into this year's plant

position of next corm

axillary buds and leaf bases

swollen stem (corm) formed last year and full of stored food

adventitious roots

previous year's corms

growing

flower-bearing stem of this year's plant

leaves of this year's plant

new corm developing contractile roots

another new corm developing from axillary bud

later

next year's terminal bud

axillary buds

new corm

contractile roots for anchoring new corms in soil

Figure 11.24 Diagrams of a corm. Solid arrows indicate movement of food materials from perennating organ to new plant or new perennating organ. Broken arrows indicate movement of food materials from the foliage leaves of this year's plant into the perennating organ.

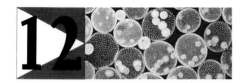

12 Growth and development

Development of the tadpole

Every sexually reproducing multicellular organism starts life as a single cell which then divides repeatedly and develops into an adult. An amphibian in the stage between being a fertilised **egg** and an **adult** is described as a **tadpole**. The development of the tadpole can be followed by observing live tadpoles of *Xenopus*, or some other amphibian such as the common frog, at the appropriate time of year (often spring), and also by studying preserved specimens, if available.

Apart from observing the external features, you may be able to look at transverse and/or longitudinal sections of the various stages.

Procedure

The young tadpole

1 Examine a newly hatched tadpole. To what extent does it look like Figure 12.1A which is based on the common frog?

2 Identify as many of the following features as you can, and consider the associated questions:

   a Tail Does this lengthen or shorten over the next few days?

   b Mucus glands To what do these attach the young tadpole?

   c External gills How many are there on each side of the head?

   d Developing mouth As yet this does not connect with the pharynx, so how does the tadpole gain nourishment at this stage?

   e S-shaped tubular heart Can you suggest why this is S-shaped?

   f Developing internal gills How many are there on each side of the head?

From hatching to metamorphosis

3 During the next three months or so (more quickly if tadpoles are kept in an aquarium in a warm room) the tadpole undergoes a series of changes which you can see for yourself by examining tadpoles at different stages of development. Identify as many of the following changes as you can, and consider the associated questions:

   a Degeneration of the attachment organ and elongation of the tail, with the result that the tadpole becomes motile. How does the tadpole use its tail for movement?

   b Development of **sense organs** (nasal sacs, eyes and inner ears).

   c Development of a mouth. On what do tadpoles feed?

   d Elongation and coiling of the **gut**. How does this suit the tadpole for its diet?

   e Replacement of the external gills by **internal gills** associated with four pairs of gill pouches. Why does this change occur?

   f Growth of a pair of **opercula** – ventro-lateral folds of skin that cover the gill openings (Figure 12.1B). What might be the function of the opercula?

   g Growth of **limb buds**. Which are visible first, the forelimbs or hindlimbs?

   h Development of a pair of **lungs** as pouches from the ventral side of the pharynx.

Metamorphosis

4 Towards the end of the third month or so the tadpole undergoes a comparatively sudden **metamorphosis** (change) into the adult, during the course of which it becomes terrestrial. Many of the adult structures are already present in rudimentary form before metamorphosis, but at this time they complete their development and become functional. By observing live and/or preserved specimens, describe the changes that happen at metamorphosis in the structures shown in the margin.

a Nasal sacs
b Eyelids
c Ears
d Mouth
e Head shape
f Limbs
g Tail
h Skin colour
i Gut length and coiling
j Gill pouches
k Lungs
l Heart and circulatory system.

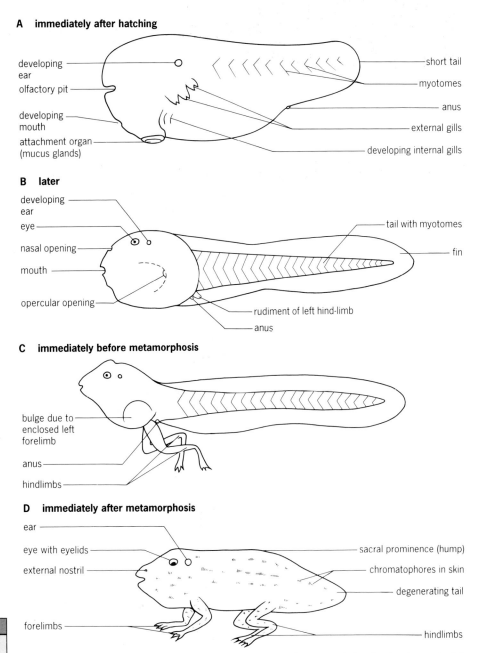

A immediately after hatching

developing ear
olfactory pit
developing mouth
attachment organ (mucus glands)
short tail
myotomes
anus
external gills
developing internal gills

B later

developing ear
eye
nasal opening
mouth
opercular opening
tail with myotomes
fin
rudiment of left hind-limb
anus

C immediately before metamorphosis

bulge due to enclosed left forelimb
anus
hindlimbs

D immediately after metamorphosis

ear
eye with eyelids
external nostril
sacral prominence (hump)
chromatophores in skin
degenerating tail
forelimbs
hindlimbs

Figure 12.1 Diagrams showing the major external changes that occur during the development of the frog tadpole. Based on the common frog *Rana temporaria*.

For consideration

1 To what extent can adult frogs be regarded as fully terrestrial?
2 Can the change from tadpole to adult amphibian really be described as a metamorphosis? How does it compare with metamorphosis in a butterfly and with puberty in humans?

12.2 PRACTICAL EXERCISE

Development of shepherd's purse embryos

In a flowering plant the following changes take place after fertilisation: the **zygote** develops into the **embryo**; the endosperm nucleus divides to form a mass of tissue, known as the **endosperm**, which surrounds and nourishes the embryo; the **ovule** develops into the **seed**, the **integuments** forming the seed coat (**testa**); and the **ovary** forms the **fruit** (**pericarp**).

These developmental changes can conveniently be seen in *Capsella bursa-pastoris*, shepherd's purse.

Procedure

1   Examine a whole plant of shepherd's purse. The youngest part of the plant is at the apex where unopened flower buds may be seen; further back open flowers should be visible; and further back still, heart-shaped fruits should be seen. Trace the developmental sequence from apex to base. Two stages are illustrated in Figure 12.2.

2   Open one of the youngest fruits and note the two rows of ovules (Figure 12.2A). Remove a few of the ovules and mount in chloral hydrate or acetocarmine. Identify the structures shown in Figure 12.3A.

3   Mount ovules of different ages in chloral hydrate. Start with ovules from fruits towards the apex of the plant, and then work your way down the stem towards the base. In each case observe intact ovules first, then gently press the coverslip with a needle so as to burst the ovule and release its embryo. If the embryo is too transparent, try mounting another one in acetocarmine.

Corrosive
Acetocarmine

Toxic
Chloral hydrate

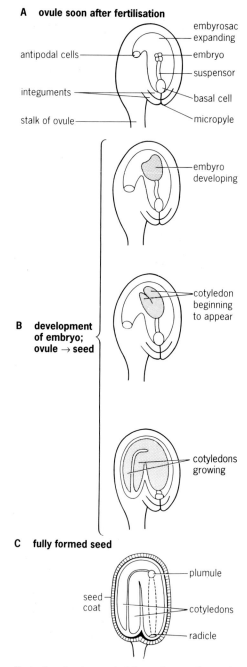

Figure 12.3 Diagrams illustrating development of the embryo and associated structures in shepherd's purse, *Capsella bursa-pastoris*. The diagrams are not all drawn to the same scale: the carpel and its contents grow steadily longer after fertilisation.

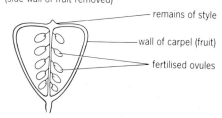

Figure 12.2 Fruit and seeds of shepherd's purse, *Capsella bursa-pastoris*.

4   Using Figure 12.3 to help you, reconstruct the sequence of stages in the develop-
    ment of the embryo and the formation of the seed. What happens to the
    endosperm and suspensor as development proceeds?
5   Supplement the investigation by examining a prepared longitudinal section of the
    fruit of shepherd's purse.

For consideration

1   What is the function of the suspensor?
2   During development the embryo bends over so the cotyledons point downwards.
    What are the consequences of this?
3   The final event in the formation of the seed is the loss of water with the result
    that the water content is reduced from approximately 80 to 10%. What is the pur-
    pose of this? Suggest how it might be achieved.

12.3 PRACTICAL EXERCISE

Seed structure

In most seeds the embryo is surrounded by endosperm tissue which serves as a food
supply during germination. In other seeds there is little or no endosperm, food being
supplied by the enlarged cotyledons. Flowering plants are divided into **mono-
cotyledons**, the seeds of which have only one cotyledon, and **dicotyledons**, the seeds
of which have two cotyledons.

Whatever other factors are required for germination, one essential factor is water:
the first clearly observable event in germination is the **imbibition** of water. As a result
of this, the embryonic tissues swell and rupture the seed coat.

In this practical you will examine seeds and identify the form in which they carry
their food reserves.

Danger
Razor blade

Procedure

1   Examine dry and soaked seeds of the following plants: broad bean, castor oil plant
    and wheat. Determine the approximate percentage increase in mass after soaking.
2   Slice longitudinally through the soaked seeds and identify the structures you
    observe, using Figures 12.4, 12.5 and 12.6 to help you.

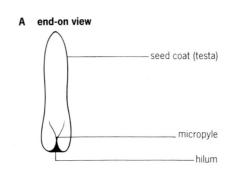

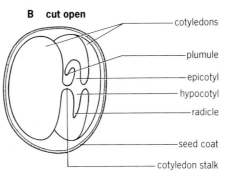

Figure 12.4 Structure of broad bean seed.

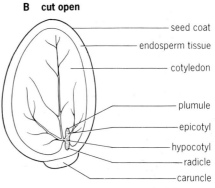

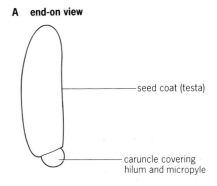

Figure 12.5 Structure of the seed of the castor
oil plant, Ricinus communis. Caruncles are usually
adaptations for dispersal by animals.

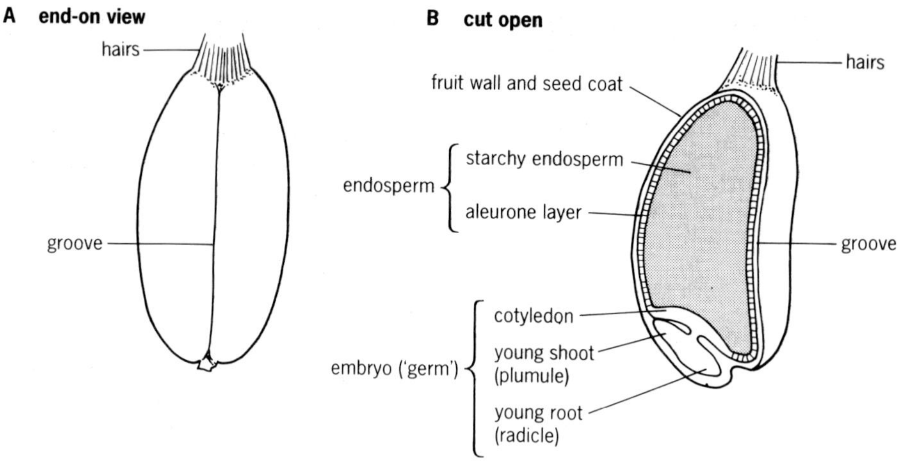

A end-on view

B cut open

Figure 12.6 Structure of a wheat grain. A wheat grain is in fact a *fruit*, the seed itself being inside.

3 Determine whether each seed is endospermic or non-endospermic and monocotyledonous or dicotyledonous.
4 Carry out food tests on different parts of the seeds of each species (see page 49). It may help to present your results in the form of a table.

For consideration

1 Does the percentage increase in mass on soaking represent the percentage increase in water content? Explain your answer.
2 Were there substantial differences in the food reserves of different parts of the various seeds?
3 What are the advantages of seeds being in a dried-out state while they are lying in the soil?
4 Why is it necessary for a seed to absorb water before it can germinate?
5 How, and by what route, do you think these seeds take up water? How might your ideas be tested?

REQUIREMENTS

Balance
Scalpel or razor blade
Reagents for food tests (see page 49)
Broad bean seed (dry)
Broad bean seed (soaked for 24–48 hours)
Castor oil seed (dry)
Castor oil seed (soaked for 48 hours)
Wheat grain (dry)
Wheat grain (soaked for 24 hours)

12.4 INVESTIGATION

Hypogeal and epigeal germination

In **hypogeal** germination the cotyledons remain below ground (*hypo* is Greek for under). In **epigeal** germination the cotyledons appear above the ground (*epi* is Greek for upon). Hyogeal germination results from elongation of the *epicotyl*. Consult Figure 12.4B and imagine what would happen if the epicotyl were to elongate – the plumule would be thrust upwards through the soil. In epigeal germination, on the other hand, the *hypocotyl* elongates with the result that the delicate cotyledons, protected by the ruptured seed coat, are pushed up above the soil surface. Here, exposed to light, the cotyledons turn green and photosynthesise.

In this investigation it is suggested that you follow the fate of germinating castor oil and broad bean seeds to determine which of these species shows hypogeal and which epigeal germination.

Guidance

You will need to soak the seeds for 24 hours and then sow them about 3 cm beneath soil level. Think about how many castor oil seeds and broad bean seeds you will need. Will you need to dig any up before they break the soil surface? How precisely will you determine whether germination is hypogeal or epigeal? You will probably find it helpful to make careful drawings or take photographs to record your findings.

For consideration

1 Which species showed hypogeal and which epigeal germination?
2 The seeds of hypogeal plants usually contain large, fleshy cotyledons – why is this?
3 The seeds of epigeal plants usually contain abundant endosperm tissue – why?
4 Although the seeds of epigeal plants usually contain abundant endosperm tissue, there are some that do not, e.g. sunflower, marrow and sycamore. How do you think such plants obtain nourishment during germination?

REQUIREMENTS

Plant pots
Potting compost
Castor oil seeds
Broad bean seeds
Camera (if available)

Toxic
Chloral hydrate

Primary growth in flowering plants

Primary growth in flowering plants takes place at the apex of the stem and root. It involves division of primary meristematic cells in **apical meristems**. To examine primary growth it is necessary to study sections and/or cleared whole mounts of young root and shoot apices. (Clearing is a process in which a chemical such as chloral hydrate is added to make the section more transparent, and thus easier to see through.)

Procedure
Root apex

1   Obtain a germinating seed of maize or some other grass (Figure 12.7). Instead of having the main root found in many plants, most grasses, including maize, develop a bundle of **adventitious** roots.
2   Cut one of the roots about 15 mm from the tip and mount in chloral hydrate.

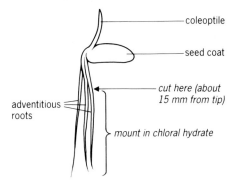

Figure 12.7 Preparation of young maize roots for viewing under the microscope.

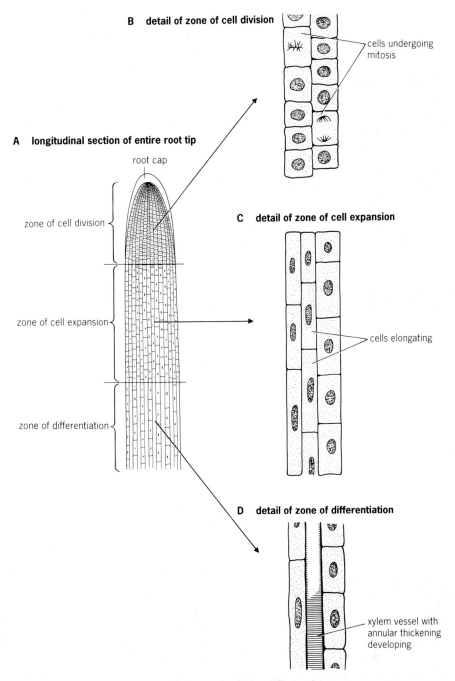

Figure 12.8 Microscopic structure of the root tip of onion (*Allium* sp.).

3 Examine under medium power, reducing the illumination as much as possible. Start with the extreme tip and work back to the older parts of the root. Note successively:
  a Root cap cells (protective);
  b Zone of cell division (cells cube-shaped, dividing mitotically);
  c Zone of cell expansion (cells progressively more elongated further back along the root);
  d Zone of differentiation (cells acquire features characteristic of specific tissues – xylem vessels with annular or spiral thickening should be evident).

4 Take a germinating pea or bean with a radicle 10–20 mm long and examine it under a hand lens or binocular microscope. Describe what you see.

5 With a sharp razor blade cut thin longitudinal sections and mount them in water or dilute glycerol. Examine under a microscope. Note the zones of cell division, expansion and differentiation. How do these relate to the **root hair zone**?

6 Examine a prepared longitudinal section of the root tip of onion (*Allium* sp.) under low and high powers (Figure 12.8). Start at the tip and work back noting, in particular, cells undergoing mitosis. Where are such cells most often found?

Procedure
Shoot apex

1 Remove the tip of the plumule of a germinating broad bean, and cut it close to its attachment to the seed.

2 Holding the isolated shoot in a piece of moistened pith (see page 79), cut transverse sections at levels **a**, **b** and **c** in Figure 12.9 and place them in water in separate labelled watch glasses.

3 Stain a thin section from each watch glass in acidified phloroglucinol, then mount in dilute glycerol.

4 Compare your sections. What conclusions can you draw regarding the development of primary tissues in the shoot?

5 Examine a longitudinal section through the shoot apex of, for example, lilac (Figure 12.10). Start at the tip and work back. How does the section compare with that of the root apex? In addition to the zones of cell division, expansion and differentiation, note the developing vascular strands, leaf primordia with vascular tissue going to them, and axillary buds.

Danger
Razor blade

Corrosive
Acidified
phloroglucinol

Highly
flammable
Acidified
phloroglucinol

REQUIREMENTS

Microscope
Hand lens or binocular microscope
Slides and coverslips
Razor blade
Watch glasses
Pith
Chloral hydrate
Acidified phloroglucinol
Dilute glycerol
Germinating maize with roots about 20 mm in length
Germinating pea or bean with radicle 10–20 mm in length
LS root tip of onion (*Allium* sp.)
LS stem apex of lilac (*Syringa* sp.)

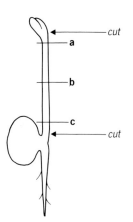
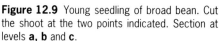

Figure 12.9 Young seedling of broad bean. Cut the shoot at the two points indicated. Section at levels **a, b** and **c**.

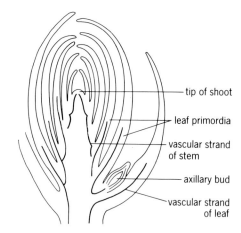

Figure 12.10 Longitudinal section of the stem apex of lilac (*Syringa* sp.).

For consideration

1 Compare the development of a primary shoot and root. Explain the differences between them in terms of the functions which these two parts of the plant have to carry out.

2 In the apical meristem of a root or shoot the cell divisions do not all occur in the same plane. Describe the planes in which they occur, and explain the contribution each makes to the developing organ.

Secondary growth in flowering plants

Primary growth is mainly concerned with growth of the plant in a *longitudinal* direction. In contrast, secondary growth is responsible for increasing the *girth* of the stem and main root(s). It occurs by division of secondary meristematic cells (**cambium**) within the primary tissues, and it results in the formation of secondary tissues. In a twig, for example, secondary growth results in the formation of **wood**. In this investigation you can attempt to reconstruct the three-dimensional internal structure of a twig by examining both temporary and prepared slides cut in various planes.

Guidance

Before beginning your investigation, carefully examine Figure 12.11 which shows the distribution of the tissues in a transverse section of a lime (*Tilia* sp.) twig in the autumn of the second year of its growth. Ensure that you know the functions of the various tissues shown.

12.6 INVESTIGATION

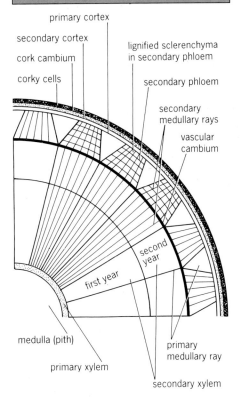

Figure 12.11 Transverse section of lime (*Tilia* sp.) twig in the autumn of its second year.

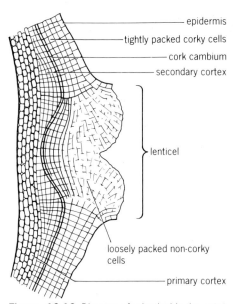

Figure 12.13 Diagram of a lenticel in the outer layers of the bark of a tree seen in section. Based on elder (*Sambucus* sp.).

Corrosive Acidified phloroglucinol   Harmful Iodine solution   Highly flammable Acidified phloroglucinol   Danger Razor blade

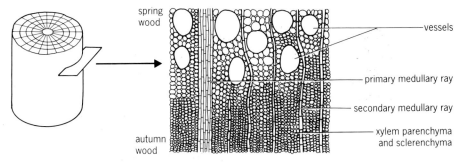
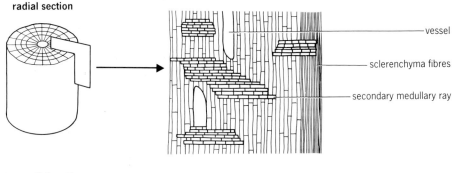
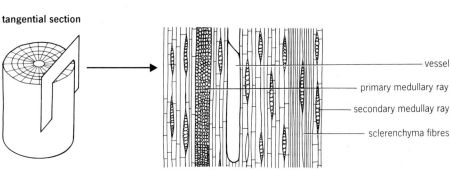

Figure 12.12 The difference between transverse, radial and tangential sections through a piece of wood.

Procedure

Reconstruct the three-dimensional anatomy of a woody twig by cutting transverse, radial and tangential sections (Figure 12.12 and Box 5.4, page 79.). Stain some sections in iodine, others in acidified phloroglucinol and mount in dilute glycerol. Supplement the information gained from your own sections by examining prepared sections.

Examine a prepared slide showing a transverse section through **cork** with a **lenticel** present. Interpret your observations by reference to Figure 12.13.

REQUIREMENTS

Microscope
Slides and coverslips
Watch glasses
Razor blade
Iodine solution
Acidified phloroglucinol
Dilute glycerol
Twig of a woody perennial, e.g. lime
   (*Tilia* sp.), oak (*Quercus* sp.) or beech
   (*Fagus* sp.)
Transverse, radial and tangential section
   of wood
TS cork showing lenticel

For consideration

1 In temperate regions, wood can be divided into spring and autumn wood. In a given growing season, which of these lies external to the other? How may the two types of wood be distinguished by their structure? What is the functional significance of this difference?
2 Where did you find starch in your twig? Why was it found there?
3 Explain the functions of the various cell types you found in your twig.
4 Make a sketch showing the distribution of tissues in a two-year old stem. Explain to yourself (or, better, to someone else!) how this pattern is arrived at during development.
5 Imagine an eighty year-old oak tree. Make a sketch of its trunk, and some of its branches and twigs. Write on the sketch the numbers of annual rings which you would expect to find at various parts of the tree.
6 What functions are performed by cork? What function is performed by lenticels?
7 Sketch the internal structure of a large, old root showing secondary growth.

12.7 PRACTICAL EXERCISE

Measurement of tropic responses of coleoptiles and roots

It is well known that stems usually grow towards light, that is, they are **positively phototropic**. In this experiment the rapid phototropic response of a coleoptile is observed and measured. The same technique can be used to measure the responses of coleoptiles and radicles to other stimuli (see 'Projects'). For this experiment you require a microscope whose eyepiece has been fitted with a micrometer scale (see Box 5.2, page 71).

Procedure

1 Bend the microscope downwards towards you, so that the tube is horizontal and the stage vertical. Darken the room and arrange for the light to strike the microscope stage from one side.
2 Select a germinating seed with a straight coleoptile. Mount it in a moist chamber constructed from a plastic syringe (Figure 12.14), with the coleoptile protruding.
3 Attach the moist chamber horizontally to a microscope slide with an elastic band. Clip the slide to the microscope stage so that the horizontal coleoptile is pointing directly towards the top of the field of view. Position it so that the tip of the coleoptile, when viewed down the microscope, corresponds exactly with the mid-point of the micrometer scale. Illuminate it from one side and observe the tip of the coleoptile for 5–15 minutes until it starts moving in a definite direction.
4 Loosen the elastic band, and rotate the moist chamber through 180° on the slide so that the other side of the coleoptile now receives the strongest illumination. Adjust the position of the moist chamber so that the coleoptile tip points toward the mid-point of the micrometer scale, as before.
5 Take readings of the position of the coleoptile tip on the micrometer at regular intervals for up to half an hour.
6 Plot the positions of the coleoptile tip against time. What conclusions can you draw?

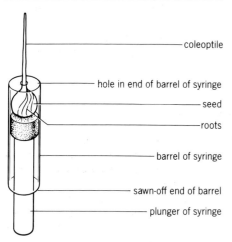

Figure 12.14 Moist chamber, constructed from a plastic syringe, for mounting a germinating seed for observations on phototropism (or other plant responses).

coleoptile
hole in end of barrel of syringe
seed
roots
barrel of syringe
sawn-off end of barrel
plunger of syringe

REQUIREMENTS

Microscope
Eyepiece with micrometer scale
Moist chamber (adapted syringe as in
   Figure 12.14)
Microscope slide
Elastic band
Lamp

Germinating seed of oat, barley or wheat
   grown in the dark at 25 °C for four
   days, long enough to have a protruding
   coleoptile

For consideration

1 State two reasons why the coleoptile was rotated through 180° at step 4 of the experiment.
2 What is the relevance of your results to the normal life of the plant?
3 Try to explain anything unexpected which happened during the experiment, or any anomalous results.

12.8 PRACTICAL EXERCISE

The detection of light in positive phototropism

The tips of seedlings exhibit growth bending towards a light source. How do they detect the direction from which the light is shining?

Procedure

1 You are provided with four photographic film cases with coloured filters in the walls. For each container, cut out two circles of filter paper of sufficient size to fit into the base, insert them and add drops of water from a dropping pipette until the paper is moist.

2 Place onto the centre of the filter paper three germinating cereal grains or seeds of 'fast plants' (see Practical exercise 11.12). Put the top on the container. Carefully place it where it will not be disturbed but will be equally illuminated from all sides.

3 Examine the seedlings at daily intervals, but never leave the tops off the containers for long. Record the directions in which the coleoptiles or hypocotyls bend, their lengths and colours. In the case of dicotyledonous fast plants, note the degree of unfolding of the cotyledons in each case.

4 Interpret your results in terms of the wavelengths of light transmitted through each filter.

For consideration

1 The containers were equally illuminated from all sides but did the seedlings necessarily receive an equal intensity of light from all sides through the filters?

2 On the basis of the absorption spectra of various pigments in the plant, suggest which pigment(s) might be absorbing the light to which the shoots are responding.

3 In direction-finding for a shoot emerging from the soil, why might it be advantageous for the shoot to respond to some wavelengths of light rather than others?

REQUIREMENTS
Four photographic film cartons in the sides of each of which three 'windows' have been cut and filters stuck. One carton should have a blue, a red and a green filter. The other three cartons should each have the same colour of filter stuck over all the windows – blue for one carton, red for a second and green for a third.
Filter paper
Scissors
Dropping pipette
Measuring scales, thin, graduated in mm
Seeds of wheat or 'fast plants' (*Brassica campestris (rapa)* L.) which have germinated to a point where the coleoptiles or hypocotyls are about 10 mm long

---

12.9 PRACTICAL EXERCISE

This practical exercise extends over more than one practical session.

Effect of auxin on leaf abscission

Deciduous trees in the northern hemisphere lose their leaves in autumn. This seems to be a response to the increasing night length as the days shorten. The changes in night length, monitored by the pigment phytochrome, probably trigger abscission by altering the concentrations of plant growth substances in the leaves.

One hypothesis is that the growth substance **auxin**, produced in the tip of a leaf, diffuses down the leaf stalk (petiole) during the summer and prevents the leaf from being shed. Leaves only fall off when the inhibition of leaf abcsission ceases. In this experiment we test this idea on geraniums (*Pelargonium* sp.).

Procedure

1 Select a mature *Pelargonium* plant with at least twelve leaves, and count the exact number of leaves.

2 By drawing numbers out of a hat, assign each leaf on the plant randomly to one of three treatments. Treatment one (the control) consists of leaves to which no special treatment is applied. In treatment two the leaf blades (laminas) are carefully removed but the stalks (petioles) are left intact. In treatment three the leaves are treated in the same way as in treatment two, i.e. the blades are removed but the petioles are left. In addition a blob of lanolin containing 1% auxin is placed on the end of each petiole.

3 Set up the treatments, and as you do so, attach a numbered string tag to each petiole indicating the treatment to which it has been subjected.

4 Keep the plant well-watered in a light place. Examine it after three weeks, and again after six weeks. Record on each occasion exactly what has happened to each leaf. Are your results consistent with the hypothesis?

For consideration

1 How could you test experimentally whether an increase in night length triggers leaf abscission?

2 If a herbivore eats a leaf blade, what happens to the petiole?

3 What are the functions of the abscission layer?

4 Which other plant growth substances, besides auxin, are involved in leaf abscission and in what way?

5 Suggest four possible advantages to deciduous trees of losing their leaves in winter.

REQUIREMENTS
String tags
Indoleacetic acid (IAA) in lanolin (1%) (dissolve the auxin in a little ethanol before mixing it into the lanolin). **Note**: the pure auxin may be toxic. A 1% solution carries no risk
Healthy leafy plant of geranium (*Pelargonium* sp.)

12.10 PRACTICAL EXERCISE

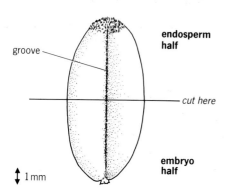

Figure 12.15 Diagram of barley grain to show where to make the transverse cut to separate the embryo and endosperm halves.

Danger
Razor blade

REQUIREMENTS

Marking pen
Bunsen burner, tripod, gauze
Beaker
Forceps
Razor blade
White tile
Oven at 30 °C
Refrigerator
Clinistix strip
Benedict's reagent
Petri dishes containing starch-iodine agar
　×8 (four containing gibberellic acid and
　four not, see below)
Barley grains ×40 (soaked in water for
　six hours before the experiment)
Prepare Petri dishes as follows:
Dissolve 200 mg soluble starch in a little
water and make up to 100 cm³. Heat until
boiling and then add 1.5 g Oxoid no. 1
agar powder. Stir vigorously until the agar
is dissolved. Then split the hot agar into
two halves. To one half add 0.5 cm³ of
100 ppm (0.01 per cent) gibberellic acid
in ethanol and stir. To the other half of the
agar add 0.5 cm³ of ethanol as the
control.

When agar cools to 60 °C, pour 10 cm³
into each of the eight Petri dishes, having
distinguished the four control dishes from
the four impregnated with GA₃.
Immediately add two drops of iodine
solution to each dish. Stir vigorously,
distributing the iodine to form a uniformly
coloured gel. Store in fridge at 4 °C until
required.

Gibberellic acid and the production of amylase in germinating barley grains

When a cereal grain germinates, the insoluble storage compounds in the endosperm, such as starch, are broken down to soluble sugars, such as maltose, which are absorbed by the growing embryo. What triggers the digestion of the starch in the endosperm by enzymes? One hypothesis suggests that the stimulus is provided by the growth substance gibberellic acid (GA_3) released from the embryo. The aim of this practical exercise is to determine whether or not gibberellic acid is necessary for germinating barley grains to release the starch-digesting enzyme amylase.

Procedure

1　You are provided with eight Petri dishes containing blue starch-iodine agar. If amylase enzymes are released into this agar, they will digest the starch and the blue colour will disappear.

2　Four of your Petri dishes have had gibberellic acid (GA_3) incorporated into the agar and four have not. Label the bases of the dishes which have received GA_3 with G END L, G EMB L, G END D and G EMB D respectively. Mark the remaining dishes END L, EMB L, END D and EMB D. In this code, G stands for gibberellic acid, END for the endosperm end of the grain, EMB for the embryo end of the grain, L for living and D for dead.

3　Place twenty barley grains in a beaker of boiling water for ten minutes. Then lift them out carefully with forceps and place them on a white tile.

4　Using a razor blade, cut each boiled grain transversely about half way down (Figure 12.15). Make sure that you can distinguish between the endosperm half and the embryo half. After each grain has been cut, transfer its endosperm and embryo halves to the appropriate D Petri dishes with the cut side of the grain exposed to the agar. The two END D dishes should each receive ten boiled endosperm halves, and the two EMB D dishes should each receive ten boiled embryo halves. Place the grains on the agar as far apart as you can.

5　Repeat step 4 with twenty unboiled grains. In this case the two END L dishes will each receive ten unboiled endosperm halves, and the two EMB L dishes will each gain ten unboiled embryo halves.

6　Place the Petri dishes in an incubator for 36 hours at 30 °C.

7　When incubation is complete, examine the dishes. For each grain in each treatment, record the diameter in mm of any clear region in the agar beneath the grain.

8　Examine the insides of the grains themselves. In which grains have the contents been liquified? Test the contents of the grains for reducing sugars with Benedict's reagent, or for glucose with Clinistix. Record your results.

9　Calculate the area of the clear region surrounding each grain (area of a circle $= \pi r^2$). Work out the average area of the clear region in each treatment and tabulate the results. If you consider it appropriate, carry out a t-test to determine whether the grains in each treatment produced significantly different quantities of amylase (see statistical appendix).

For consideration

1　Does gibberellic acid affect the production of amylase by barley grains?

2　Suggest a reason for the difference in amylase production between the boiled and unboiled grains.

3　Did your embryo halves produce some amylase? If so, how?

4　Gibberellic acid might cause the release by the aleurone layer of enzymes stored there. Alternatively, it might trigger the synthesis of enzymes as well as their release. Suggest two experiments which would distinguish between these hypotheses.

5　The brewing of beer begins with the production of maltose inside barley seeds. Suggest how this process could be speeded up.

References

Black, M. *Control Processes in Germination and Dormancy.* Oxford Biology Reader **20**, Oxford University Press, 1972.

Freeland, P.W. Gibberellic acid enhanced α-amylase synthesis in halved grains of barley (*Hordeum vulgare*): a simple laboratory demonstration. *Journal of Biological Education* **6**, 369–375, 1972.

Coppage, J. & Hill, T.A. Further experiments on gibberellin-stimulated amylase production in cereal grains. *Journal of Biological Education* **7**, 11–18, 1973.

12.11 PRACTICAL EXERCISE

REQUIREMENTS

Razor blade or scalpel
Forceps
Binocular microscope or hand lens
Pencil, red crayon and blue crayon
Watch glasses ×4
Safety goggles
Solutions of iodine, silver nitrate, phenolphthalein diphosphate and 'alkali' are prepared as follows:
Iodine – dissolve 4 g potassium iodide in 600 cm^3 distilled water, add 2.5 g iodine crystals and make up to 1 dm^3.
Silver nitrate – make up a small volume with 1.7 g per 100 cm^3 distilled water.
Phenolphthalein diphosphate – dissolve 0.5 g of the calcium salt in 100 cm^3 distilled water. Store in a refrigerator until needed and filter before use.

Petri dish containing two germinating maize grains per stage of germination investigated.
Maize seedlings: use a large-seeded variety which has been treated with a fungicide. Sow in cool, well-lit conditions about two weeks before the practical session. The maize should have germinated to the point where the radicles have emerged but not started branching, and the plumules have emerged but have not broken through the coleoptiles.
Before use, wash the seedlings thoroughly to remove soil. After handling the seedlings, wash your hands thoroughly to remove fungicide.

Localisation and activity of enzymes at various stages of maize grain germination

Firstly, familiarise yourself with the structure of a grain of maize (*Zea mays*) (Figure 12.16). On the outside, the seed and fruit walls are fused. Within the large seed, a small plate-like embryo, the potential new plant, is embedded in a large starchy endosperm, a food store.

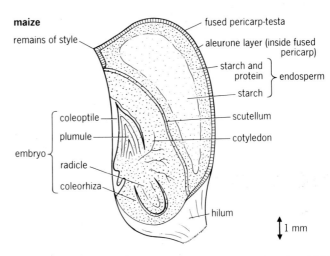

Figure 12.16 Vertical section through grain (fruit) of maize (*Zea mays*) – the old inflorescence, covered with such fruits, is sweetcorn or corn on the cob.

When a cereal grain germinates, its starch reserves are broken down. One of the enzymes involved is **starch phosphorylase**, which yields glucose.

Stages in this process can be followed in maize by using stains to detect starch, starch phosphorylase and glucose.

The procedure below describes how to stain seedlings of the same age. If, however, seeds at different stages of germination are available, the events which occur during germination can be followed in sequence.

Harmful Iodine solid

Corrosive Iodine

Corrosive silver nitrate

Toxic silver nitrate

Procedure

1. Select two maize seedlings at the same germination stage. Cut each one *carefully* down its longitudinal axis to produce a total of four half-seedlings.
2. Using forceps, place a single half-seedling into each of the three solutions provided so that the cut surface is immersed in the liquid. The three solutions contain iodine, silver nitrate and phenolphthalein diphosphate respectively. Do not get silver nitrate on your fingers, since it is corrosive and toxic and it stains.
3. Leave your half-seedlings in the solutions for at least half an hour.
4. Remove the half-seedling from the iodine. This stains starch a blue colour. Draw a diagram to show the distribution and intensity of the blue staining on the cut surface of the seedling. Ignore the brown colour of the iodine itself.
5. Remove the half-seedling from the silver nitrate. This stains reducing sugars (such as glucose) black. Draw a diagram to show the distribution and intensity of the black staining.
6. Remove the half-seedling from the phenolphthalein diphosphate solution. In the presence of starch phosphorylase enzymes the solution is hydrolysed to phenol-

phthalein, which gives a red colour in alkaline solution. Place the half-seedling in the 'alkali' solution for two minutes. Examine it and draw a diagram showing the distribution and intensity of the red colour.

For consideration

1 Account for the distribution and intensity of colours in terms of the biochemistry of seed germination. Assume that the starch phosphorylase activity is proportional to the metabolic rate of the tissues.
2 Which parts of the *embryo* are most metabolically active, and why?
3 Of what use will glucose be to the embryo?

12.12 INVESTIGATION

Effect of an impermeable testa on seed germination

The seeds of many species remain dormant for some time because the seed coat is impermeable to water and oxygen. Germination occurs sporadically when the seed coats are damaged. Seeds in this category include those of rockrose (*Helianthemum* spp.) and many members of the family Leguminosae (Fabaceae) – gorse (*Ulex* spp.), broom (*Cytisus scoparius*), vetches (*Vicia* spp.) etc.

Design and carry out an experiment to test the hypothesis that seeds of a particular species will only germinate if the testa is damaged.

Guidance

Seeds can be held in forceps and chipped with a mounted needle. They can be germinated on two layers of moistened filter paper in Petri dishes.

For consideration

1 Why do you think that undamaged seeds do not germinate? Suggest an experiment to test your hypothesis.
2 Suggest ways in which the testa of a seed in the soil might be broken down under natural conditions.
3 What effect will an impermeable testa have on the timing of germination under natural conditions? In what circumstances might this be favourable to the species?

REQUIREMENTS

Petri dishes
Whatman no. 4 filter paper (2 per dish)
Forceps
Mounted needle
Binocular microscope

Seeds of species to be tested

12.13 INVESTIGATION

Effect of gibberellic acid on hypocotyl elongation in seedlings

In Gregor Mendel's peas, those which have one or two alleles for 'tallness' may grow to a height of nearly 2 m, whereas 'short' plants that lack this allele may only reach a height of about 0.5 m. One hypothesis explaining how the alleles influence height is that the tall plants produce enough of the plant growth substance gibberellic acid (GA_3) to elongate rapidly, whereas the short plants do not produce enough growth substance to grow fast.

Gibberellic acid is effective in very small quantities (around 10^{-9} moles dm^{-3}) and its concentration in plant tissues is difficult to measure. It is possible, however, to test the hypothesis that the *absence* of gibberellic acid causes tall plants to be short. All you have to do is to add gibberellic acid (in lanolin) to short plants and see if they turn into tall ones.

Guidance

This investigation takes several weeks. Design it carefully. Pea plants (*Pisum sativum*) or rapid-cycling *Brassicas* can be used. Germinate the seeds of tall and dwarf varieties at equivalent densities in pots, but allow, when planting, for seeds which do not germinate or which become infected.

You will need to try various ways of adding the GA_3 in lanolin to the short plants without damaging their shoot meristems and hence their capacity to grow. The obvious technique is to place a dollop of lanolin containing 10^{-6} moles dm^{-3} of GA_3 on the shoot apex of each short plant, amongst the terminal leaves, when it is 8 cm tall. Since this may supply too much GA_3 to the tissue it may be wise to incorporate in the experiment some lanolin at 10^{-8} moles dm^{-3} of GA_3.

REQUIREMENTS

Seeds of tall and dwarf plants of the same
  species (e.g. pea, *Pisum sativum*, or
  rapid-cycling *Brassicas* – see Practical
  Exercise 11.12) from biological
  suppliers
To produce concentrations of gibberellic
  acid in lanolin of 10^{-6} and 10^{-8} moles
  per litre, dissolve measured masses of
  the plant growth substance into small
  quantities of ethanol before stirring into
  lanolin
Growth cabinet or greenhouse
Garden pots and soil
Metre rule

Measure the heights of all the plants at frequent intervals. Make sure that each treatment is applied to several plants. Then you can ultimately perform t-tests (see statistical appendix) to determine whether or not there is a significant difference in mean growth rate between the plants which have received extra GA_3 and those which have not.

For consideration

1 On the basis of your results, is the absence of gibberellic acid alone sufficient to account for the difference in height between the short and tall phenotypes?
2 What does the dominant allele for tallness code for?
3 Does gibberellic acid increase the rate of cell division or cause each cell to grow longer, or both. How would you investigate this?

12.14 PRACTICAL EXERCISE

This practical exercise extends over more than one practical session.

Plasmid infection of sunflower seedlings

In recent years biologists have begun to be able to move pieces of DNA from one species to another – a process known as **genetic engineering**. Genetic engineering has the potential to revolutionise our lives. It is already being used to protect plants from disease and to synthesise certain human products such as insulin. In addition, it offers the prospect of the reduction, perhaps even the eradication, of genetic disease such as sickle-cell anaemia, cystic fibrosis and muscular dystrophy.

At the same time, genetic engineering is fraught both with ethical and safety considerations. Unfortunately these greatly limit the work that can be done in schools and colleges. In this extended practical it is suggested that you follow *exactly* the following instructions in conjunction with Philip Harris' *Plant Tumour Kit*. These will enable you to inject sunflower seedlings with *Agrobacterium tumefaciens* and observe the results. In doing this you will be carrying out some of the basic practical steps in the genetic engineering of plants.

A. tumefaciens is a bacterium which is common in soil. It is a serious plant pathogen and can attack many plant species. Having entered a plant through a wound, the bacterium releases a piece of extra-chromosomal DNA known as a **plasmid**. This plasmid inserts itself into the plant DNA and then starts to make its own messenger RNA. This messenger RNA codes for proteins which result in the formation of a plant **tumour** or **gall**. In this practical, infection of sunflower seedlings with *A. tumefaciens* is followed by excision of the galls and re-isolation of the bacterium. Further plants can then be inoculated with the re-isolated bacteria.

Eye protection
must be worn

Procedure

1 Fill a large flower pot (15–20 cm diameter) with potting compost, and plant six sunflower seeds.
2 Put the pots in a well-lit, warm place and keep watered until the seedlings are about 10 cm high with a pair of cotyledons and a further pair of 'normal' leaves. (This takes approximately three to six weeks.)
3 Using a flame-sterilised inoculating loop, inoculate a tube of nutrient broth with bacteria from the *A. tumefaciens* culture (Figure 12.17 step 3). (See Box on page 149 for details of flame sterilisation.) Incubate at 30 °C for 2–4 days until the broth appears turbid.
4 Make a sterile salt solution by dissolving 0.85 g sodium chloride in 100 cm³ distilled water, and autoclave at 100 kPa (15 psi) for 15 minutes.
5 Add 1 cm³ of the turbid culture to a tube containing 9 cm³ of sterile salt solution and mix well (Figure 12.17 step 5). This is the **inoculum** of *A. tumefaciens* which you will inject into the sunflower seedlings.
6 Inoculate all six sunflower seedlings as follows: using the sterile syringe and needle, pick up a small amount of inoculum and puncture the stem close to the cotyledons, pushing the needle into the centre of the stem (Figure 12.17 step 6). The inoculating needle should be re-sterilised before picking up more bacterial inoculum and inoculating each stem.

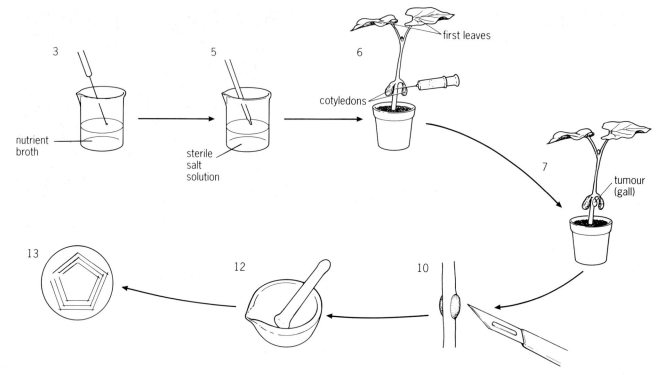

Figure 12.17 Flow diagram illustrating the stages in the infection and isolation of *Agrobacterium* from sunflower seedlings.

7 Maintain the plants in warm, well-lit conditions for a further 14–21 days, by which time they should be approximately 30 cm in height, and the tumours should have developed (Figure 12.17 step 7).

8 Loosen the cap of a bottle of nutrient agar and either autoclave or place in a saucepan of water and bring to the boil. Pour some of the hot medium into two sterile Petri dishes and allow to cool.

9 Prepare a saturated solution of sodium thiosulphate by adding the crystals provided to 50 cm³ distilled water.

10 Cut one of the galls from the stem of an infected plant using flame-sterilised scalpel and forceps (Figure 12.17 step 10).

11 Sterilise the surface of the gall by immersing in 11% v/v of a commercial sodium hypochlorite solution (e.g. bleach) for five seconds. Wear eye protection. Then neutralise by dipping the gall in the saturated sodium thiosulphate solution for five seconds.

12 Thoroughly sterilise a pestle and mortar by rinsing in alcohol. Then grind the gall, using the pestle and mortar, in 1 cm³ of sterile salt solution (Figure 12.17 step 12).

13 Streak two nutrient agar plates using a sterile inoculating loop dipped into the ground gall suspension (Figure 12.17 step 13). (See Box on page 000 for details of how to streak agar plates.) Incubate the inverted plates at 30 °C for four days.

14 Examine the plates for small, white, circular, glistening, translucent colonies of *Agrobacterium* (Figure 12.18).

15 If you want to check that the colonies really are *Agrobacterium*, stain and examine them as follows:

   a Using a sterile inoculating loop, transfer a *small* sample from a *single* colony to a drop of distilled water on a microscope slide, spreading it out to cover an area 3 cm × 1 cm.

   b Leave it to dry and fix it by passing though a Bunsen flame, avoiding overheating.

   c Cover with dimethylbenzene for one minute, then drain off the dimethylbenzene.

   d Cover with absolute alcohol for one minute, then drain off the absolute alcohol.

   e Wash with distilled water and dry.

Corrosive sodium hypochlorite

Highly flammable Dimethylbenzene

Highly flammable alcohol

Harmful Dimethylbenzene

Harmful
Gram's
iodine

Corrosive
Carbol
fuchsin

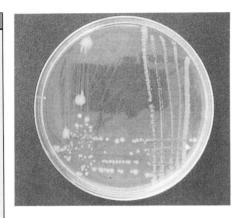

Figure 12.18 Petri dish containing agrobacterium.

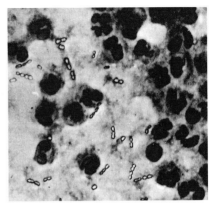

Figure 12.19 Agrobacterium under oil immersion.

f Cover with methyl violet for one minute, then drain off the stain.
g Wash with distilled water.
h Cover with Gram's iodine for one minute, then drain off the stain.
i Wash with absolute alcohol until no more colour is seen to come off.
j Cover with carbol fuchsin for one minute, then drain off the carbol fuchsin.
k Wash with distilled water and blot dry.
l Examine under the microscope, preferably using oil immersion. *Agrobacterium* cells appear as pink Gram negative (rather than violet Gram positive) rods approximately $0.8 \times 1.5–3.0$ mm (Figure 12.19).
16 Finally, autoclave the soil or plants, or treat with disinfectant, before disposal, and sterilise the flower pots.

For consideration

1 Why is it so important that sterile working conditions are maintained?
2 How could you be more confident that the bacteria you isolated from the gall are indeed *Agrobacterium*?
3 Explain how *Agrobacterium tumefaciens* could be used to transfer a gene from one plant species into another.
4 Outline the main arguments for and against the genetic engineering of plants.

12.15 PRACTICAL EXERCISE

Development of the vertebrate eye

The development of the vertebrate eye is worth studying in detail because it illustrates the organised sequence of events involved in the differentiation of a complex organ. Development proceeds under the influence of a hierarchy of **organisers**.

First the **neural tube** is formed by invagination of the mid-dorsal **ectoderm**, then the anterior end of the neural tube swells up to form the **brain**. The eye then develops as follows (Figure 12.20):

1 An **optic vesicle** is formed on each side of the head as an outgrowth from the side of the brain.
2 A **lens** is formed by thickening and invagination of the ectoderm adjacent to the optic vesicle.
3 The optic vesicle invaginates to form an **optic cup**.
4 The inner wall of the double-walled optic cup gives rise to the nervous layers of the **retina**; the outer wall gives rise to the **pigment** layer.
5 The ectoderm adjacent to the lens forms the **cornea**.

Procedure

Using prepared slides reconstruct the sequence of events that takes place as the eye develops. You will need to examine a number of slides to piece together all the stages.

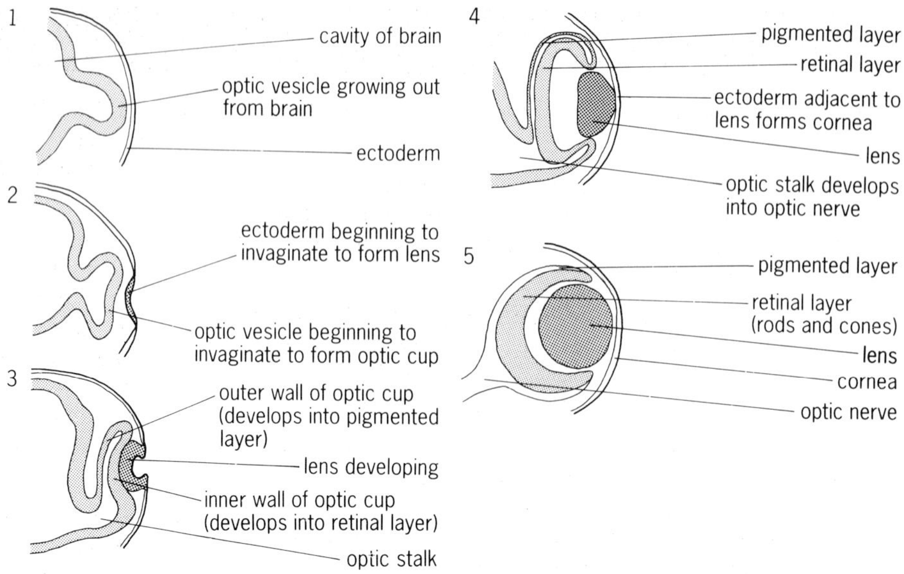

Figure 12.20 Development of the vertebrate eye as seen in transverse sections of the head of vertebrate embryos.

REQUIREMENTS

TS head of embryo (amphibian or chick) through eyes, at various stages of development

For consideration

1 Suggest what induces the formation of the neural tube, optic vesicle, lens, optic cup and cornea. How could your suggestions be tested?
2 Name two other organs or systems in a vertebrate that might develop under the influence of a hierarchy of organisers.
3 What are the advantages of development being controlled in this kind of way?

12.16 INVESTIGATION

Senescence in humans

In many organisms, the oldest individuals in a population become progressively less fit as they age. In everyday language we call this 'growing old'; using more scientific language, the process is referred to as **senescence**. Recent research suggests that senescence results from the gradual accumulation of genetic and biochemical defects. In this investigation it is suggested that you investigate the manifestations of senescence in humans.

Guidance

Make a list of all the changes that you suspect accompany senescence in humans. Examples might include changes in hair colour, skin texture, eyesight, reaction times and short-term memory. Now think about how you can measure these changes with some reliability and precision. Finally, you will need to obtain a sample of willing volunteers of varying ages prepared to subject themselves to your investigation.

For consideration

1 Does senescence start at any particular age?
2 Does the onset and progression of senescence differ for women and men?
3 How did your subjects view your investigation? Were they willing volunteers or embarrassed by your study?
4 How do people regard the prospect of 'growing old'?

PROJECTS

Before starting a project, discuss your intended procedure with your teacher.

1   Observe frog tadpoles and *either* toad *or* newt tadpoles from hatching through to metamorphosis. Compare the growth and development of the two species. Investigate how population density affects the behaviour of tadpoles.

2   Investigate factors affecting the rate at which seeds absorb water prior to germination. You may find it helpful to have access to a suitably precise analytical balance, though the need for such a balance is lessened if large sample sizes of seeds are used.

3   Study the development of flowers, relating your findings to what you know of primary and secondary growth. Remember that a flower consists of a series of modified leaves typically arranged in four whorls around a central stem (see page 217). You should find that different species show variations from the descriptions given in most textbooks, not only in obvious features like the number of petals and sepals, but also in the details of ovary and embryo sac structure.

4   Investigate one or more of the following responses:
   (i)   the response to directional illumination of a coleoptile whose tip has been removed.
   (ii) the response of a coleoptile to gravity.
   (iii) the response of a radicle to directional illumination.
   (iv) the response of a radicle to gravity.
   (v)   the response to gravity of a radicle whose root cap has been removed.
   In each case you will have to think out carefully how best to apply the stimulus. Draw such conclusions as you can, and carry out other experiments of your choice to throw light on how coleoptiles and radicles respond to stimuli. In some of the experiments use the technique of mounting a germinating seed in a moist chamber and viewing it under the microscope (Practical Exercise 12.7).

5   In the experiments in which a germinating seed is mounted in a moist chamber and viewed under the microscope (Practical Exercise 12.7) and in which seedlings are exposed to light filters (Practical Exercise 12.8) determine the region of the coleoptile which detects the stimulus. Compare the responses of intact seedlings with those that have had different lengths of their coleoptile tips excised.

6   It is claimed that in many species seed germination is inhibited by the presence of leaf canopies above the seeds. Test this assertion with weed seeds on moistened filter paper in Petri dishes with and without a permanent covering of leaves.

7   Examine changes in photosynthetic pigments, and in the concentrations of starch and glucose, in ageing leaves of various ages, and speculate on the value to the plant of these trends. Pigments can be separated by thin layer or paper chromatography (see Practical Exercise 6.9). Starch levels can be estimated with iodine solution and glucose levels can be estimated with a Benedict's test. See Gill, J., Howell, P. and Saunders, T. The biology of ageing in leaves. *Journal of Biological Education* **22** (3), 167, 1988.

8   Investigate the effects of various treatments intended to prevent the senescence of commercially important crops, such as green bananas, carnations or lettuce. Possible methods of preservation include clingfilm, refrigeration, sealing in polythene bags, and, for flowers, anti-bacterial agents in the water. For background information read Hobson, G. Slowing the deterioration of fruits and vegetables after harvest. *Journal of Biological Education* **26** (2), 100–105, 1992.

9   How do members of the public view the advent of genetic engineering? You will need to carry out a study using a questionnaire (see page 180). Distinguish between the genetic engineering of: microorganisms (for example, to produce human insulin), plants (for example, to make them more resistant to certain diseases), animals (for example, to increase the milk yield of cows), and humans (for example, to treat cystic fibrosis). You might choose to investigate the null hypothesis that a person's attitude towards genetic engineering is unaffected by their gender, age or scientific knowledge.

10 Investigate how the production of β-amylase by the aleurone layer of barley seed is influenced by gibberellic acid (see page 222).

11 Study senescence in dogs or cats and compare your results with those obtained from humans (see page 228).

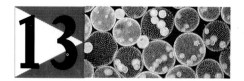

13 Genetics

Monohybrid inheritance in tobacco seedlings

In this investigation you will be provided with a sample of tobacco seeds obtained from one plant. Your job is to grow the seeds to the point where you can identify two **phenotypes** (distinct characters) in the plants, and then predict the **genotypes** (genetic constitutions) of the parent plants.

Guidance

Sow the seeds in flat trays or pots at a density of not more than one seed to 4 cm². Keep in a warm, light place and water every two or three days, but without water-logging the plants. After about 15 to 20 days, observe and describe any differences between the seedlings with respect to such features as colour of the cotyledons, colour and hairiness of the stems and the shape of the leaves. Count the number of tobacco plants showing each feature. Calculate the ratio between them and draw such conclusions as you can.

For consideration

1 From your results, predict the *genetic* constitution of the parent plants and calculate what *phenotypic* ratios you would expect among the offspring.
2 How close are your actual ratios to those predicted? Use the chi-squared test to analyse them statistically (see page 253).

REQUIREMENTS

Tray of soil approx. 40 × 20 cm *or* small pots
Potting compost
Seeds of monohybrid tobacco (*Nicotiniana tabacum*)

Monohybrid and dihybrid inheritance in maize

In maize, *Zea mays* (corn), a single cob (ear) is covered with several hundred kernels which represent the fruits. Each kernel contains a single seed. Each seed contains a diploid embryo formed as a result of a single fertilisation. The fertilisations which created the different seeds are independent of each other.

Maize kernels display a number of easily recognised characteristics such as colour and shape: thus they may be purple or yellow, smooth or shrunken, etc. In this practical it is suggested that you examine the phenotypes of the kernels on a number of cobs and make deductions about the genotypes of the parent plants.

Procedure

Monohybrid inheritance

1 Examine cobs **A** and **B**. For each cob, count the number of yellow and purple kernels and determine the ratio between them. Do you think it is sufficient to count the kernels in one (or several) rows, or should all the kernels in the cob be counted?
2 Which is the genetically dominant colour, yellow or purple?
3 What can you say about the genotypes of the yellow and purple kernels on cob **A**?
4 What can you say about the genotypes of the yellow and purple kernels on cob **B**?
5 Consider the parents of the kernels on cob **A**. What is the genotype of each for kernel colour?
6 Consider the parents of the kernels on cob **B**. What is the genotype of each for kernel colour?
7 Construct genetic diagrams to illustrate the crosses involved in the production of cobs **A** and **B**.
8 Examine cob **C** and notice that some kernels are more shiny than others. Determine the ratio between the two types.
9 The shiny and non-shiny kernels in cob **C** differ in their starch content. Carefully shave off the top of a kernel of each type with a razor or scalpel and stain the cut surfaces with iodine solution. Notice any differences. A blue-black colour indicates

Harmful
Iodine
solution

Danger
Razor blade

starch, a red colour dextrin. Dextrin is a carbohydrate intermediate in size between maltose and starch.

Dihybrid inheritance

1 Examine cobs **D** and **E**. The kernels differ from each other with respect to two pairs of characteristics; each is yellow or purple, *and* wrinkled or smooth.

2 In each of cobs **D** and **E**, estimate or count the number of kernels that are:
   a yellow and wrinkled;
   b yellow and smooth;
   c purple and wrinkled;
   d purple and smooth.

3 Construct genetic diagrams illustrating the possible crosses involved in the production of cobs **D** and **E**.

For consideration

1 In terms of relationships within a human family, describe the relationship between two kernels belonging to the same maize cob.

2 Which of the five cobs could have been the result of self-pollination?

3 What tentative conclusions about the way genes work can you draw from your study on cob **C**?

REQUIREMENTS

Maize (corn) cobs showing segregation for the following kernel characters:
  Cob **A**: yellow, purple (monohybrid)
  Cob **B**: yellow, purple (a different monohybrid ratio)
  Cob **C**: non-shiny (starchy), shiny (waxy) (monohybrid)
  Cob **D**: yellow, purple, wrinkled, smooth (dihybrid)
  Cob **E**: yellow, purple, wrinkled, smooth (a different dihybrid ratio)
Razor or scalpel

13.1 BOX # Handling Drosophila

Drosophila, the fruit fly, is an ideal animal for experimental genetics. It can be kept easily in the laboratory, and at 25 °C the life cycle takes only 10–14 days.

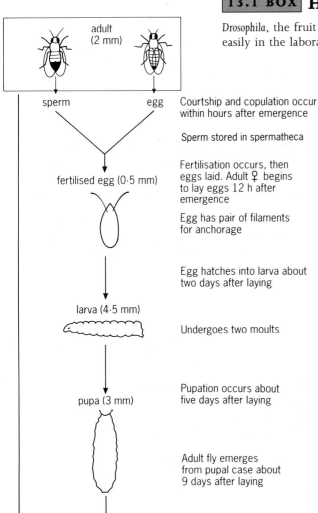

Illustration 1 Life cycle of the fruit fly, *Drosophila melanogaster*. The times apply to fruit flies kept at 25 °C.

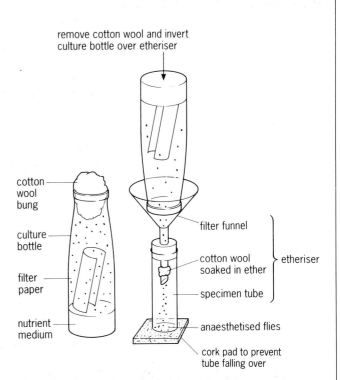

Illustration 2 Method of anaesthetising *Drosophila*.

	male	female

1	rounded abdomen	pointed abdomen
2	black transverse stripes at posterior end of abdomen so close together they appear as a single dark blob	black transverse stripes at posterior end of abdomen narrow and clearly separated
3	pair of chitinous claspers on ventral side of abdomen at posterior end	claspers absent

Highly flammable Ether

4	row of small bristles (sex comb) on first tarsal joint of forelegs 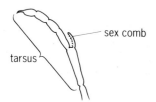	sex combs absent

Illustration 3 Differences between male and female *Drosophila melanogaster*.

Moreover, a single female lays between 80 and 200 eggs, so it does not take long to produce a large population and genetic ratios can be determined with a fair degree of precision. The species most often used in the laboratory is *D. melanogaster*.

Before you can do any genetic investigations using *Drosophila* you need to learn how to handle the flies, recognise the different strains and tell males from females.

Rearing the flies

Fruit flies used in experimental work are descendants of wild species that feed on yeasts and plant sugars such as are found on damaged fruits. In the laboratory fruit flies can be cultured in bottles containing an appropriate nutrient medium.

The life cycle is summarised in Illustration 1. After mating, the female stores sperm in a sperm store known as a spermotheca, from which a large number of eggs can be fertilised. Once laid, the eggs develop into larvae which burrow into the nutrient medium.

After two moults the larvae leave the medium and crawl up into drier parts of the bottle, usually onto the sides and up a roll of filter paper provided for the purpose. They then pupate and after a few days the adults emerge and the cycle can start again.

Examination of live flies

Examine a culture bottle containing a **pure line** of flies, that is, a population of flies that are homozygous at one or more key loci. Adult flies of both sexes should be present. It doesn't matter whether or not larvae and pupae are present.

In order to examine the adult flies in more detail, they must first be anaesthetised. One technique is as follows (Illustration 2):

1 Extinguish all naked flames and pipette a few drops of ether onto the cotton wool of an 'etheriser'. Return unwanted ether to the bottle and replace the stopper immediately: ether fumes are dangerous.
2 Tap the culture bottle so that any adult flies are dislodged from the mouth of the bottle and from the cotton wool bung.
3 Quickly remove the cotton wool bung and place the funnel of the etheriser over the open mouth of the culture bottle. Now turn the etheriser and culture bottle upside down and tap the culture bottle gently until at least ten flies have entered the etheriser. Then replace the stopper of the culture bottle.
4 Occasionally tap the etheriser while the flies are still moving. This will help prevent the flies from coming into contact with the cotton wool soaked in ether, which can kill them.
5 As soon as the flies in the etheriser stop moving, remove the top of the etheriser and tip the flies onto a while tile or piece of paper.
6 Examine the flies under a hand lens or binocular microscope and identify their gender and strain as indicated below. A fine paintbrush can be used to move unconscious flies. Anaesthetised *Drosophila* usually remain unconscious for five to ten minutes. Avoid giving them too much ether or you will kill them.

Sexing fruit flies

Male and female *Drosophila* can be distinguished as shown in Illustration 3. Note that shortly after emergence from the pupae, adult flies are pale coloured and have incompletely expanded wings.

Recognising different strains

Normal *Drosophila* have round, red eyes, grey bodies and wings that are slightly longer than the abdomen. Most of the common **mutants** show differences in these characteristics. For example: vestigial-winged *Drosophila* have very short wings; ebony *Drosophila* have black bodies; and white-eyed *Drosophila* have white eyes.

Examine at least two strains of *Drosophila* and ensure you can distinguish the adult males and adult females of each strain.

13.3 PRACTICAL EXERCISE

This practical exercise requires four laboratory sessions over a period of four weeks.

Monohybrid inheritance in *Drosophila*

To perform a simple monohybrid cross between two different strains you will need virgin females. Females do not mate until at least eight hours after they have emerged from their pupae. The simplest way, therefore, to obtain virgin females from a culture bottle with a large number of pupae is to remove all the adult flies early in the morning (say, 8.30 a.m.) and then later on the same day (say, 3.30 p.m.). You then anaesthetise the adult flies that have emerged during the day and separate them into males and females. The females will be virgins and can be used as outlined in the procedure below.

In this practical it is suggested that you cross normal (often referred to as **wild type**) and vestigial-winged flies and follow the results through the F_1 into the F_2.

Setting up a parental cross

Highly
flammable
Ether

1 Transfer five virgin pure-breeding normal females and five pure-breeding vestigial-winged males into a new bottle containing culture medium. To do this, anaesthetise the flies, taking care not to over-anaesthetise them, and tip them onto a white surface. Then gently lift them, one by one, into the new culture bottle which should be placed on its side. Leave the bottle on its side until the flies recover, so that they do not become stuck in the medium.

2 Label the bottle with your name, indicating the cross which you have set up as follows:

$$\text{P } ♀ \text{ normal} \times ♂ \text{ vg (date)}$$

3 When you are sure that at least two female and two male flies have recovered from the anaesthetic and are moving freely, put your labelled bottle in an incubator at 25 °C.

4 *One week later*, when the eggs have hatched into larvae, remove the parent flies. The F_1 adult flies should emerge over a period of several days, approximately 10–14 days after the cross was set up.

Examining the results of the parental cross and setting up an F_1 cross

Highly
flammable
Ether

1 Anaesthetise *all* the F_1 flies that have resulted from your parental cross, taking care, as before, not to over-anaesthetise them. Tip them onto a white surface and count the number of flies in each of the following four categories:
   a female normal;
   b female vestigial-winged;
   c male normal;
   d male vestigial-winged.

   Produce a hypothesis to explain your results. Predict the result of crossing the F_1 flies amongst themselves.

2 Now cross the F_1 flies among themselves by transferring five female and five male flies to a new culture bottle and incubate at 25 °C. In this case it doesn't matter whether or not the females are virgins. Label your culture bottle so that it records the details both of the new cross *and* of the original parental cross from which the F_1 flies came.

Examination of F_2 flies

Highly
flammable
Ether

1 One week after the F_1 cross was set up, remove the adult flies from the culture bottle.

2 Allow a further week to elapse and then anaesthetise all the adult flies, examine them carefully and classify them into the same four categories, namely:
   a female normal;
   b female vestigial-winged;
   c male normal;
   d male vestigial-winged.

3 Produce a hypothesis to explain your results. Is this hypothesis the same as the one you suggested *before* setting up the F_1 cross? Use the chi-squared test (see page 253) to test whether your observed results differ significantly from your expected results.

For consideration

1   Why were pure-breeding flies used for the parental cross?
2   Should the reciprocal cross have been set up, i.e. vestigial-winged females and normal males? If not, explain why not.
3   When the parental cross was set up it was important that the adult females were virgins. However, this was not the case when the F_1 cross was set up. Why the difference?
4   Why was it never necessary for the *males* to be virgins?
5   Why was it necessary to remove the parent flies before the F_1 flies emerged from their pupae?

13.4 PRACTICAL EXERCISE

Genetic constitution of maize pollen

Gametes formed by an organism that is heterozygous at a particular locus differ in their genetic constitution: approximately half contain one of the alleles; the other half contain the other allele. Although the results of monohybrid crosses provide excellent evidence in support of this, the assertion is difficult to test directly as genetic differences seldom reveal themselves in gametes. However, an exception to this is provided by the inheritance of starchiness in maize.

Theoretical background

In maize a distinction can be made between starchy and non-starchy plants. Non-starchy plants contain dextrin instead of starch – dextrin being a carbohydrate intermediate in size between maltose and starch. Fortunately for our purposes, dextrin stains red with iodine solution whereas starch, of course, stains blue-black. This allows us to distinguish the two phenotypes.

Consider a heterozygous maize plant resulting from a cross between starchy and non-starchy parents. Starchiness is controlled by a single gene, so the heterozygous plant will have one allele for starchiness and one for non-starchiness. Now the alleles responsible for this condition determine the presence or absence of starch in maize pollen grains as well as in adult plants. So pollen grains produced by a heterozygous plant should be starchy and non-starchy in approximately equal numbers. In this practical we shall test this prediction.

Procedure

⚠
Harmful
Iodine
solution

1   You are provided with a floret of a heterozygous maize plant. With mounted needles, tear off the enveloping bracts and remove one of the anthers.
2   Place the anther in a drop of iodine solution on a microscope slide. With your needles break the anther open and tease out the pollen grains. Put a coverslip on and wait for the iodine solution to react with the starch and dextrin.
3   View the pollen grains under the medium power lens of a microscope. If they appear uniform, alter the illumination. Don't illuminate too brightly. The most common reason for finding it difficult to see the difference between the two types of pollen grain is because there is too much light.
4   Count a large sample of pollen grains (at least 50). Do your results confirm or refute the prediction that the heterozygous plant produces two types of gametes in approximately equal numbers?

For consideration

1   Which of Mendel's laws is given considerable support by the results of this practical? Explain fully.
2   What significance, if any, is there for the conclusions you have drawn in the fact that, strictly speaking, pollen grains are not gametes?
3   Do you consider that a *failure* to demonstrate the existence of genetically distinct types of gametes would seriously undermine Mendel's theory? Explain your answer.

Relationship between genes and chromosomes in Drosophila

Highly flammable Ether

Unfortunately it is not possible to look at an organism's chromosomes under the microscope and say which particular genes occur on each one. However, it is possible to draw certain conclusions about the relationship between genes and chromosomes by carrying out breeding experiments. Once again we shall rely on *Drosophila*. You will need to use the techniques described in Box 13.1 on page 231. Remember, when using ether, to extinguish all naked flames and minimise the amount of ether fumes.

Experiment 1

1 Set up a cross between normal virgin females and brown-eyed, vestigial-winged males. Remember to label your culture bottle. After one week remove the parent flies, and after a further week examine the F_1 offspring.
2 Now cross the F_1 flies amongst themselves and carry the study through to the F_2. Don't forget to remove the F_1 flies before the F_2 flies emerge.
3 Examine the F_2 flies, recording the number of individuals showing each combination of characteristics.
4 Try to explain your results.

Experiment 2

1 Set up a cross between white-eyed, yellow-bodied virgin females and normal (i.e. red-eyed, grey-bodied) male flies. Remember to label the culture bottle. After one week remove the parent flies, and after a further week examine the F_1 offspring. There could be up to eight possible phenotypes, namely:
   a white-eyed, yellow-bodied female;   e white-eyed, yellow-bodied male;
   b white-eyed, grey-bodied female;   f white-eyed, grey-bodied male;
   c red-eyed, yellow-bodied female;   g red-eyed, yellow-bodied male;
   d red-eyed, grey-bodied female;   h red-eyed, grey-bodied male;

2 Produce a hypothesis to explain your results. What results would you expect to get if you crossed the F_1 flies among themselves?
3 Now cross the F_1 flies among themselves, and carry the study through to the F_2. As before, do not forget to remove the F_1 flies.
4 Examine the F_2 flies, recording the different phenotypes. Is your hypothesis confirmed or refuted?

Experiment 3

1 Set up a cross between white-eyed, yellow-bodied males and normal females. Proceed exactly as in Experiment 2.
2 Record, and attempt to explain, the results obtained in both the F_1 and F_2 generations.

For consideration

1 What do your results tell you about the relationship between the genes responsible for the brown eye and vestigial wing conditions?
2 What conclusions can you draw regarding the relationship between the genes responsible for white eye, yellow body and sex?
3 What further experiments would need to be done to build up a complete picture of *Drosophila*'s chromosomes and the genes they carry?

REQUIREMENTS

Hand lens *or* binocular microscope
White tile *or* paper
Fine paintbrush
Etheriser
Culture bottles
Pure-breeding normal (wild type) flies
Pure-breeding brown-eyed, vestigial-winged flies
Pure-breeding white-eyed, yellow-bodied flies

Survey to investigate the relationship between human eye colour and hair colour

In humans, both eye colour and hair colour show considerable variation. In this investigation it is suggested that you carry out a survey to determine the extent of this variation and see whether the two characteristics are independent of each other or correlate with one another.

Guidance

Make a *preliminary* attempt to describe the range of human eye colours and hair colours. Now think about how you can record these colours more systematically. You might try building up a reference collection, using Polaroid snaps. Or you might get hold of household paint cards that portray large numbers of different colours.

Once you have decided how to record hair colour and eye colour, record these characteristics for a large number of people. If at all possible, some of these people should be related to each other. However, exercise sensitivity in this regard. Not all families consist of full siblings with their biological parents.

Once you have got *some* results, begin to analyse them. You will need to think carefully about how to present and interpret them. Three dimensional graphs may be a possibility, with eye colour along one axis, hair colour along another and frequency along a third. However, you may feel that eye and hair colour cannot each be mapped on a single axis. If you have access to a computer with a colour monitor and a statistics or graphics package, you may find them a help. Think about how your results can be analysed statistically (see pages 247–256).

For consideration

1 Would you say that these two characteristics show **discrete variation** or **continuous variation**?
2 To what extent do eye and hair colour correlate with each other?
3 Can you produce any tentative explanations of your results?
4 Is it true that people with black hair tend to have dark eyes, and people with blond hair, blue eyes?
5 What do your results, if you have any, for the distribution of eye and hair colour within families, suggest about the genetics of these characteristics?

Making models to illustrate DNA, RNA and protein synthesis

If you think that research necessarily means using sophisticated techniques and complicated apparatus, it is sobering to reflect that Watson and Crick found that building models, using little more than stands, clamps and pieces of wire, was an essential step in unravelling the structure of **DNA** and understanding how it works (Figure 13.1). In this investigation you will have a modest opportunity to follow in their footsteps.

Procedure

Using match sticks, plasticine of different colours, pipe cleaners and any other suitable materials, construct two-dimensional models (i.e. models which lie flat on a table) to illustrate each of the following:

The molecular structure of DNA

Show the relationship between the **sugar**, **phosphate** and **organic bases**, the molecular basis of the helical configuration and the complementary relationship between the bases.

How DNA replicates

Build a short length of DNA made up of, say, five pairs of **nucleotides**. Construct ten further nucleotides with the appropriate bases. Now make your DNA **replicate**.

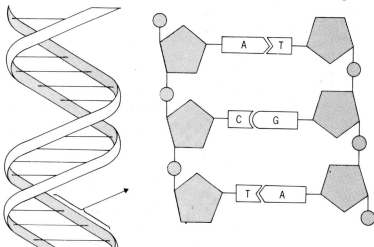

Figure 13.1 The Watson-Crick model of DNA.

Formation of messenger RNA

Show how DNA is **transcribed** into **messenger RNA** – one of the two strands of the DNA serving as the **template** for the synthesis of the RNA.

How messenger RNA controls the assembly of a protein

Make models of **amino acids**, **transfer RNA** molecules and a short length of messenger RNA. Show how the sequence of bases in the messenger RNA is **translated** into **protein** structure.

The action of polyribosomes

Make models of two or more **ribosomes**. Move the ribosomes in convoy along a strand of messenger RNA and show how **polypeptides** are formed.

The three-dimensional structure of DNA

If time and opportunity allow, try building a three-dimensional model of DNA. Represent the shapes of the individual nucleotides as accurately as possible.

For consideration

1 Why do you think Watson and Crick found it necessary to build models of DNA?
2 When Watson and Crick built their model of DNA they paid particular attention to the shape (stereochemistry) of the four bases. Why?
3 Modify your models to show how cells cope with **introns**, the unexpressed portions of DNA that are excised after transcription and before translation.

REQUIREMENTS

Eight different colours of plasticine
   (modelling clay)
Match sticks
Pipe cleaners

13.8 PRACTICAL EXERCISE

Distribution of DNA and RNA in root-tip cells

One piece of evidence supporting the DNA–RNA theory of genetic control is that RNA is found in the cytoplasm as well as in the nucleus, but DNA is mainly confined to the nucleus. In this practical the distribution of DNA and RNA in undifferentiated cells is investigated by staining with chemicals specific for each nucleic acid. Two techniques can be tried: the Feulgen technique stains only the DNA; the methyl green-pyronin technique stains both DNA and RNA – but different colours. For both techniques root-tip cells of bean provide suitable material.

Testing for DNA with Feulgen stain

The technique involves hydrolysing the DNA with acid. This liberates aldehydes which re-store the red colour to bleached Feulgen solution. Take care – Feulgen reagent is an irritant.

1 The roots should be fixed in acetic ethanol for two hours before proceeding further.
2 Transfer the fixed material to *either* 1.0 mol dm^{-3} HCl at 60 °C for six minutes in an oven, *or*, wearing eye protection, 50% HCl at room temperature for fifteen minutes. This treatment hydrolyses the DNA and macerates the tissue.
3 Transfer the root to a watch glass of colourless Feulgen reagent for one to two hours. If time is short the reaction can be accelerated by placing the watch glass on a warm surface.
4 Cut off and discard all but the terminal 3 mm of the root. Transfer the root tip to a microscope slide and add acetocarmine (which intensifies the Feulgen stain).
5 Tease out the stained root tip and put a coverslip over it. Place a piece of filter paper on the coverslip and press gently so as to spread out the tissue and soak up surplus stain.
6 Examine under low and high power. Where is the DNA distributed in the cells?

Testing for DNA and RNA with methyl green-pyronin stain

The stain is a mixture of methyl green and pyronin. DNA takes up methyl green, and RNA the pyronin. This enables the two types of nucleic acid to be distinguished, at least in good preparations.

1 Ensure that all naked flames are extinguished, then fix the roots in absolute ethanol for 30 minutes before proceeding further.
2 With a sharp razor blade cut thin *longitudinal* sections of the terminal 3 mm of a root. Place the sections on a slide and cover with aqueous methyl green-pyronin stain for 30 minutes.
3 Draw off the stain with a pipette and replace with distilled water. Change the water several times so as to wash the sections thoroughly.

REQUIREMENTS

Microscope
Oven at 60 °C
Slides and coverslips
Watch glasses
Razor blade
Filter paper
Hydrochloric acid (1.0 mol dm^{-3})
Feulgen solution
Methyl green-pyronin stain
Distilled water
Acetocarmine Feulgen reagent
   methylgreen pyronin
Acetic ethanol
Absolute ethanol
Safety goggles
Bean roots

Danger
Razor
blade

Highly
flammable
Absolute ethanol
Acetic methyl
green-pyronin
stain

Irritant
Feulgen
solution

Corrosive
Hydrochloric
acid
Feulgen
solution

Eye protection
must be worn

Note: To obtain roots
Germinate broad bean seeds 10 days before the practical. When the radicle is 1.5 cm long, cut off the tip to stimulate the growth of lateral roots.
Preparation of Feulgen's reagent
Dissolve 1.0 g basic fuchsin in 200 cm³ boiling distilled water. Filter. Add 30 cm³ hydrochloric acid (1.0 mol dm⁻³) and 3.0 g potassium metabisulphite to the filtrate. Allow to bleach for 24 hours in the dark. If the solution is still coloured, the residual colour should be absorb stoppered bottle in the dark.
Preparation of methyl green-pyronin stain
Mix 0.15 g of methyl green and 0.25 g pyronin in 2.5 cm³ of ethanol and 20 cm³ of glycerol. Make up to 100 cm³ with 0.5% carbolic acid.

4   Mount the sections in distilled water and view under low and high powers. DNA should be stained blue-green, RNA red.

For consideration

1   From your observations in this practical what predictions can be made about the way the nucleus communicates with the cytoplasm in controlling the development of the cell?

2   DNA is not entirely confined to the nucleus; small amounts occur in the cytoplasm. Whereabouts in the cytoplasm is DNA found and what is it doing there?

13.9 INVESTIGATION

Colour and banding in the European field snail (*Cepaea nemoralis*)

In the European field snail (*Cepaea nemoralis*), individuals differ greatly in the appearance of their shells (Figure 13.2). This is the result of genetically-determined differences in the colours and banding patterns of the shells. The background colour of the shell may be yellow, pink or brown. In addition, the number of black bands on the shell varies from no bands at all to as many as five.

In this investigation we shall investigate the reason for this variation. You will only have time to scratch the surface of variation in *Cepaea nemoralis*. The species has been intensively studied since the 1950s and hundreds of papers have been written on its population genetics.

Guidance

First find some field snails and observe their appearance and distribution. Field snails are widely distributed in woods, hedges and grassland throughout the British Isles except northern parts of Scotland. You will need to devise an unambiguous way of describing and categorising the snails' shells (Figure 13.3). Then generate some hypotheses in an attempt to explain the variation in shell colour and banding pattern. For example, you might predict that some forms are more visible to birds, and therefore more susceptible to predation. Visibility will be a feature both of a snail's shell *and* of the background colour and appearance of its habitat. Or you might predict that some forms warm up more quickly and are therefore at an advantage in cooler places. Or you might predict that some sort of **sexual selection** is going on, in which individuals either avoid or are attracted to other individuals of similar shell appearance.

Having generated one or more hypotheses, think carefully how you can test your ideas and then carry out an investigation to test at least one of them. You will probably want to work in an area with two or more contrasting habitats (e.g. grassland and woodland).

Figure 13.2 European field snails (*Cepaea nemoralis*) showing some of the variation in this species.

A   B   C   D   E   F

Figure 13.3 Some examples of variation in the European field snail. **A** Yellow shell with five bands and a dark lip (opening to the shell). **B** Pink shell with a dark lip but no bands. **C** Brown shell with only the central band present. **D** Yellow shell with the bands present but unpigmented, making them translucent, and an unpigmented lip. **E** Yellow shell with five bands but an unpigmented lip. **F** Pink shell with only the central and two lower bands present.

REQUIREMENTS

Access to site with European field snails
(*Cepaea nemoralis*). Species-rich
grassland with adjoining hedges is often
suitable.

13.10 INVESTIGATION

Highly
flammable
Ether

REQUIREMENTS

Hand lens *or* binocular microscope
White tile *or* paper
Fine paintbrush
Etheriser
Culture bottles
Pure-breeding male red-eyed *Drosophila*
Pure-breeding virgin female red-eyed
    Drosophila
Pure-breeding male white-eyed *Drosophila*
Pure-breeding virgin female white-eyed
    Drosophila

13.11 PRACTICAL EXERCISE

For consideration

1 What tentative conclusions can you draw from your investigation?
2 Do you feel that the frequencies of the different forms you have determined are likely to be accurate in view of the fact that some forms will be more camouflaged than others to your eyes? In what ways might this problem have affected your results and how could you eliminate it?
3 How could you investigate the genetic basis of any differences you have observed?

The fitness of the white-eyed allele in Drosophila

As discussed on page 233, numerous **mutants**, or different forms, are known in the fruit fly, *Drosophila melanogaster*. In this investigation it is suggested that you study whether individuals with white eyes are fitter or less fit than individuals with red eyes.

Guidance

In order to see whether the allele for white eyes is fitter than the allele for red eyes or not, you will need to set up breeding colonies of *Drosophila*, using the techniques described in the Box 13.1 on page 231, and then follow the resulting populations for at least two generations. The principle is to set up colonies in which there is competition between white-eyed and red-eyed individuals. Here are two possible starting breeding colonies, though you may think of others:
a Three red-eyed males, three white-eyed males and six red-eyed females;
b Six red-eyed males, three white-eyed females and three red-eyed females.

However you proceed, the important thing once the colonies are set up is to count the number of individuals with different phenotypes over at least two generations. You should then be in a position to:
a Work out whether one allele is dominant or whether they are codominant;
b Determine whether the alleles occur on the autosomal or sex chromosomes;
c Predict the ratios of phenotypes you would expect to see in successive generations from your answers to (**a**) and (**b**) and your knowledge of Mendelian genetics;
d Compare your observed phenotypic ratios with your expected phenotypic ratios (if necessary using the chi-squared test explained on page 253);
e Determine whether the allele for white eyes has the same fitness as the allele for red eyes.

For consideration

1 Is red-eyed dominant to white-eyed, *vice versa* or are the two alleles codominant?
2 Are the alleles autosomal or sex-linked?
3 Did you find that the allele for white eyes has the same fitness as the allele for red eyes?
4 Why was it necessary to follow the breeding colonies for at least two generations?

Selective predation of coloured prey

In many species, **genetic polymorphisms** occur. In these, two or more genetically-determined phenotypes coexist in a population. In some species, genetic polymorphisms result from the behaviour of predators. The peppered moth, *Biston betularia*, is the best known example. In this species, individuals spend much of the day resting on tree trunks, a dangerous past-time as birds find the moths very palatable. The normal speckled white form of the moth does best in unpolluted parts of Britain, where tree trunks are often covered in pale-coloured lichens. In such areas, the dark form is conspicuous. The dark form does best in industrial areas where pollution kills off the lichens and darkens tree trunks. In these areas, the speckled white form is the more obvious.

   In this practical it is suggested that you make pastry 'baits' as prey and see whether students, acting as predators, find some colours easier to find than others.

Procedure

1 Sort washed river gravel into paler ('white') and darker ('brown') piles. Put onto separate trays.
2 Make pastry 'baits' using one part lard (or vegetarian equivalent) to three parts plain flour. Add edible colouring dyes and form the pastry into pellets approximately 7 mm × 5 mm. Try to get white baits the same colour as the white river

gravel and brown baits the same colour as the brown river gravel.

3 Randomly place the same number of white and brown baits on the tray with white gravel. (If the tray is $30\,cm \times 20\,cm$, a total of 24 baits would be suitable.) You can half bury the baits provided you treat the two colours the same.

4 Ask a fellow student to choose the first ten baits they see. Make a note of how many baits of each colour they choose.

5 Replace the baits and repeat step 4 with another student. Again, record your results. Continue until you have results from ten students.

6 Carry out steps 3 to 5, but using the tray with the brown gravel and new students.

For consideration

1 What can you conclude from your results?

2 Explain the significance of your results for the maintenance of genetic polymorphisms in the wild.

3 What difference do you think it would have made if you had carried out the practical with only one student instead of twenty different ones? After you have made your prediction, you might like to carry out the practical with only one student and see whether your prediction is correct.

Reference

Allen, J.A., Anderson, K.P. and Tucker, G.M. 1987. More than meets the eye – a simulation of natural selection, *Journal of Biological Education*, **21**, 301–305.

REQUIREMENTS
Washed river gravel (average maximum diameter approximately 10 mm), 10 kg (obtainable from builders' merchants)
Cooking lard (or vegetarian equivalent), 100 g
Plain flour, 300 g
Edible colouring dyes – brown, black and orange (obtainable from certain supermarkets or from wholesalers)

▷ PROJECTS

Before starting a project, discuss your intended procedure with your teacher.

1 Investigate the inheritance of coat colour in cats by studying adult females and their young.

2 Carry out a survey to investigate the extent to which colour blindness in humans is sex-linked.

3 Visit farms that keep cattle and study the inheritance of such characters as coat colour, the presence of horns or milk yield.

4 Try crossing different varieties of a plant species (e.g. a garden vegetable) to determine some of the inheritance patterns involved.

5 If you keep freshwater aquarium fish, investigate the genetics of the different forms of guppies.

6 ⚠ Investigate the inheritance of either brown eyes or ebony body in *Drosophila*.

7 ⚠ Continue your study of the inheritance of wing length in *Drosophila* by breeding the **F₂** flies in the Practical Exercise, page 233 into the third and fourth generation. Do you find that the ratio of the two phenotypes to one another remains constant or changes with succeeding generations? Think of possible explanations of your findings and investigate them further.

8 ⚠ Identify a character in *Drosophila* which appears to show **continuous variation**. (In humans examples of continuous variation include height, hair colour and intelligence.) Don't forget to consider behavioural as well as morphological characters. Set up a selective breeding programme to see whether there is a genetic component to such variation.

9 ⚠ Set up colonies of *Drosophila* with at least two genotypes in large containers (e.g. 2 litre soft drinks containers) and follow them for several generations. For example, start off with equal numbers of grey-bodied and ebony-bodied individuals and each generation sample the population to determine the ratio of the phenotypes. Interpret your findings as best you can.

10 ⚠ It has been suggested that when white-eyed male *Drosophila*

individuals are very rare in a population dominated by red-eyed individuals, they may actually enjoy greater reproductive success than red-eyed males. Test this hypothesis by setting up breeding colonies with different ratios of red-eyed to white-eyed males. Think carefully about your experimental design before starting.

11 ⚠ Investigate whether the fitness of vestigial-winged *Drosophila* individuals relative to normal-winged individuals depends on the population density. You will need to set up breeding colonies with different densities, either by using containers that differ in size or by setting up, and maintaining, colonies with different numbers of individuals.

12 Carry out the 13.11 Practical Exercise 'Selected predation of coloured prey' (page 239) with birds instead of students as the predators. Modify the procedure as you think fit. You will need to place trays with bait at bird tables. Ensure you use bird tables regularly visited by birds.

13 Design and construct a board game to teach the principles behind the Hardy-Weinberg equation. Evaluate your game.

14 Test the hypothesis that people who are red-green colour blind are better at distinguishing different shades of green from one another than people who are not red-green colour blind. Explain how this hypothesis, if correct, might help explain the high incidence of red-green colour blindness (which is a sex-linked trait found in about 8% of males and about 1% of females).

15 Write a computer programme to predict the primary sequence of a polypeptide from the sequence of bases in the gene responsible for its synthesis. (If you can write a computer programme to predict a polypeptide's tertiary structure you will almost certainly be awarded a Nobel Prize!) Modify your programme to consider the effect of gene mutations.

16 Find out all you can about James Watson, Francis Crick, Rosalind Franklin and Maurice Wilkins in the years leading up to the discovery of the structure of DNA in 1953. To what extent did their personalities and other factors seem to have been related to their ways of working as scientists?

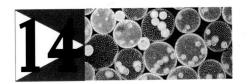

Evolution

The vertebrate pentadactyl limb: an exercise in homology

Homologous structures are features of different organisms believed by biologists to share a common ancestor, even though they may differ in function. So, for example, the spines of cacti are believed to be homologous with the leaf stalks of other flowering plants. On the other hand, the wings of insects and birds are not thought to be homologous; they are described as **analogous**, meaning that they share the same function, but differ in their ancestry.

A further example of homology is thought to be provided by the **pentadactyl limb** of vertebrates, so called because typically it terminates in five digits. It is possessed by amphibians, reptiles, mammals and birds. However, in the course of evolution, the pentadactyl limb appears to have undergone considerable modification in different groups. These modifications have involved enlargement, fusion, degeneration or, in some cases, total loss of certain components.

In this practical exercise you will examine the limbs of various **tetrapods** (four-limbed animals) and observe the extent to which they conform to, or depart from, the typical structure of a pentadactyl limb. In each case, try to correlate the structure of the limb with the function it performs.

Procedure

Study Figure 14.1. This shows the anatomy of a generalised pentadactyl limb. Notice that the diagram shows both of a fore-limb and a hind-limb. How many bones are shown in each wrist and each ankle?

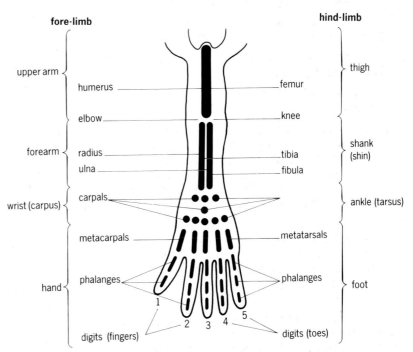

Figure 14.1 A generalised pentadactyl limb. This kind of limb, often in a greatly modified form, is possessed by amphibians, reptiles, mammals and birds, i.e. all vertebrates except fish. The edge of the limb which generally points towards the body is to the left, the edge of the limb which generally points away from the body being to the right. The fore- and hind-limbs both confirm to the pattern illustrated: the nomenclature used for each is shown to the left and right of the diagram respectively.

Rabbit

1   Examine the fore- and hind-limb bones of a rabbit. Identify the component parts, regarding the carpus and tarsus as single units for the moment. To what extent does each limb depart from the generalised pentadactyl pattern?

2   Now examine the carpus and tarsus in detail. Are all the component bones present? If not, what do you think has happened to them? What functional explanation would you suggest for the modifications seen in the carpus and tarsus?

Frog

1   Examine the fore- and hind-limb bones of a frog. Again, regarding the carpus and tarsus as single units, identify the component parts of each limb. To what extent do the fore- and hind-limbs differ from each other, and how do they depart from the generalised pentadactyl pattern? How would you explain the differences?

2   Now examine the carpus and tarsus in detail. How would you explain the structure of the carpus and tarsus in this animal?

Bird

1   Examine the hind-limb of a bird. This is more modified than that of either the rabbit or frog. Try to work out what has happened in the course of evolution. What are the likely functional reasons for the modifications?

2   Now examine the fore-limb. This is even more modified. Again, try to work out what may have happened in the course of evolution and suggest functional reasons for these modifications. If you have access to an intact wing with the skin and feathers in position, this may help you in your interpretations.

Other tetrapods

If available, examine the fore- and hind-limbs of other mammals, or photographs of them, e.g. human, monkey, pig, mole, bat, etc. In each case note the extent to which the bones of the limb depart from the generalised pentadactyl limb and interpret, in functional terms, the modifications you observe.

For consideration

1   Are you convinced that the pentadactyl limbs which you have examined share a common ancestor, or are you sceptical or unsure? What further information, if any, would you need to be more certain?

2   Birds' wings are covered with feathers. With what structures in other vertebrates might feathers be homologous? How might you test your suggestion? If time permits, examine a feather under the microscope. What functions do feathers perform and how do these relate to their structure?

REQUIREMENTS

Hand lens
Skeleton of fore- and hind-limb of rabbit
Skeleton of fore- and hind-limb of frog
Skeleton of fore- and hind-limb of bird (e.g. pigeon)
Intact wing of bird
Other limb skeletons of tetrapods (or photographs thereof) as available

---

14.2 INVESTIGATION

Variation in leaf and flower morphology in daisies

Variation within a species provides the 'raw material' for **natural selection**. Darwin and Wallace independently realised that inherited variation could lead to evolutionary change over time. Suppose, to take a hypothetical example, a species of bee shows variation in its hairiness and suppose that the climate changes so that it becomes colder. The hairier bees may now be more likely to survive and so, on average, produce more offspring. Over time, natural selection will cause the species to become more hairy.

In this investigation it is suggested that you look at variation in daisies with a view to assessing its possible evolutionary significance.

Guidance

Daisies are found growing in lawns or other short grassland and all belong to the one species *Bellis perennis* (daisy) (Figure 14.2). Daisies are convenient for our purpose because you can be sure that all the individuals you examine come from the one species. This is important because natural selection works *within* species, as some individuals survive and reproduce more than the rest.

The first thing to do is to find a population of daisies. Ideally you should have access to over 100 individuals and they should not all come from a single clump. Having found some daisies, examine them carefully noting their growth form, leaves and flowers.

Figure 14.2 Daisies (*Bellis perennis*) in flower.

Now look at *one* daisy in detail and describe it as fully as you can. Think about every part of the plant above ground. (There is no need to dig any daisies up.) Most of your description will be **quantitative**, e.g. the number of white 'petals', the number of leaves, the length and width of each leaf. However, some of your descriptions may be **qualitative** (e.g. colour). Make a particular effort to record any characters which you suspect show some variation. It would be a good idea to keep a record of where each plant was. This will help prevent you from measuring the same plant twice, and mean that later you can see whether any of the characters you have measured vary from place to place.

Once you have collected *some* data, make a preliminary analysis and presentation of your results. Try, for example, plotting a **frequency distribution histogram** with frequency (i.e. number of individuals) up the vertical axis and variation in a character (e.g. number of petals) along the horizontal axis (see page 6). Is there much variation? What sort of distribution have you found? Does the variation appear to be **discrete** (so that there are only a few classes of individuals, as in the number of fingers humans have) or **continuous** (as in human height)?

Your preliminary analysis may cause you to think of new ways of collecting or recording data before you complete your survey.

For consideration

1 Comment on the amount of variation you found.
2 Suggest what possible evolutionary significance, if any, such variation might have.
3 Do some characters appear to be correlated with others? For example, is leaf length correlated with leaf breadth? If some correlations are found, why do you think this is?
4 Did you find any evidence that there is more variation *between* different clumps of daisies than *within* a clump? Whether you did or didn't, suggest two hypotheses to explain your findings.
5 Do you think daisies reproduce vegetatively or sexually or both? What significance does this have for your findings?

14.3 INVESTIGATION

The struggle for existence among seedlings

Inherited variation between individuals is not enough for natural selection to occur. For natural selection to take place one **genotype** must be **fitter** than another. Fitter genotypes become more frequent in succeeding generations. In other words, they outcompete less fit genotypes. In this investigation it is suggested that you follow the fortunes of two intraspecific forms to see if one variety is fitter than the other one.

Guidance

You need to sow seeds of two forms within a species. These forms must belong to the same species as natural selection operates within species. One possibility is to sow seeds of two different varieties (e.g. lettuce). Different commercial varieties of the same species can be obtained from garden centres. Choose varieties that differ in leaf morphology so that you can distinguish them without too much difficulty as they grow. Another possibility is to sow seeds of different genotypes of tomato. These can be chosen with differences in such characters as cotyledon colour, stem colour and stem hairiness.

Sow the seeds in flat trays or pots. Ensure that you sow *equal* numbers of each variety in each tray or pot, but *vary* the densities. For example, you might have ten pots, each with two plants of one form and two plants of the other form (i.e. four plants in total in each pot); ten pots, each with five plants of one form and five plants of the other form; ten pots, each with ten plants of one form and ten plants of the other form; ten pots, each with twenty plants of one form and twenty plants of the other form. You may want to use toothpicks to mark the presence of each form in case it is difficult to distinguish the different forms as they grow.

Keep in a warm, light place and water every two or three days, but without water-logging the plants. At weekly intervals, observe and describe any differences between the seedlings. Count the number of plants showing each feature. Calculate the ratio between them each week. Continue the investigation for as many weeks as is feasible.

For consideration

1 Did you find any evidence that one genotype is fitter than the other?
2 What effect, if any, did density have?
3 How could this investigation be improved?

14.4 INVESTIGATION

Evolution of the multicellular state

The development of multicellularity was an important step in evolution. How did it arise? One way of tackling this question is to look at certain unicellular and small multicellular organisms living today. In doing this one must bear in mind that, although it may be tempting to regard such organisms as 'primitive', they are themselves the products of many millions of years of evolution. They may be markedly different from those organisms that did give rise to the multicellular state, perhaps some 800 million years ago.

Guidance

Examine under the light microscope live representatives of the following organisms, all of which are green algae in the phylum Chlorophyta (Kingdom Protoctista):

> *Chlamydomonas*
> *Gonium* or *Pandorina* or *Eudorina*
> *Volvox*

Approximately how many cells are there in each representative of these species? How does the trend observed within this group of organisms *suggest* that the multicellular state may have evolved?

Now examine *Pleurococcus*, another green alga, under the light microscope. Note that it occurs either as a single cell or as small groups of cells. In the small groups of cells are the cells intimately united or just 'stuck together'? How do you think the group condition arises?

Finally, examine a live specimen and/or a prepared slide of *Opalina*, a unicellular flagellate in the phylum Zoomastigina (Kingdom Protoctista). Approximately how many nuclei does the organism have? What light does the anatomy of this organism shed on the question of the origins of multicellularity?

For consideration

1 Would you describe *Volvox* as a colony of unicellular organisms or as a multicellular organism? Defend your answer.
2 From your observations in this investigation summarise possible ways in which the multicellular state may have arisen.
3 Why is it unlikely that *Opalina*, itself, is the ancestor of multicellular animals?
4 There is a group of free-living flatworms (phylum Platyhelminthes) called acoels (class Turbellaria, order Acoela). These organisms are small marine flatworms usually less than 2 mm in length. They are of interest to us because the cell membranes between their adjoining cells are incompletely formed. Do you think this provides any clues as to how multicellular animals may have arisen?
5 Describe the advantages and disadvantages which a multicellular organism exhibits compared to a similar unicell. Why did multicellularity evolve?

Biohazard
Opalina

REQUIREMENTS

Microscope
Slides and coverslips
Chlamydomonas, living
Gonium or *Pandorina* or *Eudorina*, living
Volvox, living
Opalina, living (from the contents of the rectum of a frog or toad) and/or prepared slide
Pleurococcus, living (from green bark of a tree trunk) and/or prepared slide

14.5 INVESTIGATION

Evolution of seed plants; examination of club mosses and conifers

One of the major events in evolution was the evolution of the flowering plants that dominate the world's vegetation today. We have already looked at the life cycle of a moss (page 190) and a fern (page 192), and at reproduction in flowering plants (page 187). In this investigation we shall look at the reproductive structures of club mosses and conifers and see to what extent these organisms lie between mosses and ferns, on the one hand, and flowering plants, on the other.

Club mosses (Kingdom Plantae, phylum Lycopodophyta)

In a moss or a fern, all the **spores** formed are the same size. For this reason the plants are said to be **homosporous**. However, some plants form two distinct types of spores.

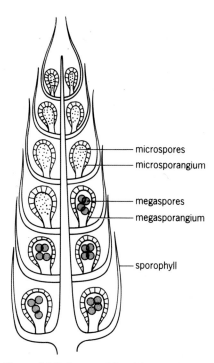

Figure 14.3 A cone of the club moss *Selaginella* showing megaspores within megasporangia and microspores within microsporangia.

Such plants are said to be **heterosporous** and an example is *Selaginella*. *Selaginella* is one of the club mosses (phylum Lycopodophyta). As in mosses and ferns, the spores are formed in specialised spore-bearing structures called **sporangia**. The sporangia are formed on special leaves (the **sporophylls**) which are densely packed to form cone-like structures projecting from the main stem (Figure 14.3). The sporophylls bear two types of sporangia:

- **Microsporangia** produce a large number of tiny **microspores**, each of which can grow into a small sperm-producing male gametophyte.
- **Megasporangia** produce a small number of large **megaspores** (usually four), each of which can grow into a relatively large female gametophyte.

The life cycle of *Selaginella* is compared with that of the common fern *Dryopteris* in Figure 14.4.

Guidance

Examine slides of the reproductive structures of *Selaginella*. Identify sporophylls, megasporangia, megaspores, microsporangia and microspores. Calculate, approximately, the ratio of the volume of a megaspore to that of a microspore. Estimate, approximately, the ratio of the number of microspores to megaspores produced.

Conifers (Kingdom Plantae, phylum Coniferophyta)

In conifers, as in club mosses, the sporophylls are grouped together to form cone-like structures. However, in conifers cones are either female or male, unlike the case in club mosses where each 'cone' produces both megasporangia and microsporangia. In conifers, female cones contain ovules (Figure 14.5A), while male cones contain **pollen sacs** (microsporangia) which produce **pollen** (Figure 14.5B).

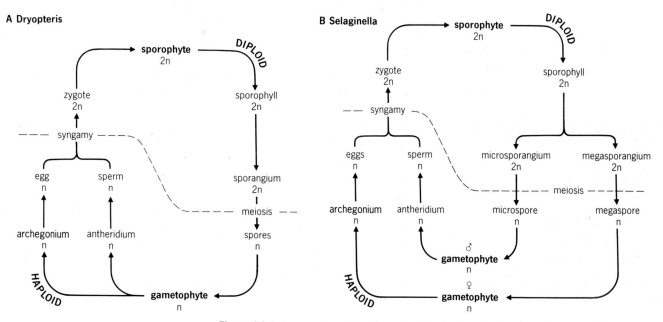

Figure 14.4 A comparison of the life cycle of the fern *Dryopteris* and the club moss *Selaginella*. Note that *Dryopteris*, in common with other ferns, produces only one type of spore, whereas *Selaginella* produces both megaspores and microspores.

Guidance

Obtain cones of different sizes from one or more species of conifer. Carefully dissect the cones and identify whether each is male or female. How many ovules does each sporophyll in a female cone bear? How many pollen sacs does each sporophyll in a male cone bear?

For consideration

1 Explain how the reproductive structures of *Selaginella* differ from those of a moss.
2 Theoreticians have predicted that the total investment in female reproductive structures by a plant should approximately equal that in male reproductive structures.

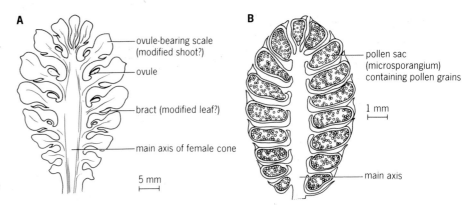

Figure 14.5 A Half-section through the female cone of a Scots pine, *Pinus sylvestris*.
B Half-section through the male cone of a Scots pine. Notice the different scales. The female cone is much larger than the male.

REQUIREMENTS

Microscope
Dissection instruments
Selaginella (prepared slide through a 'cone')
Male and female conifer cones (e.g. *Pinus, Abies* or *Picea*)

From your estimates in *Selaginella* of the relative numbers and sizes of megaspores and microspores do you agree or disagree with this conclusion?

3 List the evolutionary events needed for a club moss to have evolved into a conifer. (Note that it is not at all certain that this event happened in evolution. It is possible that both club mosses and conifers may have evolved separately from another ancestor.)

4 Conifers produce seeds, but mosses and club mosses do not. Explain what a seed is in terms of life-cycle terminology (megaspore, microspore, etc.) and suggest some advantages which caused seeds to evolve in conifers and flowering plants.

5 Why did heterospory evolve?

 PROJECTS

Before starting a project, discuss your intended procedure with your teacher.

1 Examine entire skeletons of different vertebrates. What other structures besides the limbs appear to be homologous with each other? Compare such structures and try to explain the differences between them in functional terms.

2 Deductions about the evolutionary relationships of organisms can sometimes be made by studies of their early developmental stages. Examine, and if necessary dissect, the early stages of some of the following: mosses, liverworts, ferns, club mosses, conifers, monocots and dicots. What conclusions can you draw?

3 Find out how creationists account for the present-day geographical distribution of organisms, trends in the fossil record and the other main lines of evidence thought by most biologists to favour evolution. Carry out a survey to find out how many people hold creationist as opposed to evolutionary ideas.

4 Germinate seeds of different species on blotting papers with different concentrations of salt. Are there differences *between* species in salt tolerance?

5 Germinate seeds of a species which has a short life cycle, such as *Brassica campestris* (page 200), on blotting papers with different concentrations of salt. Is there any variation in salt tolerance *within* this species? If there is, try growing the plants that are most tolerant through to reproduction and see if the seeds they produce are, on average, more tolerant to salt.

6 Carry out a survey to see if differences in fur colour and lengths in cats are associated with differences in hunting success or longevity (as reported by the cats' owners). If possible, find out what colours and lengths are most common in feral cat colonies. What do your findings tell you about natural selection and cat coats?

7 Carry out a survey to see if there is any relationship in humans between height and the number of children a person has. Investigate males and females separately. Does natural selection appear to be operating on human height? Explain your results.

8 One of the necessary conditions for natural selection is that more individuals are produced than can possibly survive. For different species of plants and animals work out the average number of offspring an individual produces in its life. You will need to determine the number of offspring produced each time an individual of the species reproduces and multiply this by the number of times an individual reproduces during its lifetime. Explain any differences you find between species. Don't investigate only animals.

9 ⚠ Lead produced by anti-knock agents in petrol (lead tetraethyl) has contaminated roadsides throughout Britain. The concentration of lead in the soil decreases with distance from a busy road. If you have permission from the land owner, select individual plants of the same species from various distances away from a main road and test their tolerance to various concentrations of lead chloride in solution culture. Explain how this tolerance could have been selected for. Alternatively, the study can be carried out on different varieties of the same species grown from seed. A suitable species is creeping red fescue (*Festuca rubra*) and seeds of the varieties Merlin and Dawson can be obtained from Philip Harris Education.

10 Set up cultures of *Volvox*. Is the number of cells in a single 'individual' constant or affected by environmental conditions? How exactly does such a complex 'individual' reproduce itself?

11 Dissect male and female cones of a number of different conifers. Compare your findings with those obtained from the dissection of a number of angiosperm flowers. Precisely how do the ovules of gymnosperms differ from angiosperms? Can you find any consistent differences between the seeds of conifers and angiosperms?

Appendix

Statistical analysis

Much biological work produces data that need to be analysed. The aim of this appendix is to help you to carry out your analysis of data, and to make it easier for you to draw conclusions from your results and understand what is going on.

What are data?

Data are things like the heights of plants, the number of species growing in a wood and the colours of flowers. Most data are **quantitative**. This means that they are measured in numbers, for example height in centimetres or mass in kilograms. However, some data are **qualitative**, for example flower colour. We will concentrate on quantitative data because having data in the form of numbers makes analysis more feasible. Usually qualitative data can be converted into quantitative data, making analysis easier. For example, colours can be represented by numbers that are the wavelengths of light of these colours. Thus blue is approximately 450 nm, green 510 nm, yellow 570 nm, and so on.

Analysing your data: Introduction

Analysis of data means doing something with the numbers to help you interpret your findings. Here is an example based on real data. Suppose you work out the density (i.e. specific gravity) of a piece of wood belonging to a species we will call species A. Now suppose you repeat the exercise a further four times with different pieces of wood, but all belonging to the same species, species A. Now imagine you carry the exercise out with five pieces of another species, species B. All in all you get 10 bits of data, as follows:

Density of wood of species A: 0.76, 0.74, 0.75, 0.72, 0.71.
Density of wood of species B: 0.68, 0.67, 0.72, 0.69, 0.66.

After getting these results, the best thing to do is to look at them and think about them. By inspection it seems likely that the density of the wood of species A is greater than that of species B, but how can we be sure? In this case, the first thing to do is to calculate the **mean**.

Calculating means

You have almost certainly calculated means before. All you have to do is to add up the individual values and divide by the total number of measurements. So, in this case, the mean for species A is:

$$(0.76 + 0.74 + 0.75 + 0.72 + 0.71) \div 5 = 0.736$$

The general formula is:

$$\bar{x} = \Sigma x / n$$

where:

$\bar{x}$ is the mean
Σ stands for 'sum of'
x refers to the individual values of the sample
n is the total number of individual values in the sample.

Repeating this exercise with species B, we find that the mean density of the wood of species B is 0.684. Now 0.684 is less than 0.736, so we might feel confident in concluding that species A has denser wood than species B. However, it is worth thinking about these data a bit more carefully.

For a start, note that *some* of the individual measurements of the density of the wood of species A are equal to, or even less than, certain of the individual measurements of the density of the wood of species B. How can we be *certain* that the difference between 0.736 and 0.684 isn't just the result of chance? The answer is that we *can't* be certain. However, we can use statistics to see how *confident* we can be about our conclusions. This is an important distinction. Statistics is not about certainties; it is about what statisticians call **degrees of confidence**.

Degrees of confidence

The easiest way to explain what is meant by degrees of confidence is to give an example. Suppose a bag contains a large number of marbles, some of which are red and some of which are yellow. Imagine now that ten marbles are drawn at random from the bag, and that eight are red and two yellow. We conclude that the bag may well contain more red than yellow marbles, but we can't be certain of this. Imagine now that a further ten marbles are drawn at random from the bag and that this time nine are red and one yellow. By now we are even more confident that there are more red than yellow marbles in the bag. But just *how* confident would we have to be to satisfy ourselves that this really is the case?

By convention, statisticians like to be at least 95% certain of something before drawing any conclusions! Another way of saying this is that statisticians like to draw conclusions only if the chance of their being wrong is less than one in 20, i.e. 5%. Let us return to our earlier example of the density of the wood of two different species, A and B. For a statistician to be satisfied that the average density of the wood of the two species *really* is different, we need to show that the probability of the *observed* difference being due to *chance* is less than 5%, i.e. less than 0.05. Finding that the probability of the observed difference being due to chance is less than 5% is sometimes referred to as being *confident at the 5% level*.

Another way of putting this is to say that we first *assume* that the densities of the woods of the two species are *not* different. This is our **null hypothesis**, so called because our assumption, i.e. hypothesis, is that there is *no* difference between the two woods. We then *reject* this null hypothesis only if we are 95% sure it is wrong.

The statistical tests that follow involve making calculations to determine how confident we can be about drawing conclusions, in other words about *rejecting* a null hypothesis. Some of these tests are made much easier if a calculator with certain statistical functions is available. These requirements are explained under the description of each test.

Different sorts of statistical tests

There are hundreds of different statistical tests, and each makes certain assumptions. For our purposes we can concentrate on three different tests. These tests are widely used in biology and the assumptions they make are valid for most sorts of biological data.

To decide which test you want, answer the following questions.

1   *Are you interested in seeing whether there are significant differences between the means of two sets of data?* (For example, does one species of animal grow faster than another, or does adding fertiliser make a difference to the height of plants?) If the answer to this question is 'yes', go to the section below on '**Testing the difference between two means**'. If, however, the answer to this question is 'no', go to question 2.

2   *Are you interested in seeing whether the ratio of your results is what you expect?* (For example, does a genetics ratio differ significantly from the 3 to 1 ratio you expected?) If the answer to this question is 'yes', go to the section below on '**Seeing if observed numbers differ from expected numbers**'. If, however, the answer to this question is 'no', go to question 3.

3   *Are you interested in seeing whether two sets of data are correlated?* (For example, do plants with bigger flowers attract more insects, or are people who smoke less fit than other people?) If the answer to this question is 'yes', go to the section below on '**Finding out if a correlation exists**'. If, however, the answer to this question, as to questions 1 and 2, is 'no', then unfortunately we can't help you. You might like to consult a mathematics teacher or one of the books on statistics listed on page 258. As we said earlier, there are hundreds of different statistical tests and we've only chosen three.

Testing the difference between two means

To test the significance of the difference between two means, we need first to calculate **standard deviations.** The standard deviation is a measure of the extent to which individual measurements *vary* around the mean. The greater the variation among the individual measurements, the larger the standard deviation; the less the variation among the individual measurements, the smaller the standard deviation.

It helps to have a calculator that works out standard deviations. If you *don't* have such a calculator, read the next section entitled 'Calculating standard deviations'. If you *do* have a calculator that works out standard deviations, you may want to skip this section and go to the section entitled 'Using a calculator to obtain standard deviations'.

Calculating standard deviations

The standard deviation, s_x, is given by the following formula:

$$s_x = \sqrt{\frac{\Sigma x^2 - \frac{(\Sigma x)^2}{n}}{n-1}}$$

where:

Σ stands for 'sum of'
x refers to the individual values of the sample
n is the total number of individual values in the sample.

An example may help. We shall go back to our earlier data on the density of the wood of species A. The five individual values, i.e. values of x, were: 0.76, 0.74, 0.75, 0.72 and 0.71. The sum of these five values, i.e. Σx, equals 3.68. Using these values of x and Σx in the above formula, we have:

$$s_x = \sqrt{\frac{(0.76^2 + 0.74^2 + 0.75^2 + 0.72^2 + 0.71^2) - \frac{(3.68)^2}{5}}{4}}$$

$$= \sqrt{\frac{2.7102 - 2.7085}{4}}$$

$$= 0.021$$

Using a calculator to obtain standard deviations

You may need to have your calculator in standard deviation mode, and type the data into a memory. Then there will be a key, often labelled $\bar{x}$. This key gives you the mean of the data. Another key, often labelled s or σ, gives you the standard deviation. If you have the key σ_{n-1} or s_{n-1} use it in preference to σ_n or s_n for working out the standard deviation.

Using standard deviations to calculate the significance of the difference between two means

If you have a very posh calculator (or access to a statistical package) you may have a key labelled t. This stands for **t-test** because that is the name of the test we are going to carry out. If you do have such a key, use it as instructed by the calculator or statistical package and go to step 8 below. If you don't have a key labelled t, proceed as follows:

1 Work out the means of the two sets of data. Each set must have at least three figures, but the numbers of figures in each set need not be the same.
2 Subtract the smaller mean from the larger one.
3 Work out the standard deviation of one set of data. Multiply this number by itself (i.e. square it) and divide it by the number of pieces of data in that set of data.
4 Work out the standard deviation of the other set of data. Multiply this number by itself (i.e. square it) and divide it by the number of pieces of data in that set of data.
5 Add together the figures you calculated in steps 3 and 4.
6 Take the square root of the figure calculated in step 5. You have now calculated what is called the **standard error**.
7 Divide the difference between the two means (step 2) by the figure calculated in step 6. This is your t value.
8 Now use Table A.1 to see whether your value of t could be expected by chance. Note that you need to know something called the **degrees of freedom**. For a t-test, the degrees of freedom is simply two less than the total number of individual measurements in the two samples.

Table A.1   Table of t values (based on Zar).

Degrees of freedom				t		
1	1.00	3.08	6.31	12.71	63.66	636.62
2	0.82	1.89	2.92	4.30	9.93	31.60
3	0.77	1.64	2.35	3.18	5.84	12.92
4	0.74	1.53	2.13	2.78	4.60	8.61
5	0.73	1.48	2.02	2.57	4.03	6.87
6	0.72	1.44	1.94	2.45	3.71	5.96
7	0.71	1.42	1.90	2.37	3.50	5.41
8	0.71	1.40	1.86	2.31	3.36	5.04
9	0.70	1.38	1.83	2.26	3.25	4.78
10	0.70	1.37	1.81	2.23	3.17	4.59
11	0.70	1.36	1.80	2.20	3.11	4.44
12	0.70	1.36	1.78	2.18	3.06	4.32
13	0.69	1.35	1.77	2.16	3.01	4.22
14	0.69	1.35	1.76	2.15	2.98	4.14
15	0.69	1.34	1.75	2.13	2.95	4.07
16	0.69	1.34	1.75	2.12	2.92	4.02
17	0.69	1.33	1.74	2.11	2.90	3.97
18	0.69	1.33	1.73	2.10	2.88	3.92
19	0.69	1.33	1.73	2.09	2.86	3.88
20	0.69	1.33	1.73	2.09	2.85	3.85
21	0.69	1.32	1.72	2.08	2.83	3.82
22	0.69	1.32	1.72	2.07	2.82	3.79
24	0.69	1.32	1.71	2.06	2.80	3.75
26	0.68	1.32	1.71	2.06	2.78	3.71
28	0.68	1.31	1.70	2.05	2.76	3.67
30	0.68	1.31	1.70	2.04	2.75	3.65
35	0.68	1.31	1.69	2.03	2.72	3.59
40	0.68	1.30	1.68	2.02	2.70	3.55
45	0.68	1.30	1.68	2.01	2.70	3.52
50	0.68	1.30	1.68	2.01	2.68	3.50
60	0.68	1.30	1.67	2.00	2.66	3.46
70	0.68	1.29	1.67	1.99	2.65	3.44
80	0.68	1.29	1.66	1.99	2.64	3.42
90	0.68	1.29	1.66	1.99	2.63	3.40
100	0.68	1.29	1.66	1.99	2.63	3.39
Probability (P) that chance alone could produce the difference	0.50 (50%)	0.20 (20%)	0.10 (10%)	0.05 (5%)	0.01 (1%)	0.001 (0.1%)

- If your value of t is *bigger* than the critical value shaded in Table A.1 you can be at least 95% confident that the difference between the means is significant. Your result is said to be **statistically significant** and you can reject the null hypothesis that there is no difference between the means.
- If your value of t is *smaller* than the critical value shaded in Table A.1 you are less than 95% confident that the difference between the means is significant. Your result is not statistically significant and you cannot reject the null hypothesis that there is no difference between the means.

All this may look rather formidable, so perhaps an example will help. We shall use the data listed earlier on the density of the wood of two different species, A and B. Our null hypothesis is that there is no difference between the densities of the woods of the two species.

1   Mean density of species A = 0.736; mean density of species B = 0.684.
2   Difference between the means = 0.052.
3   Standard deviation of the density of species A multiplied by itself divided by the number of pieces of data in that set of data = 0.021 × 0.021 ÷ 5 = 0.0000882.
4   Standard deviation of the density of species B multiplied by itself divided by the number of pieces of data in that set of data = 0.023 × 0.023 ÷ 5 = 0.0001058.
5   The sum of the figures calculated in steps 3 and 4 = 0.0000882 + 0.0001058 = 0.000194.

6 The square root of the figure calculated in step 5 = 0.0139.

7 The difference between the two means (step 2) divided by the figure calculated in step 6 = 0.052 ÷ 0.0139 = 3.74.

8 It is obvious that 3.74 is much greater than the critical value of t, which for a total number of pieces of data of 10, i.e. 8 degrees of freedom, equals 2.31. This means that we are at least 95% confident that the mean density of the wood of species A differs from the mean density of the wood of species B.

We can sum up the way to calculate the value of t by these steps as follows:

$$t = \frac{\text{mean of X} - \text{mean of Y}}{\text{standard error}}$$

$$= \frac{\overline{x} - \overline{y}}{\sqrt{\dfrac{(s_x)^2}{n_x} + \dfrac{(s_y)^2}{n_y}}}$$

where:

$\overline{x}$ equals the mean of sample X
$\overline{y}$ equals the mean of sample Y
s_x is the standard deviation of x
s_y is the standard deviation of y
n_x is the number of individual measurements in sample X
n_y is the number of individual measurements in sample Y.

The degrees of freedom are equal to $n_x + n_y - 2$.

One final point. Note that if there really is a difference between the means of X and Y, the greater the values of n_x and n_y – in other words the larger the sample sizes – the greater the value of t. This means that the larger your sample sizes, the more likely you are to detect a significant difference, if one exists. You really need a minimum of half a dozen individual measurements in each sample.

BOX A.1 **How does the t–test work?**

So far we have given no explanation as to how calculating t enables us to decide whether the difference between two means is significant or not. There is no need to know this to be able to carry out a t-test. Indeed, there is no requirement for you to understand why any statistical test works. However, if you are interested in understanding how a t-test works, this box gives a *partial* explanation. A full explanation would take us into complex mathematics beyond the scope of this book.

The normal distribution

When measurements of a particular characteristic showing continuous variation, such as the height of people or the density of pieces of wood, are made on a large number of individuals in a population, a graph of frequency against the characteristic often falls approximately on a **normal distribution curve**. An example of a normal distribution curve is shown in Illustration 1. The curve is bell-shaped. Its position and its shape depend solely on its mean and standard deviation. The larger the standard deviation, the flatter and more spread out the curve.

The value of the normal distribution curve for our purposes is that one standard deviation on either side of the mean encloses some 68% of the area under the curve. Two standard deviations (to be more exact, 1.96 standard deviations) on either side of the curve enclose 95% of the area under the curve. The two curves labelled A and B in Illustration 2, and drawn with continuous lines, show the curves which we should expect if we had measured and plotted the densities of hundreds of individual pieces of wood from species A and B.

Standard error

We used a total of five measurements of wood density to calculate the mean density of the wood of species A, and we obtained a value of 0.736. Obviously

(continued)

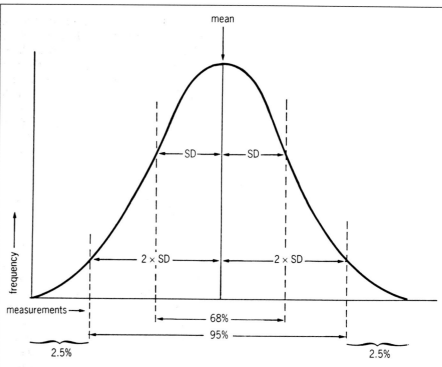

Illustration 1 Diagram of the normal distribution curve.

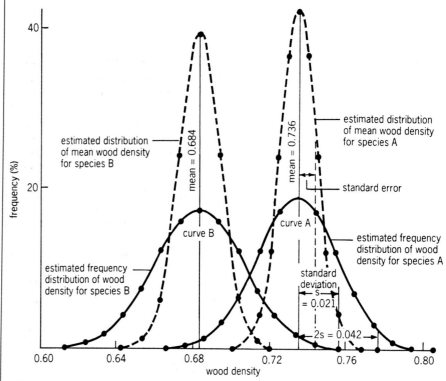

Illustration 2 Normal distribution curves for the wood density data.

this value, calculated from a mere five measurements, is unlikely to equal precisely the *actual* mean density of the wood of species A. Now, the more measurements of wood density we made before calculating the mean, the closer we should expect our calculated mean to lie to the actual mean.

This is where the argument gets a bit tricky. Suppose we made a large number of estimates of the mean density of the wood of species A, each time using n

(continued)

individual measurements to calculate each mean. (In the example we worked out earlier, n equalled five.) In such a case the estimates of the mean lie on a normal distribution. As you might expect, the mean of these estimates will lie close to, but will probably not exactly equal, the actual mean. If we calculate the standard deviation of the estimated means we find that this equals $s/\sqrt{n}$, where s, as before, equals the standard deviation of the individual measurements. The standard deviation of the estimated means is generally referred to as the standard deviation of the mean, or simply the **standard error**. As it equals $s/\sqrt{n}$, it is always smaller than the standard deviation of the individual measurements, by a factor $\sqrt{n}$.

In the case of the densities of woods of species A and B we have:

$$
\begin{aligned}
s_A &= 0.021 \\
n_A &= 5 \\
s_A/\sqrt{n_A} &= 0.021 / \sqrt{5} = 0.009 \\
s_B &= 0.021 \\
n_B &= 5 \\
s_B/\sqrt{n_B} &= 0.023 / \sqrt{5} = 0.010
\end{aligned}
$$

The two curves in Illustration 2 drawn with broken lines show the curves which we should expect if we had calculated the mean densities of hundreds of samples of wood from species A and B where each sample contained five individual measurements. These curves show the normal distributions for the means. They are taller and more pointed than curves A and B which show the normal distributions for the individual measurements. It is because they are taller and more pointed that they overlap less. And it is because they overlap only very slightly that we can be confident that the means are different.

Seeing if observed numbers differ from expected numbers

To see if observed numbers differ from expected numbers you need to work out exactly what your expected numbers are. An example will help. Suppose you cross two plants each of which is heterozygous at the same locus. We can represent this as Aa × Aa. Now if A is dominant to a, you might expect to get a 3:1 ratio of phenotypes among the offspring, e.g. red flowers:white flowers. Let us suppose you actually classify 50 offspring and find that the ratio is 40 red:10 white. The question is, does this ratio of 4:1 differ *significantly* from the expected one of 3:1?

The first thing to do is to work out the expected numbers. In this case we expect one quarter of the 50 offspring (i.e. $50 \times 0.25 = 12.5$) to have one set of characteristics (white flowers), and three-quarters (i.e. $50 \times 0.75 = 37.5$) to have the other set of characteristics (red flowers). It may look odd to expect non-whole numbers, but this is the only way to get a ratio of exactly 3:1 (i.e. 37.5 red:12.5 white).

Now we complete the following table:

	red	white
Observed (O)	40	10
Expected (E)	37.5	12.5
O–E	2.5	–2.5
(O–E)^2	6.25	6.25
(O–E)^2 / E	0.17	0.5
Sum of {(O–E)^2 / E} = 0.17 + 0.5 =	0.67	

Here 0.67 is called the **chi-squared value** or χ^2 **value**. The bigger it is, the greater the chance that the observed results differ significantly from the expected ones. To see if the difference is significant, use Table A.2. Note that you need to know the number of classes of data to work out the degrees of freedom. For a chi-squared test, the degrees of freedom is simply one less than the number of classes of data. In our example the number of classes of data equals two, because each offspring fell into one of two classes. If the expected ratio had been 1:2:1 (e.g. red:pink:white), the number of classes of data would have been three and the expected numbers would not have been 37.5 and 12.5 but 12.5, 25 and 12.5.

Table A.2 Table of χ^2 values (based on Fisher).

Degrees of freedom	Number of classes	χ^2						
1	2	0.016	0.46	1.64	2.71	3.84	6.64	10.83
2	3	0.21	1.39	3.22	4.61	5.99	9.21	13.82
3	4	0.58	2.37	4.64	6.25	7.82	11.34	16.27
4	5	1.06	3.36	5.99	7.78	9.49	13.28	18.47
Probability (P) that chance alone could produce the deviation		0.90 (90%)	0.50 (50%)	0.20 (20%)	0.10 (10%)	0.05 (5%)	0.01 (1%)	0.001 (0.01%)

If your value of chi-squared is bigger than the critical value shaded in Table A.2, you can be at least 95% confident that the difference between the observed and expected results is significant. Your result is said to be statistically significant. You can see that in our example the value of chi-squared we calculated (0.67) is much smaller than the critical value for one degree of freedom (3.84). This means that the ratio of 40:10 is not significantly different from a 3:1 ratio.

The general formula you need to carry out this sort of test, called a **chi-squared test** (or χ^2-test), is given by:

$$\chi^2 = \Sigma \{(O - E)^2 / E\}$$

The degrees of freedom is equal to one less than the number of classes. As always in statistics, the more data the better. For technical reasons a chi-squared test needs each expected value to equal at least 4.

Finding out if a correlation exists

To find out if a significant correlation exists between two variables you first need to know the **correlation coefficient**. The most sensitive test to find out if a significant correlation exists requires you to work out the **Pearson product–moment correlation coefficient**, abbreviated to **r**. Unfortunately it is extremely long-winded to calculate r, which means that you really need a calculator (or a statistical package) that works it out for you.

A less sensitive test to find out if a significant correlation exists requires you to work out the **Spearman rank correlation coefficient**, abbreviated to r_s. If you *don't* have a calculator or statistical package that works out r, use the section below titled 'Calculating the Spearman rank correlation coefficient'. If you *can* calculate r, you may want to skip this section and go straight on to the section titled 'Interpreting correlation coefficients'.

Calculating the Spearman rank correlation coefficient

Although calculating the Spearman rank correlation coefficient is slightly less likely to reveal the existence of a correlation, it makes fewer mathematical assumptions than the test based on the Pearson product–moment correlation coefficient. So although you are less likely to conclude that a correlation exists, if you *do* conclude that one exists, your conclusion is more likely to be valid.

The test based on the Spearman rank correlation coefficient has one other advantage. This is that, as its name suggests, it can be used on *ranked* data. For example, you could use it to see if people are less fit if they smoke heavily, even if you can't *quantify* their fitness or the amount they smoke, provided you can *rank* their fitness and the amount they smoke.

Here is an example to show you how to calculate the Spearman rank correlation coefficient, r_s. The data in the margin shows gill mass and body mass in the crab *Pachygrapus crassipes*:

Our null hypothesis is that there is no correlation between body mass and gill mass. It's always best to plot your data on a scatter graph (see page 6) to see if a correlation seems to exist before embarking on any calculations of correlation coefficients. In this case plotting the data, or visualising it in your mind's eye if you are can do that sort of thing, shows that it is likely that a significant correlation does exist.

Body mass / g	Gill mass / mg
14.4	159
15.2	179
11.3	100
2.5	45
22.7	384
14.9	230
1.4	100
15.8	320
4.2	80
15.4	220
9.5	210

To calculate r_s, the next thing to do is to rank the data. (This is why r_s is referred to as the Spearman rank correlation coefficient.) For each column, rank the data from 1 (the largest value) downwards. For our example, the following results:

Body mass / g	rank	Gill mass / mg	rank
14.4	6	159	7
15.2	4	179	6
11.3	7	100	8.5
2.5	10	45	11
22.7	1	384	1
14.9	5	230	3
1.4	11	100	8.5
15.8	2	320	2
4.2	9	80	10
15.4	3	220	4
9.5	8	210	5

Notice that because there are two gill masses the same (100 mg) they are given a rank of 8.5 on the grounds that they share ranks 8 and 9.

These two ranks are labelled R_1 and R_2 – it makes no difference which is which. The Spearman rank correlation coefficient is given by:

$$r_s = 1 - \frac{6\Sigma(R_1 - R_2)^2}{n(n^2 - 1)}$$

In the above example we have:

$$\Sigma(R_1 - R_2)^2 = (6-7)^2 + (4-6)^2 + (7-8.5)^2 + \ldots + (8-5)^2 = 29.5$$
$$n = 11$$

So:

$$r_s = 0.87$$

Interpreting correlation coefficients

The value of a calculated correlation coefficient lies between -1 and $+1$. A correlation coefficient of close to -1 means that there is a strong *negative* relationship between the two variables. This means that an *increase* in one variable (e.g. height of a tree) is accompanied by a *decrease* in the other variable (e.g. amount of light reaching the ground).

A correlation coefficient of close to $+1$ means that there is a strong *positive* relationship between the two variables. This means that an *increase* in one variable (e.g. mass of an animal) is accompanied by an *increase* in the other variable (e.g. amount of food consumed each day).

A correlation coefficient of close to 0 means that the relationship between the two variables is weak or non-existent.

Having obtained a value for your correlation coefficient, use either Table A.3 or Table A.4 to see if it differs significantly from 0. Use Table A.3 if you have calculated the Pearson product–moment correlation coefficient, r, and Table A.4 if you have calculated the Spearman rank correlation coefficient, r_s. Note that in neither case are degrees of freedom required, simply the number of points used to calculate the correlation coefficient.

For example, if data on the heights of different meadow buttercup plants and the number of flowers they produce were obtained from 10 plants, r would have to exceed 0.63 for the relationship to be significant at the 5% level, while r_s would have to exceed 0.65.

A final important piece of information. You need more points on your scatter graph to reveal a significant correlation if your test is based on the Spearman rank correlation coefficient than if it is based on the Pearson product-moment correlation coefficient. Get at *least* ten points if using the Spearman rank correlation coefficient, and at *least* six if using the Pearson product-moment correlation coefficient.

Table A.3 Table of r values (based on Zar).

Number of points						
3	0.71	0.95	0.99	1.00	–	–
4	0.50	0.80	0.90	0.95	0.99	1.00
5	0.40	0.69	0.81	0.88	0.96	0.99
6	0.35	0.61	0.73	0.81	0.92	0.97
7	0.31	0.55	0.67	0.76	0.88	0.95
8	0.28	0.51	0.62	0.71	0.83	0.93
9	0.26	0.47	0.58	0.67	0.80	0.90
10	0.24	0.44	0.55	0.63	0.77	0.87
12	0.22	0.40	0.50	0.58	0.71	0.82
14	0.20	0.37	0.46	0.53	0.66	0.78
16	0.18	0.34	0.43	0.50	0.62	0.74
18	0.17	0.32	0.40	0.47	0.59	0.71
20	0.16	0.30	0.38	0.44	0.56	0.68
25	0.14	0.27	0.34	0.40	0.51	0.62
30	0.13	0.24	0.31	0.36	0.46	0.57
40	0.11	0.21	0.26	0.31	0.40	0.50
50	0.10	0.18	0.24	0.28	0.36	0.45
60	0.09	0.17	0.21	0.25	0.33	0.41
70	0.08	0.16	0.20	0.24	0.31	0.39
80	0.08	0.15	0.19	0.22	0.29	0.36
90	0.07	0.14	0.17	0.21	0.27	0.34
100	0.07	0.13	0.17	0.20	0.26	0.32
Probability (P) that chance alone could produce the correlation	0.50 (50%)	0.20 (20%)	0.10 (10%)	0.05 (5%)	0.01 (1%)	0.001 (0.1%)

Table A.4 Table of r_s values (based on Zar).

Number of points			r_s			
4	0.60	1.00	–	–	–	–
5	0.50	0.80	0.90	–	–	–
6	0.37	0.66	0.83	0.89	1.00	–
7	0.32	0.57	0.71	0.79	0.93	1.00
8	0.31	0.52	0.64	0.74	0.88	0.98
9	0.27	0.48	0.60	0.70	0.83	0.93
10	0.25	0.46	0.56	0.65	0.79	0.90
12	0.22	0.41	0.50	0.59	0.73	0.85
14	0.20	0.37	0.46	0.54	0.68	0.80
16	0.18	0.34	0.43	0.50	0.64	0.76
18	0.17	0.32	0.40	0.47	0.60	0.73
20	0.16	0.30	0.38	0.45	0.57	0.70
25	0.14	0.27	0.34	0.40	0.51	0.63
30	0.13	0.24	0.31	0.36	0.47	0.58
40	0.11	0.21	0.26	0.31	0.41	0.51
50	0.10	0.18	0.24	0.28	0.36	0.46
60	0.09	0.17	0.21	0.26	0.33	0.42
70	0.08	0.16	0.20	0.24	0.31	0.39
80	0.08	0.15	0.19	0.22	0.29	0.36
90	0.07	0.14	0.17	0.21	0.27	0.34
100	0.07	0.13	0.17	0.20	0.26	0.33
Probability (P) that chance alone could produce the correlation	0.50 (50%)	0.20 (20%)	0.10 (10%)	0.05 (5%)	0.01 (1%)	0.001 (0.1%)

References

Webb, N. and Blackmore, R. 1985 *Statistics for Biologists*, Cambridge University Press. Very clearly written in a chatty style.

Parker, R.E. 1979 *Introductory Statistics for Biology*, Edward Arnold – reprinted in 1993 by Cambridge University Press. A classic, clear introduction to the subject.

Carter, D.C. *et al.* 1981 *Mathematics in Biology*, Nelson. A general introduction to the use of mathematical techniques in biology with many practical examples.

Zar, J.H. 1984 *Biostatistical Analysis*, Prentice-Hall International. All the tables you need (and lots that you don't) for statistical analysis.